ADDITION AND SUBTRACTION FACTS

Understanding Whole Numbers

Polly is buying dog food for her puppy. Which can will cost Polly the least amount of money?

We want to know which can has the lowest price. We know the prices for the different dog

foods are _____, _____ and _____.
To compare the 3 prices, we can find them on a number line.

40   41   42   43   44   45   46   47   48   49   50

✔ The set of **whole numbers** starts with 0 and goes as far as we need it to go. The whole numbers 0, 1, 2, 3, 4, 5, 6, 7, 8 and 9 are called **digits.** On a number line, the number to the right is always greater.

49 is greater than **45**   **49 > 45**

✔ A number to the left is always less.

43 is less than **45**   **43 < 45**

The dog food that will cost Polly the least costs _____.

Getting Started

Write the missing whole numbers.

1. 26, ____, 28   2. ____ comes after 89.   3. 58 is between ____ and _____.

Compare these numbers. Write < or > in the circle.

4. 32 ◯ 38   5. 76 ◯ 53   6. 27 ◯ 72

Write the numbers in order from least to greatest.

7. 32, 46, 15   ____, ____, ____   8. 13, 43, 29   ____, ____, ____

1

Practice

Write the missing whole numbers.

1. 35, 36, ___, ___

2. ___, ___, 48, 49

3. 63, 62, ___, ___

4. 91, ___, ___, 94

5. 7, ___, ___,10, ___

6. ___, ___, ___, 20, 21

7. 82, ___, 80, ___, 78

8. ___ comes after 49.

9. ___ is between 56 and 58.

10. 77 is between ___ and ___.

Compare these numbers. Write < or > in the circle.

11. 39 ◯ 36

12. 73 ◯ 17

13. 21 ◯ 30

14. 17 ◯ 16

15. 81 ◯ 89

16. 32 ◯ 42

17. 63 ◯ 36

18. 22 ◯ 33

19. 89 ◯ 40

20. 25 ◯ 29

21. 57 ◯ 51

22. 48 ◯ 40

23. 48 ◯ 50

24. 96 ◯ 99

25. 15 ◯ 35

Write the numbers in order from least to greatest.

26. 75, 36, 48

___, ___, ___

27. 35, 87, 29

___, ___, ___

28. 23, 57, 45

___, ___, ___

29. 83, 47, 58

___, ___, ___

30. 22, 57, 39

___, ___, ___

31. 18, 81, 88

___, ___, ___

32. 25, 36, 12, 19

___, ___, ___, ___

33. 47, 58, 75, 21

___, ___, ___, ___

34. 67, 9, 42, 83

___, ___, ___, ___

Reviewing Addition Facts

Aaron left home early one morning to walk to the library, before he went to school. How many blocks did he walk on his way to school?

We want to know the number of blocks Aaron walked all together.

We know that he walked _____ blocks from his house to the library.

He walked another _____ blocks from the library to school.
To find the total number of blocks, we add

_____ and _____.

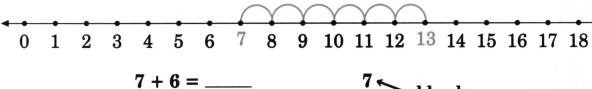

$$0 \quad 1 \quad 2 \quad 3 \quad 4 \quad 5 \quad 6 \quad 7 \quad 8 \quad 9 \quad 10 \quad 11 \quad 12 \quad 13 \quad 14 \quad 15 \quad 16 \quad 17 \quad 18$$

7 + 6 = _____
↗ ↖ ↑
addends sum

$$\begin{array}{r} 7 \\ + 6 \\ \hline \end{array}$$ ← addends
← sum

$7 + 6 = 13$ is called a **number sentence.**

Aaron walked _____ blocks from his home to school.

Getting Started

Complete the number sentences.

1. $4 + 2 =$ _____   2. $7 + 9 =$ _____   3. $8 + 3 =$ _____

4. $2 + 9 =$ _____   5. $5 + 6 =$ _____   6. $8 + 8 =$ _____

Add.

7. $\begin{array}{r} 8 \\ + 7 \\ \hline \end{array}$ 8. $\begin{array}{r} 4 \\ + 1 \\ \hline \end{array}$ 9. $\begin{array}{r} 9 \\ + 9 \\ \hline \end{array}$ 10. $\begin{array}{r} 5 \\ + 5 \\ \hline \end{array}$ 11. $\begin{array}{r} 3 \\ + 6 \\ \hline \end{array}$ 12. $\begin{array}{r} 9 \\ + 4 \\ \hline \end{array}$

3

Practice

Complete the number sentences.

1. $7 + 1 =$ ___   2. $7 + 7 =$ ___   3. $2 + 1 =$ ___   4. $6 + 9 =$ ___

5. $8 + 5 =$ ___   6. $4 + 4 =$ ___   7. $1 + 1 =$ ___   8. $5 + 9 =$ ___

9. $9 + 3 =$ ___   10. $6 + 8 =$ ___   11. $8 + 2 =$ ___   12. $7 + 6 =$ ___

13. $7 + 8 =$ ___   14. $2 + 4 =$ ___   15. $8 + 9 =$ ___   16. $8 + 4 =$ ___

Add.

17. $\begin{array}{r} 7 \\ + 4 \\ \hline \end{array}$ 18. $\begin{array}{r} 5 \\ + 2 \\ \hline \end{array}$ 19. $\begin{array}{r} 4 \\ + 3 \\ \hline \end{array}$ 20. $\begin{array}{r} 9 \\ + 5 \\ \hline \end{array}$ 21. $\begin{array}{r} 2 \\ + 6 \\ \hline \end{array}$ 22. $\begin{array}{r} 1 \\ + 8 \\ \hline \end{array}$

23. $\begin{array}{r} 3 \\ + 8 \\ \hline \end{array}$ 24. $\begin{array}{r} 5 \\ + 4 \\ \hline \end{array}$ 25. $\begin{array}{r} 9 \\ + 1 \\ \hline \end{array}$ 26. $\begin{array}{r} 9 \\ + 8 \\ \hline \end{array}$ 27. $\begin{array}{r} 2 \\ + 7 \\ \hline \end{array}$ 28. $\begin{array}{r} 9 \\ + 7 \\ \hline \end{array}$

29. $\begin{array}{r} 1 \\ + 3 \\ \hline \end{array}$ 30. $\begin{array}{r} 5 \\ + 7 \\ \hline \end{array}$ 31. $\begin{array}{r} 1 \\ + 6 \\ \hline \end{array}$ 32. $\begin{array}{r} 3 \\ + 9 \\ \hline \end{array}$ 33. $\begin{array}{r} 3 \\ + 3 \\ \hline \end{array}$ 34. $\begin{array}{r} 4 \\ + 9 \\ \hline \end{array}$

35. $\begin{array}{r} 2 \\ + 8 \\ \hline \end{array}$ 36. $\begin{array}{r} 1 \\ + 7 \\ \hline \end{array}$ 37. $\begin{array}{r} 1 \\ + 2 \\ \hline \end{array}$ 38. $\begin{array}{r} 8 \\ + 6 \\ \hline \end{array}$ 39. $\begin{array}{r} 1 \\ + 9 \\ \hline \end{array}$ 40. $\begin{array}{r} 3 \\ + 4 \\ \hline \end{array}$

41. $\begin{array}{r} 3 \\ + 2 \\ \hline \end{array}$ 42. $\begin{array}{r} 6 \\ + 1 \\ \hline \end{array}$ 43. $\begin{array}{r} 8 \\ + 1 \\ \hline \end{array}$ 44. $\begin{array}{r} 2 \\ + 2 \\ \hline \end{array}$ 45. $\begin{array}{r} 4 \\ + 7 \\ \hline \end{array}$ 46. $\begin{array}{r} 5 \\ + 8 \\ \hline \end{array}$

Apply

Solve these problems.

47. Megan bought a wool scarf for $7 and a pair of mittens for $6. How much did she spend?

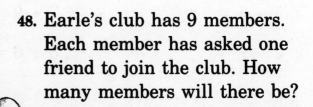

48. Earle's club has 9 members. Each member has asked one friend to join the club. How many members will there be?

4

Column Addition

The first United States astronauts orbited the earth in 1962.
How many orbits did these Americans complete in that year?

Date	Astronaut	Orbits
February 20	John Glenn	3
May 24	Scott Carpenter	3
October 3	Wally Schirra	6

We want to find the total number of orbits all the astronauts made in 1962.

We know that Glenn orbited _____ times;

Carpenter, _____ times; and Schirra, _____ times.

To find this **total** or **sum,** we add _____,

_____ and _____.

We can add only two numbers at a time.

Add down.
$$\begin{array}{r} 3 \\ 3 \\ + 6 \end{array}\Big\} \underline{\quad}$$

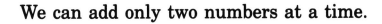

$$\begin{array}{r} 3 \\ 3 \\ + 6 \end{array}\Big\} \underline{\quad}$$ Add up to check.

The American astronauts completed _____ orbits in 1962.

Getting Started

Add and check.

1.
$$\begin{array}{r} 1 \\ 3 \\ + 5 \end{array}$$

2.
$$\begin{array}{r} 2 \\ 6 \\ + 3 \end{array}$$

3.
$$\begin{array}{r} 3 \\ 4 \\ + 2 \end{array}$$

4.
$$\begin{array}{r} 6 \\ 3 \\ + 1 \end{array}$$

5.
$$\begin{array}{r} 7 \\ 1 \\ + 7 \end{array}$$

6.
$$\begin{array}{r} 6 \\ 3 \\ 2 \\ + 4 \end{array}$$

7.
$$\begin{array}{r} 3 \\ 2 \\ 4 \\ + 9 \end{array}$$

8.
$$\begin{array}{r} 5 \\ 4 \\ 5 \\ + 3 \end{array}$$

9.
$$\begin{array}{r} 7 \\ 2 \\ 3 \\ 5 \\ + 1 \end{array}$$

10.
$$\begin{array}{r} 8 \\ 1 \\ 6 \\ 2 \\ + 2 \end{array}$$

Practice

Add and check.

1.	6	2.	2	3.	2	4.	8	5.	6
	3		3		7		1		3
	+ 6		+ 4		+ 2		+ 4		+ 2

6.	4	7.	1	8.	5	9.	5	10.	7
	5		6		2		2		2
	+ 3		+ 3		+ 5		+ 1		+ 6

11.	2	12.	6	13.	4	14.	3	15.	9
	5		2		2		1		1
	+ 3		+ 3		+ 7		+ 6		+ 5

16.	8	17.	1	18.	5	19.	5	20.	6
	1		6		3		1		1
	5		3		4		6		3
	1		+ 7		+ 1		+ 2		5
	+ 4								+ 3

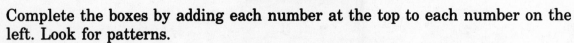

EXCURSION

Complete the boxes by adding each number at the top to each number on the left. Look for patterns.

+	5	3	7
8			
18			
28			
38			
48			
58			

+	2	6	4
9			
19			
29			
39			
49			
59			

+	9	7	5
7			
27			
47			
67			
87			
97			

Understanding Addition Properties

Understanding the basic properties of addition can help you find sums more easily.

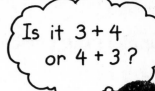

> **Order Property**
> We can add in any order.

$$3 + 4 = \underline{\hspace{1cm}} \qquad 4 + 3 = \underline{\hspace{1cm}}$$

> **Grouping Property**
> We can change the grouping.
> Remember to add the numbers in the parentheses first.

$$(5 + 3) + 6 = ? \qquad 5 + (3 + 6) = ?$$

$$\underline{\hspace{1cm}} + 6 = \underline{\hspace{1cm}} \qquad 5 + \underline{\hspace{1cm}} = \underline{\hspace{1cm}}$$

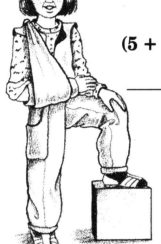

> **Zero Property**
> Adding zero does not affect the answer.

$$6 + 0 = \underline{\hspace{1cm}} \qquad 0 + 3 = \underline{\hspace{1cm}}$$

Getting Started

Complete the number sentences.

1. $5 + 0 = \underline{\hspace{1cm}}$
2. $(6 + 3) + 2 = \underline{\hspace{1cm}}$
3. $0 + 9 = \underline{\hspace{1cm}}$

4. $4 + (0 + 6) = \underline{\hspace{1cm}}$
5. $(2 + 7) + 0 = \underline{\hspace{1cm}}$
6. $5 + (3 + 5) = \underline{\hspace{1cm}}$

Add and check.

7.
$$\begin{array}{r} 6 \\ 2 \\ + 4 \\ \hline \end{array}$$

8.
$$\begin{array}{r} 3 \\ 9 \\ + 4 \\ \hline \end{array}$$

9.
$$\begin{array}{r} 9 \\ 3 \\ 0 \\ + 2 \\ \hline \end{array}$$

10.
$$\begin{array}{r} 1 \\ 4 \\ 5 \\ 3 \\ + 4 \\ \hline \end{array}$$

11.
$$\begin{array}{r} 7 \\ 5 \\ 0 \\ 3 \\ + 2 \\ \hline \end{array}$$

Practice

Complete the number sentences.

1. 7 + 0 = ___

2. (4 + 2) + 7 = ___

3. 0 + 8 = ___

4. (8 + 0) + 2 = ___

5. 5 + (8 + 1) = ___

6. (7 + 2) + 3 = ___

7. (0 + 6) + 9 = ___

8. (6 + 0) + 9 = ___

9. 4 + (6 + 3) = ___

10. (2 + 5) + 8 = ___

11. 8 + (5 + 2) = ___

12. 3 + (4 + 5) = ___

13. 6 + (2 + 0) = ___

14. 4 + (3 + 6) = ___

15. (5 + 0) + 5 = ___

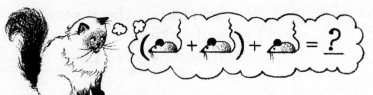

Add and check.

16.
```
  5
  3
+ 2
```

17.
```
  2
  7
+ 0
```

18.
```
  0
  8
+ 6
```

19.
```
  1
  7
+ 2
```

20.
```
  6
  0
+ 8
```

21.
```
  4
  0
+ 7
```

22.
```
  3
  8
+ 0
```

23.
```
  8
  1
+ 5
```

24.
```
  7
  1
+ 8
```

25.
```
  9
  0
+ 4
```

26.
```
  0
  5
+ 0
```

27.
```
  3
  6
+ 1
```

28.
```
  5
  9
+ 1
```

29.
```
  2
  2
+ 5
```

30.
```
  8
  0
+ 6
```

31.
```
  9
  0
  6
+ 4
```

32.
```
  1
  4
  3
+ 0
```

33.
```
  4
  5
  3
+ 2
```

34.
```
  6
  8
  0
+ 5
```

35.
```
  7
  2
  5
+ 2
```

36.
```
  3
  0
  8
  2
+ 4
```

37.
```
  2
  4
  3
  4
+ 2
```

38.
```
  5
  4
  2
  1
+ 6
```

39.
```
  1
  0
  5
  8
+ 2
```

40.
```
  4
  4
  3
  3
+ 3
```

Reviewing Subtraction Facts

Rinaldo's goal for this year
is to read 12 books. So far,
he has read 5 books. How many
books must Rinaldo read to
reach his goal?

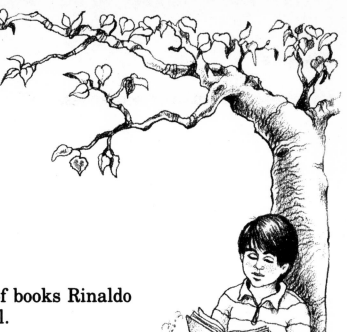

We want to know the number of books Rinaldo
must still read to reach his goal.

Rinaldo's goal is to read _____ books.

He has read _____ books so far this year.
To find the number of books he needs to read,

we subtract _____ from _____.

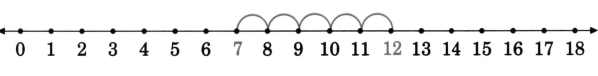

$$12 - 5 = \underline{}$$
$$\uparrow \qquad \uparrow \qquad \uparrow$$
minuend subtrahend difference

$$12 \leftarrow \text{minuend}$$
$$-\ 5 \leftarrow \text{subtrahend}$$
$$ \leftarrow \text{difference}$$

Rinaldo wants to read _____ more books this year.

Getting Started

Complete the number sentences.

1. $8 - 7 =$ _____   2. $11 - 3 =$ _____   3. $15 - 9 =$ _____   4. $12 - 5 =$ _____

5. $10 - 8 =$ _____   6. $8 - 6 =$ _____   7. $18 - 9 =$ _____   8. $13 - 4 =$ _____

Subtract.

9. $\begin{array}{r} 11 \\ -\ 4 \\ \hline \end{array}$
10. $\begin{array}{r} 5 \\ -3 \\ \hline \end{array}$
11. $\begin{array}{r} 8 \\ -3 \\ \hline \end{array}$
12. $\begin{array}{r} 14 \\ -\ 8 \\ \hline \end{array}$
13. $\begin{array}{r} 6 \\ -3 \\ \hline \end{array}$
14. $\begin{array}{r} 10 \\ -\ 4 \\ \hline \end{array}$

9

Practice

Complete the number sentences.

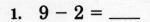

1. $9 - 2 = $ ___
2. $6 - 2 = $ ___
3. $4 - 1 = $ ___
4. $7 - 3 = $ ___

5. $15 - 8 = $ ___
6. $4 - 3 = $ ___
7. $11 - 8 = $ ___
8. $13 - 5 = $ ___

9. $2 - 1 = $ ___
10. $10 - 3 = $ ___
11. $5 - 1 = $ ___
12. $6 - 5 = $ ___

13. $9 - 8 = $ ___
14. $13 - 9 = $ ___
15. $14 - 5 = $ ___
16. $8 - 1 = $ ___

17. $15 - 6 = $ ___
18. $9 - 9 = $ ___

Subtract.

19.
$$\begin{array}{r} 10 \\ -\ 1 \\ \hline \end{array}$$
20.
$$\begin{array}{r} 9 \\ -\ 6 \\ \hline \end{array}$$
21.
$$\begin{array}{r} 12 \\ -\ 8 \\ \hline \end{array}$$
22.
$$\begin{array}{r} 10 \\ -\ 7 \\ \hline \end{array}$$
23.
$$\begin{array}{r} 9 \\ -\ 4 \\ \hline \end{array}$$
24.
$$\begin{array}{r} 3 \\ -\ 1 \\ \hline \end{array}$$

25.
$$\begin{array}{r} 12 \\ -\ 4 \\ \hline \end{array}$$
26.
$$\begin{array}{r} 11 \\ -\ 2 \\ \hline \end{array}$$
27.
$$\begin{array}{r} 4 \\ -\ 2 \\ \hline \end{array}$$
28.
$$\begin{array}{r} 14 \\ -\ 9 \\ \hline \end{array}$$
29.
$$\begin{array}{r} 14 \\ -\ 6 \\ \hline \end{array}$$
30.
$$\begin{array}{r} 11 \\ -\ 6 \\ \hline \end{array}$$

31.
$$\begin{array}{r} 17 \\ -\ 8 \\ \hline \end{array}$$
32.
$$\begin{array}{r} 9 \\ -\ 1 \\ \hline \end{array}$$
33.
$$\begin{array}{r} 10 \\ -\ 2 \\ \hline \end{array}$$
34.
$$\begin{array}{r} 16 \\ -\ 7 \\ \hline \end{array}$$
35.
$$\begin{array}{r} 7 \\ -\ 4 \\ \hline \end{array}$$
36.
$$\begin{array}{r} 13 \\ -\ 8 \\ \hline \end{array}$$

37.
$$\begin{array}{r} 16 \\ -\ 9 \\ \hline \end{array}$$
38.
$$\begin{array}{r} 10 \\ -\ 6 \\ \hline \end{array}$$
39.
$$\begin{array}{r} 9 \\ -\ 7 \\ \hline \end{array}$$
40.
$$\begin{array}{r} 15 \\ -\ 6 \\ \hline \end{array}$$
41.
$$\begin{array}{r} 12 \\ -\ 7 \\ \hline \end{array}$$
42.
$$\begin{array}{r} 11 \\ -\ 9 \\ \hline \end{array}$$

43.
$$\begin{array}{r} 10 \\ -\ 9 \\ \hline \end{array}$$
44.
$$\begin{array}{r} 7 \\ -\ 6 \\ \hline \end{array}$$
45.
$$\begin{array}{r} 12 \\ -\ 3 \\ \hline \end{array}$$
46.
$$\begin{array}{r} 11 \\ -\ 7 \\ \hline \end{array}$$
47.
$$\begin{array}{r} 10 \\ -\ 5 \\ \hline \end{array}$$
48.
$$\begin{array}{r} 14 \\ -\ 7 \\ \hline \end{array}$$

Apply

Solve these problems.

49. Butch made 9 sandwiches. His brothers ate 7 of them for lunch. How many sandwiches does Butch have left to eat?

50. Suzanne bought toothpaste for $2, and a toothbrush for $1. How much change will she receive from a $10 bill?

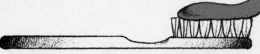

Understanding Subtraction Properties

Understanding the properties of subtraction
can help you find **differences** more easily.

What do I get when I subtract 0?

Zero Properties	
Subtracting zero does not affect the answer.	Subtracting a number from itself leaves zero.

$8 - 0 = $ _____ $7 - 7 = $ _____

$3 - 0 = $ _____ $0 - 0 = $ _____

Checking Subtraction
Addition and subtraction check each other.

What's the best way to check subtraction?

$8 - 5 = $ _____ $8 - 3 = $ _____

$3 + 5 = $ _____ $5 + 3 = $ _____

These four number sentences are
called a **fact family.**

✔ Remember that the order of the numbers
in a subtraction sentence is always important.

$3 - 2$ is *not* the same as $2 - 3$.

Getting Started

Complete the number sentences.

1. $7 - 7 = $ ___   2. $5 - 0 = $ ___   3. $4 - 0 = $ ___   4. $6 - 6 = $ ___

5. $8 - 8 = $ ___   6. $9 - 0 = $ ___   7. $5 - 5 = $ ___   8. $3 - 0 = $ ___

Subtract and check.

9. $\begin{array}{r} 14 \\ -\ 6 \\ \hline \end{array}$
10. $\begin{array}{r} 9 \\ -2 \\ \hline \end{array}$
11. $\begin{array}{r} 6 \\ -0 \\ \hline \end{array}$
12. $\begin{array}{r} 17 \\ -\ 8 \\ \hline \end{array}$
13. $\begin{array}{r} 12 \\ -\ 7 \\ \hline \end{array}$
14. $\begin{array}{r} 10 \\ -\ 6 \\ \hline \end{array}$

Practice

Complete the number sentences.

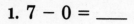

1. $7 - 0 =$ ____
2. $0 - 0 =$ ____
3. $10 - 3 =$ ____
4. $6 - 6 =$ ____

5. $8 - 3 =$ ____
6. $2 - 1 =$ ____
7. $9 - 0 =$ ____
8. $3 - 0 =$ ____

9. $4 - 4 =$ ____
10. $11 - 3 =$ ____
11. $7 - 4 =$ ____
12. $1 - 1 =$ ____

Subtract and check.

13. $\begin{array}{r} 11 \\ -\ 6 \\ \hline \end{array}$
14. $\begin{array}{r} 6 \\ -1 \\ \hline \end{array}$
15. $\begin{array}{r} 14 \\ -\ 7 \\ \hline \end{array}$
16. $\begin{array}{r} 9 \\ -5 \\ \hline \end{array}$
17. $\begin{array}{r} 4 \\ -1 \\ \hline \end{array}$
18. $\begin{array}{r} 12 \\ -\ 4 \\ \hline \end{array}$

19. $\begin{array}{r} 11 \\ -\ 7 \\ \hline \end{array}$
20. $\begin{array}{r} 10 \\ -\ 7 \\ \hline \end{array}$
21. $\begin{array}{r} 8 \\ -5 \\ \hline \end{array}$
22. $\begin{array}{r} 16 \\ -\ 8 \\ \hline \end{array}$
23. $\begin{array}{r} 13 \\ -\ 8 \\ \hline \end{array}$
24. $\begin{array}{r} 10 \\ -\ 4 \\ \hline \end{array}$

25. $\begin{array}{r} 15 \\ -\ 9 \\ \hline \end{array}$
26. $\begin{array}{r} 5 \\ -0 \\ \hline \end{array}$
27. $\begin{array}{r} 13 \\ -\ 4 \\ \hline \end{array}$
28. $\begin{array}{r} 11 \\ -\ 8 \\ \hline \end{array}$
29. $\begin{array}{r} 6 \\ -3 \\ \hline \end{array}$
30. $\begin{array}{r} 14 \\ -\ 9 \\ \hline \end{array}$

31. $\begin{array}{r} 9 \\ -2 \\ \hline \end{array}$
32. $\begin{array}{r} 13 \\ -\ 6 \\ \hline \end{array}$
33. $\begin{array}{r} 12 \\ -\ 7 \\ \hline \end{array}$
34. $\begin{array}{r} 16 \\ -\ 9 \\ \hline \end{array}$
35. $\begin{array}{r} 4 \\ -0 \\ \hline \end{array}$
36. $\begin{array}{r} 8 \\ -2 \\ \hline \end{array}$

37. $\begin{array}{r} 15 \\ -\ 8 \\ \hline \end{array}$
38. $\begin{array}{r} 1 \\ -0 \\ \hline \end{array}$
39. $\begin{array}{r} 11 \\ -\ 4 \\ \hline \end{array}$
40. $\begin{array}{r} 18 \\ -\ 9 \\ \hline \end{array}$
41. $\begin{array}{r} 12 \\ -\ 8 \\ \hline \end{array}$
42. $\begin{array}{r} 9 \\ -6 \\ \hline \end{array}$

43. $\begin{array}{r} 3 \\ -3 \\ \hline \end{array}$
44. $\begin{array}{r} 10 \\ -\ 6 \\ \hline \end{array}$
45. $\begin{array}{r} 8 \\ -8 \\ \hline \end{array}$
46. $\begin{array}{r} 10 \\ -\ 9 \\ \hline \end{array}$
47. $\begin{array}{r} 13 \\ -\ 7 \\ \hline \end{array}$
48. $\begin{array}{r} 17 \\ -\ 9 \\ \hline \end{array}$

49. $\begin{array}{r} 9 \\ -4 \\ \hline \end{array}$
50. $\begin{array}{r} 9 \\ -9 \\ \hline \end{array}$
51. $\begin{array}{r} 10 \\ -\ 2 \\ \hline \end{array}$
52. $\begin{array}{r} 8 \\ -0 \\ \hline \end{array}$
53. $\begin{array}{r} 14 \\ -\ 5 \\ \hline \end{array}$
54. $\begin{array}{r} 12 \\ -\ 9 \\ \hline \end{array}$

55. $\begin{array}{r} 7 \\ -5 \\ \hline \end{array}$
56. $\begin{array}{r} 17 \\ -\ 8 \\ \hline \end{array}$
57. $\begin{array}{r} 9 \\ -8 \\ \hline \end{array}$
58. $\begin{array}{r} 7 \\ -7 \\ \hline \end{array}$
59. $\begin{array}{r} 6 \\ -0 \\ \hline \end{array}$
60. $\begin{array}{r} 13 \\ -\ 9 \\ \hline \end{array}$

61. $\begin{array}{r} 14 \\ -\ 8 \\ \hline \end{array}$
62. $\begin{array}{r} 5 \\ -5 \\ \hline \end{array}$
63. $\begin{array}{r} 2 \\ -0 \\ \hline \end{array}$
64. $\begin{array}{r} 15 \\ -\ 6 \\ \hline \end{array}$
65. $\begin{array}{r} 2 \\ -2 \\ \hline \end{array}$
66. $\begin{array}{r} 12 \\ -\ 5 \\ \hline \end{array}$

Finding Missing Addends

Yan-Wah belongs to the photography club and she is saving money to buy a camera. So far, she has saved $9. How much more does Yan-Wah need?

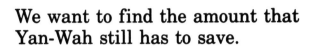

We want to find the amount that Yan-Wah still has to save.

We know that the camera costs _____.

Yan-Wah has saved _____ so far. We can write this problem as an addition sentence, and let the letter *n* stand for the missing addend.

$$\$9 + n = \$17$$

To solve this problem, we think of a related subtraction sentence from the same fact family.

$$\$17 - \$9 = n$$

Since $\$17 - \$9 =$ _____, $n =$ _____.

Yan-Wah still needs _____ to buy the camera.

Getting Started

Write related subtraction sentences.

1. $5 + n = 12$ 2. $n + 7 = 16$ 3. $6 + n = 14$ 4. $n + 7 = 13$

Use subtraction sentences to help find the missing addends.

5. $6 + n = 10$ 6. $n + 3 = 7$ 7. $n + 4 = 12$ 8. $7 + n = 15$

   $n =$ ___ $n =$ ___ $n =$ ___ $n =$ ___

9. $\begin{array}{r} 8 \\ + n \\ \hline 11 \end{array}$ 10. $\begin{array}{r} n \\ + 9 \\ \hline 16 \end{array}$ 11. $\begin{array}{r} 8 \\ + n \\ \hline 15 \end{array}$ 12. $\begin{array}{r} n \\ + 9 \\ \hline 18 \end{array}$

   $n =$ ___ $n =$ ___ $n =$ ___ $n =$ ___

13

Practice

Write related subtraction sentences.

1. $7 + n = 10$ 2. $4 + n = 12$ 3. $n + 9 = 15$ 4. $n + 6 = 14$

5. $9 + n = 18$ 6. $n + 6 = 13$ 7. $3 + n = 3$ 8. $n + 8 = 10$

9. $6 + n = 14$ 10. $8 + n = 14$ 11. $9 + n = 16$ 12. $8 + n = 12$

Use subtraction sentences to help find the missing addends.

13. $3 + n = 5$ 14. $7 + n = 8$ 15. $n + 6 = 12$ 16. $4 + n = 10$

$n = \underline{}$ $n = \underline{}$ $n = \underline{}$ $n = \underline{}$

17. $7 + n = 14$ 18. $n + 9 = 16$ 19. $n + 8 = 16$ 20. $9 + n = 14$

$n = \underline{}$ $n = \underline{}$ $n = \underline{}$ $n = \underline{}$

21. $n + 6 = 13$ 22. $n + 8 = 12$ 23. $7 + n = 16$ 24. $8 + n = 13$

$n = \underline{}$ $n = \underline{}$ $n = \underline{}$ $n = \underline{}$

25. $\begin{array}{r} 6 \\ + n \\ \hline 11 \end{array}$ 26. $\begin{array}{r} n \\ + 9 \\ \hline 14 \end{array}$ 27. $\begin{array}{r} 4 \\ + n \\ \hline 13 \end{array}$ 28. $\begin{array}{r} 8 \\ + n \\ \hline 15 \end{array}$

$n = \underline{}$ $n = \underline{}$ $n = \underline{}$ $n = \underline{}$

29. $\begin{array}{r} n \\ + 2 \\ \hline 5 \end{array}$ 30. $\begin{array}{r} 8 \\ + n \\ \hline 9 \end{array}$ 31. $\begin{array}{r} 3 \\ + n \\ \hline 7 \end{array}$ 32. $\begin{array}{r} n \\ + 5 \\ \hline 8 \end{array}$

$n = \underline{}$ $n = \underline{}$ $n = \underline{}$ $n = \underline{}$

33. $\begin{array}{r} 7 \\ + n \\ \hline 12 \end{array}$ 34. $\begin{array}{r} n \\ + 3 \\ \hline 3 \end{array}$ 35. $\begin{array}{r} 9 \\ + n \\ \hline 15 \end{array}$ 36. $\begin{array}{r} 8 \\ + n \\ \hline 16 \end{array}$

$n = \underline{}$ $n = \underline{}$ $n = \underline{}$ $n = \underline{}$

Using a Four-step Plan

Of the 1,576 children enrolled in Roosevelt School, 757 are girls. Of the 76 students absent today, 27 are girls. How many boys attend Roosevelt? How many boys are present?

★ **SEE**

We need to find:
  the number of boys who attend Roosevelt School.
  the number of boys who are absent.
  the number of boys who are present.
We know:
  the total number of students is _____.

  the number of girls is _____.

  there are _____ students who are absent.

  there are _____ girls who are absent.

★ **PLAN**

To find out how many boys attend Roosevelt

School, we subtract _____ from _____.
To find out how many boys are absent, we subtract

_____ from _____. To find the number of boys who are present, we find the difference between the total number of boys, and the number of boys who are absent.

★ **DO**

$$\begin{array}{r} 1{,}576 \\ -\ \ 757 \\ \hline \end{array}$$ boys

$$\begin{array}{r} 76 \\ -27 \\ \hline \end{array}$$ boys absent

$$\begin{array}{r} 819 \\ -\ 49 \\ \hline \end{array}$$ boys present

_____ boys attend Roosevelt School. _____ boys are present today.

★ **CHECK**

$$\begin{array}{r} 757 \\ +\ \boxed{} \\ \hline 1{,}576 \end{array}$$ students enrolled

$$\begin{array}{r} 49 \\ +27 \\ \hline \boxed{} \end{array}$$ students absent

$$\begin{array}{r} \boxed{} \\ +\ 49 \\ \hline \boxed{} \end{array}$$ boys

15

Apply

Solve these problems. Remember to use the four-step plan.

1. Marcia wants to buy a camera for $49.99. She has saved $31.27 and will earn $5.00 babysitting on Saturday. How much more will she need to buy the camera?

2. There are 157 fourth graders at Watson School. At lunch, 43 students go home to eat, 27 bring their lunches and the rest buy their lunches. How many students buy their lunches?

3. The book Frank is reading has 135 pages. He has finished reading 81 pages. If Frank is to finish the book in six days, how many pages must he read each day?

4. Karen wants to bring a birthday treat for her class. There are 24 students and one teacher in the class. She bought 4 boxes of granola bars with 5 granola bars in each. How many more granola bars does she need?

5. Read Exercise 3 again. What if Frank is to finish the book in nine days instead of six? Now how many pages must he read each day?

6. Donuts cost $3.50 a dozen at Aunt Molly's Bakery and 30¢ each at Uncle Don's Diner. At whose place would it cost less to buy 3 dozen donuts?

7. There are 157 fourth graders at Watson School. Forty-three of them walk to school. Some of the others ride bicycles and others ride on school buses. What do you need to know to tell how many fourth-grade students ride in school buses?

8. You have $10.00 to spend. It costs 50¢ to take the bus downtown. You buy a pencil-and-pen set for $2.98, a notebook for $3.98, and paper for $1.99. Can you buy a ruler for 49¢ and still have enough money left to take the bus home?

Practicing Addition Facts

2 +1	7 +2	7 +4	1 +3	1 +8	2 +3	3 +2	7 +9	1 +4	4 +4
3 +0	5 +5	8 +6	6 +0	2 +9	0 +6	3 +1	6 +3	6 +5	7 +6
9 +1	7 +0	5 +2	2 +2	1 +2	2 +6	9 +4	5 +3	7 +3	6 +8
0 +9	9 +9	3 +3	1 +6	9 +0	0 +2	7 +7	0 +3	4 +7	0 +5
7 +8	5 +6	1 +1	2 +4	5 +9	2 +5	5 +4	1 +0	7 +1	3 +5
8 +8	9 +2	5 +7	1 +7	5 +8	0 +4	6 +9	6 +7	4 +9	7 +5
9 +6	5 +1	4 +3	6 +1	8 +1	2 +0	8 +2	3 +8	6 +2	3 +7
6 +4	4 +0	9 +5	0 +7	3 +4	4 +1	8 +9	1 +8	0 +1	9 +3
8 +7	1 +5	8 +0	3 +9	8 +4	4 +2	3 +6	8 +3	5 +0	2 +8
1 +9	0 +8	6 +6	0 +0	2 +7	4 +5	9 +7	9 +8	4 +6	8 +5

Practicing Subtraction Facts

$\begin{array}{r} 6 \\ -5 \\ \hline \end{array}$	$\begin{array}{r} 13 \\ -9 \\ \hline \end{array}$	$\begin{array}{r} 9 \\ -6 \\ \hline \end{array}$	$\begin{array}{r} 12 \\ -8 \\ \hline \end{array}$	$\begin{array}{r} 11 \\ -2 \\ \hline \end{array}$	$\begin{array}{r} 9 \\ -1 \\ \hline \end{array}$	$\begin{array}{r} 2 \\ -2 \\ \hline \end{array}$	$\begin{array}{r} 10 \\ -6 \\ \hline \end{array}$	$\begin{array}{r} 7 \\ -6 \\ \hline \end{array}$	$\begin{array}{r} 13 \\ -6 \\ \hline \end{array}$

| $\begin{array}{r} 16 \\ -9 \\ \hline \end{array}$ | $\begin{array}{r} 15 \\ -7 \\ \hline \end{array}$ | $\begin{array}{r} 7 \\ -5 \\ \hline \end{array}$ | $\begin{array}{r} 14 \\ -9 \\ \hline \end{array}$ | $\begin{array}{r} 17 \\ -8 \\ \hline \end{array}$ | $\begin{array}{r} 12 \\ -6 \\ \hline \end{array}$ | $\begin{array}{r} 8 \\ -5 \\ \hline \end{array}$ | $\begin{array}{r} 12 \\ -7 \\ \hline \end{array}$ | $\begin{array}{r} 5 \\ -4 \\ \hline \end{array}$ | $\begin{array}{r} 10 \\ -9 \\ \hline \end{array}$ |

| $\begin{array}{r} 11 \\ -9 \\ \hline \end{array}$ | $\begin{array}{r} 9 \\ -9 \\ \hline \end{array}$ | $\begin{array}{r} 12 \\ -9 \\ \hline \end{array}$ | $\begin{array}{r} 16 \\ -8 \\ \hline \end{array}$ | $\begin{array}{r} 9 \\ -5 \\ \hline \end{array}$ | $\begin{array}{r} 6 \\ -1 \\ \hline \end{array}$ | $\begin{array}{r} 8 \\ -8 \\ \hline \end{array}$ | $\begin{array}{r} 16 \\ -7 \\ \hline \end{array}$ | $\begin{array}{r} 9 \\ -7 \\ \hline \end{array}$ | $\begin{array}{r} 5 \\ -2 \\ \hline \end{array}$ |

| $\begin{array}{r} 6 \\ -4 \\ \hline \end{array}$ | $\begin{array}{r} 11 \\ -7 \\ \hline \end{array}$ | $\begin{array}{r} 4 \\ -2 \\ \hline \end{array}$ | $\begin{array}{r} 11 \\ -6 \\ \hline \end{array}$ | $\begin{array}{r} 14 \\ -7 \\ \hline \end{array}$ | $\begin{array}{r} 15 \\ -6 \\ \hline \end{array}$ | $\begin{array}{r} 7 \\ -4 \\ \hline \end{array}$ | $\begin{array}{r} 2 \\ -0 \\ \hline \end{array}$ | $\begin{array}{r} 14 \\ -6 \\ \hline \end{array}$ | $\begin{array}{r} 17 \\ -9 \\ \hline \end{array}$ |

| $\begin{array}{r} 6 \\ -6 \\ \hline \end{array}$ | $\begin{array}{r} 13 \\ -8 \\ \hline \end{array}$ | $\begin{array}{r} 10 \\ -5 \\ \hline \end{array}$ | $\begin{array}{r} 3 \\ -0 \\ \hline \end{array}$ | $\begin{array}{r} 11 \\ -5 \\ \hline \end{array}$ | $\begin{array}{r} 9 \\ -3 \\ \hline \end{array}$ | $\begin{array}{r} 0 \\ -0 \\ \hline \end{array}$ | $\begin{array}{r} 7 \\ -2 \\ \hline \end{array}$ | $\begin{array}{r} 13 \\ -7 \\ \hline \end{array}$ | $\begin{array}{r} 12 \\ -3 \\ \hline \end{array}$ |

| $\begin{array}{r} 3 \\ -1 \\ \hline \end{array}$ | $\begin{array}{r} 1 \\ -0 \\ \hline \end{array}$ | $\begin{array}{r} 12 \\ -4 \\ \hline \end{array}$ | $\begin{array}{r} 9 \\ -4 \\ \hline \end{array}$ | $\begin{array}{r} 10 \\ -7 \\ \hline \end{array}$ | $\begin{array}{r} 7 \\ -7 \\ \hline \end{array}$ | $\begin{array}{r} 8 \\ -1 \\ \hline \end{array}$ | $\begin{array}{r} 14 \\ -5 \\ \hline \end{array}$ | $\begin{array}{r} 6 \\ -0 \\ \hline \end{array}$ | $\begin{array}{r} 9 \\ -8 \\ \hline \end{array}$ |

| $\begin{array}{r} 15 \\ -9 \\ \hline \end{array}$ | $\begin{array}{r} 8 \\ -7 \\ \hline \end{array}$ | $\begin{array}{r} 10 \\ -8 \\ \hline \end{array}$ | $\begin{array}{r} 18 \\ -9 \\ \hline \end{array}$ | $\begin{array}{r} 8 \\ -0 \\ \hline \end{array}$ | $\begin{array}{r} 13 \\ -4 \\ \hline \end{array}$ | $\begin{array}{r} 7 \\ -0 \\ \hline \end{array}$ | $\begin{array}{r} 3 \\ -2 \\ \hline \end{array}$ | $\begin{array}{r} 12 \\ -5 \\ \hline \end{array}$ | $\begin{array}{r} 14 \\ -8 \\ \hline \end{array}$ |

| $\begin{array}{r} 8 \\ -4 \\ \hline \end{array}$ | $\begin{array}{r} 11 \\ -3 \\ \hline \end{array}$ | $\begin{array}{r} 8 \\ -6 \\ \hline \end{array}$ | $\begin{array}{r} 4 \\ -0 \\ \hline \end{array}$ | $\begin{array}{r} 7 \\ -3 \\ \hline \end{array}$ | $\begin{array}{r} 10 \\ -4 \\ \hline \end{array}$ | $\begin{array}{r} 11 \\ -4 \\ \hline \end{array}$ | $\begin{array}{r} 5 \\ -3 \\ \hline \end{array}$ | $\begin{array}{r} 1 \\ -1 \\ \hline \end{array}$ | $\begin{array}{r} 8 \\ -3 \\ \hline \end{array}$ |

| $\begin{array}{r} 8 \\ -2 \\ \hline \end{array}$ | $\begin{array}{r} 6 \\ -3 \\ \hline \end{array}$ | $\begin{array}{r} 5 \\ -5 \\ \hline \end{array}$ | $\begin{array}{r} 4 \\ -1 \\ \hline \end{array}$ | $\begin{array}{r} 9 \\ -0 \\ \hline \end{array}$ | $\begin{array}{r} 3 \\ -3 \\ \hline \end{array}$ | $\begin{array}{r} 11 \\ -8 \\ \hline \end{array}$ | $\begin{array}{r} 2 \\ -1 \\ \hline \end{array}$ | $\begin{array}{r} 10 \\ -1 \\ \hline \end{array}$ | $\begin{array}{r} 4 \\ -4 \\ \hline \end{array}$ |

| $\begin{array}{r} 9 \\ -2 \\ \hline \end{array}$ | $\begin{array}{r} 7 \\ -1 \\ \hline \end{array}$ | $\begin{array}{r} 6 \\ -2 \\ \hline \end{array}$ | $\begin{array}{r} 5 \\ -0 \\ \hline \end{array}$ | $\begin{array}{r} 15 \\ -8 \\ \hline \end{array}$ | $\begin{array}{r} 4 \\ -3 \\ \hline \end{array}$ | $\begin{array}{r} 13 \\ -5 \\ \hline \end{array}$ | $\begin{array}{r} 10 \\ -3 \\ \hline \end{array}$ | $\begin{array}{r} 5 \\ -1 \\ \hline \end{array}$ | $\begin{array}{r} 10 \\ -2 \\ \hline \end{array}$ |

Compare these numbers.

1. 15 ◯ 19   **2.** 26 ◯ 62   **3.** 36 ◯ 39   **4.** 78 ◯ 70

Add.

5. $4 + 4 = $ _____   **6.** $7 + 3 = $ _____   **7.** $8 + 7 = $ _____   **8.** $5 + 9 = $ _____

9. $\begin{array}{r} 5 \\ + 6 \\ \hline \end{array}$ **10.** $\begin{array}{r} 9 \\ + 9 \\ \hline \end{array}$ **11.** $\begin{array}{r} 8 \\ + 3 \\ \hline \end{array}$ **12.** $\begin{array}{r} 4 \\ 6 \\ + 2 \\ \hline \end{array}$

13. $\begin{array}{r} 3 \\ 1 \\ + 4 \\ \hline \end{array}$ **14.** $\begin{array}{r} 5 \\ 2 \\ 6 \\ + 1 \\ \hline \end{array}$ **15.** $\begin{array}{r} 8 \\ 1 \\ 5 \\ + 3 \\ \hline \end{array}$ **16.** $\begin{array}{r} 4 \\ 5 \\ 3 \\ 3 \\ 6 \\ + 1 \\ \hline \end{array}$

17. $(5 + 2) + 3 = $ _____   **18.** $2 + (8 + 0) = $ _____   **19.** $(7 + 5) + 2 = $ _____

20. $3 + (6 + 3) = $ _____   **21.** $(4 + 0) + 9 = $ _____   **22.** $7 + (5 + 2) = $ _____

Subtract.

23. $9 - 6 = $ _____   **24.** $14 - 7 = $ _____   **25.** $11 - 8 = $ _____   **26.** $15 - 6 = $ _____

27. $\begin{array}{r} 8 \\ - 3 \\ \hline \end{array}$ **28.** $\begin{array}{r} 16 \\ - 8 \\ \hline \end{array}$ **29.** $\begin{array}{r} 12 \\ - 9 \\ \hline \end{array}$ **30.** $\begin{array}{r} 7 \\ - 7 \\ \hline \end{array}$

Write the missing addends.

31. $5 + n = 8$ **32.** $n + 7 = 13$ **33.** $\begin{array}{r} 6 \\ + n \\ \hline 13 \end{array}$ **34.** $\begin{array}{r} 11 \\ + \ n \\ \hline 19 \end{array}$

$n = $ _____ $n = $ _____ $n = $ _____ $n = $ _____

Circle the letter of the correct answer.

1 23 ◯ 36

   a <
   b >

2 46 ◯ 41

   a <
   b >

3 3 + 4

   a 5
   b 6
   c 7
   d NG

4 5 + 6

   a 11
   b 12
   c 13
   d NG

5   9
  + 6

   a 12
   b 14
   c 16
   d NG

6   4
  + 8

   a 11
   b 12
   c 13
   d NG

7   4
    3
  + 5

   a 11
   b 13
   c 12
   d NG

8 8 + (3 + 5)

   a 8
   b 16
   c 17
   d NG

9 7 − 3

   a 6
   b 8
   c 10
   d NG

10 15 − 7

   a 6
   b 7
   c 8
   d NG

11   1 4
  − 6

   a 8
   b 7
   c 6
   d NG

12   8
  − 8

   a 0
   b 4
   c 8
   d NG

13 $7 + n = 12$
     $n = ?$

   a 7
   b 19
   c 5
   d NG

14 $n + 2 = 8$
     $n = ?$

   a 6
   b 8
   c 10
   d NG

 score

Understanding Hundreds, Tens and Ones

Linda bought flower stickers to add to her collection. How many did she buy?

Linda bought _____ pages of 100 stickers each.

She bought _____ strips of 10 stickers each.

She also bought _____ individual stickers.
We say she bought **two hundred forty-three**

stickers, and write it as _____.

Study the number in this place value chart.

In the number, **243,**

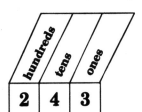

— the digit _____ is in the **ones** place.

— the digit _____ is in the **tens** place.

— the digit _____ is in the **hundreds** place.

Linda bought _____ stickers.

Getting Started

Write the numbers.

1. two hundred seventy-seven _____   2. nine hundred twenty-six _____

Write the place value of the red digits.

3. 276 _____   4. 385 _____   5. 620 _____

Write the missing words.

6. 132 one _____ thirty-two   7. 753 _____ hundred fifty-three

Practice

Write the numbers.

1.  _____

2. 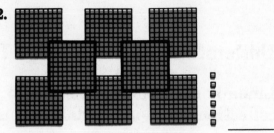 _____

3. three hundred fifty-two _____

4. six hundred ninety _____

5. two hundred seventy-eight _____

6. five hundred nineteen _____

7. four hundred ninety-nine _____

8. one hundred seven _____

9. eight hundred sixty-five _____

10. seven hundred eleven _____

Write the place value of the red digits.

11. 186 _____

12. 26 _____

13. 159 _____

14. 637 _____

15. 575 _____

16. 150 _____

17. 320 _____

18. 215 _____

19. 259 _____

20. 707 _____

21. 60 _____

22. 99 _____

23. 561 _____

24. 800 _____

25. 825 _____

Write the missing words.

26. 333 three hundred _____-three

27. 923 nine _____ twenty-three

28. 600 _____ hundred

29. 201 _____ hundred _____

30. 575 five _____ seventy-_____

31. 815 eight hundred _____

22

Understanding Dollars and Cents

Artiss is the treasurer for the drama club.
He is sorting the coins he has collected for
membership dues. He puts the pennies
into penny tubes. How much money,
in pennies, has Artiss collected?

I have 46 pennies extra.

There are _____ pennies in a dollar.

Artiss has _____ pennies in the penny tubes.

He has _____ more pennies that are not in a tube.
We say Artiss has saved **three dollars and**

forty-six cents, and write it as _____.
To understand the total amount of money that
Artiss has, study this place value chart.

In the amount, **$3.46,**

dollars	dimes	pennies
3	4	6

the digit _____ is in the **pennies** place.

the digit _____ is in the **dimes** place.

the digit _____ is in the **dollars** place.

✔ Remember to include the dollar sign and decimal
point in writing amounts of money.

Artiss has collected _____ in pennies.

Getting Started

Write the amounts.

1.  _____

2. 8 dollars and 30 pennies _____

3. 85 cents _____

4. 4 dollars _____

Practice

Write the amounts.

1.  _____

2. 3 dollars and 15 cents _____   3. 2 dollars and 4 dimes _____

4. 5 dimes and 6 cents _____   5. 7 dollars and 27 cents _____

6. 4 dollars, 2 dimes, and 8 pennies _____

7. 6 dollars and 2 dimes _____   8. 9 dollars and 99 cents _____

9. 1 dollar and 5 cents _____   10. 5 dollars and 89 cents _____

11. 2 dollars, 7 dimes and 0 pennies _____

EXCURSION

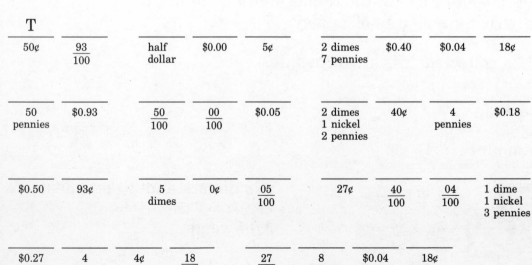

Where is the noisy drummer going?

To find out, match the letters on the chart with the money values below. The first one is done for you.

A = forty cents   K = eighteen cents
B = twenty-seven cents   N = four cents
E = five cents   O = ninety-three cents
H = zero   T = fifty cents

T								
50¢	$\frac{93}{100}$	half dollar	$0.00	5¢	2 dimes 7 pennies	$0.40	$0.04	18¢
50 pennies	$0.93	$\frac{50}{100}$	$\frac{00}{100}$	$0.05	2 dimes 1 nickel 2 pennies	40¢	4 pennies	$0.18
$0.50	93¢	5 dimes	0¢	$\frac{05}{100}$	27¢	$\frac{40}{100}$	$\frac{04}{100}$	1 dime 1 nickel 3 pennies
$0.27	4 dimes	4¢	$\frac{18}{100}$	$\frac{27}{100}$	8 nickels	$0.04	18¢	

24

Counting Money

Help Onida count the money she has collected from the customers on her paper route.

We count:

We say:

twenty
forty
sixty

seventy

seventy-five
eighty

eighty-one
eighty-two
eighty-three

eighty-three fifty
eighty-three seventy-five
eighty-three eighty-five
eighty-three ninety
eighty-three ninety-one
eighty-three ninety-two
eighty-three ninety-three

✔ Remember to include the dollar signs and decimal points.

Onida has collected _____.

Getting Started

Write the total amounts.

1.

_____

2.

_____

Practice

Write the total amounts.

1.

_____

2.

_____

3.

_____

4.

_____

5.

_____

6.

_____

7.

_____

8.

_____

Understanding Thousands

Roberto is taking inventory of the stickers that the bookstore has to sell. How many stickers are in stock?

Roberto counts _____ envelopes of 1,000 stickers each.

He has _____ sheets of 100 stickers each.

Roberto also has _____ strips of 10 stickers

each, and _____ individual stickers.
We say that Roberto counts **three thousand, two hundred fifty-six** stickers. We write the number as _____.

To understand the total number of stickers, study this place value chart.

In the number, **3,256,**

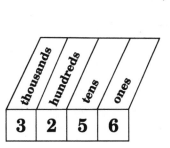

the digit _____ is in the ones place.

the digit _____ is in the tens place.

the digit _____ is in the hundreds place.

the digit _____ is in the thousands place.

Roberto counts _____ stickers in the bookstore.

Getting Started

Write the number.

1. five thousand, two hundred twenty-three _____

Write the place value of the red digits.

2. 3,275 _____   3. 1,086 _____   4. 4,390 _____   5. 6,005 _____

Write the missing words.

6. 1,900 one _____, nine hundred   7. 6,040 six thousand, _____

27

Practice

Write the numbers.

1. three thousand, six hundred fifty-seven _____

2. one thousand, ninety-four _____

3. eight thousand, two hundred eighty-three _____

4. four thousand, eight hundred eleven _____

5. two thousand one _____

Write the place value of the red digits.

6. 5,075 _____   7. 7,421 _____   8. 2,555 _____

9. 4,020 _____   10. 9,500 _____   11. 6,226 _____

Write the missing words.

12. 7,946 _____ thousand, nine _____ forty-six

13. 9,216 nine thousand, _____ hundred _____

EXCURSION

Checks can be used in place of cash to buy things.

October 1 ,1988

Payable to *Jiffy Auto Sales* $8,799.00

Eight thousand, seven hundred ninety-nine and 00/100 Dollars

John E. Cashmore

Write these dollar amounts in words, as you would write them on a check.

1. $3,075.00 _____ Dollars

2. $9,103.75 _____ Dollars

3. $1,240.16 _____ Dollars

4. $5,815.01 _____ Dollars

Comparing Numbers

The Parana River is in South America. The Mississippi River is in North America. Which river is longer?

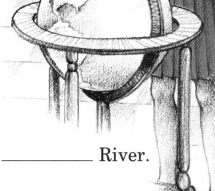

Principal Rivers of the World	
River	Length
Amazon	4,000 miles
Mississippi	2,348 miles
Nile	4,145 miles
Parana	2,485 miles

We want to know if the Parana or the Mississippi River is longer.

We know that the Parana River is _____ miles long.

The length of the Mississippi River is _____ miles.

To find the longer river, we compare their lengths.

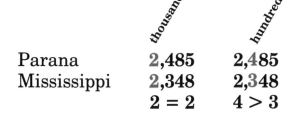

	thousands	hundreds
Parana	**2,485**	**2,485**
Mississippi	**2,348**	**2,348**
	2 = 2	4 > 3

We say 2,485 is greater than 2,348.

We write _____ > _____.

The _____ River is longer than the _____ River.

Getting Started

Compare these numbers. Write < or > in the circle.

1. 583 ◯ 581   2. 325 ◯ 383   3. 216 ◯ 410

4. 7,919 ◯ 8,215   5. 8,096 ◯ 8,039   6. 5,416 ◯ 5,420

Write the numbers in order from least to greatest.

7. 3,715, 4,210, 1,650   8. 3,748, 3,750, 3,746   9. 8,050, 8,196, 8,100

____, ____, ____   ____, ____, ____   ____, ____, ____

10. Write the names of the principal rivers in order, from shortest to longest.

_____   _____   _____   _____

Practice

Compare these numbers. Write < or > in the circle.

1. 468 ◯ 463   2. 297 ◯ 300   3. 897 ◯ 879

4. 3,246 ◯ 3,252   5. 6,485 ◯ 6,481   6. 8,296 ◯ 8,290

7. 5,084 ◯ 5,163   8. 7,006 ◯ 7,002   9. 4,561 ◯ 4,651

10. 8,000 ◯ 9,000   11. 1,250 ◯ 850   12. 2,080 ◯ 2,079

13. 6,361 ◯ 6,362   14. 8,207 ◯ 8,702   15. 3,500 ◯ 3,499

Write the numbers in order from least to greatest.

16. 468, 686, 560   17. 212, 235, 210   18. 376, 372, 378

——, ——, ——   ——, ——, ——   ——, ——, ——

19. 3,210, 3,240, 3,260   20. 8,512, 7,416, 7,800   21. 5,286, 5,179, 5,280

——, ——, ——   ——, ——, ——   ——, ——, ——

22. 7,427, 7,430, 7,425   23. 9,000, 8,967, 9,967   24. 4,241, 4,421, 4,124

——, ——, ——   ——, ——, ——   ——, ——, ——

Apply

Solve these problems.

25. The Ohio River is 975 miles long. The Red River is 1,270 miles long. Which river is longer?

26. Great Bear Lake is 1,463 feet deep. Lake Superior is 1,333 feet deep. Which lake is deeper?

27. The Verrazano-Narrows Bridge is 4,260 feet long. The Golden Gate Bridge is 4,200 feet long. Which bridge is longer?

28. The Lincoln Tunnel is 8,216 feet long. The Holland Tunnel is 8,557 feet long. Which tunnel is longer?

Rounding Numbers

Mr. Sanchez is buying his wife a birthday
present along with paper to wrap it.
Estimate the cost of each item by rounding.

We want to estimate the cost of each item
by rounding.
We know the cost of wrapping paper is _____.

The earrings cost _____ and the gold bracelet costs _____.

> To round a number to a particular
> place value, locate the digit to be
> rounded.

If the digit to the right is 0, 1,
2, 3 or 4, the digit we are
rounding stays the same. All
the digits to the right are
replaced by zeros.

$62 is rounded to _____.

✔ Sometimes it makes
more sense to round a
number to another place
value. We round $135 to
$140, rather than $100,
because $140 is a closer
estimate to the cost of the
bracelet.

If the digit to the right is 5, 6,
7, 8 or 9, the digit we are
rounding is raised one. All
digits to the right are replaced
by zeros.

39¢ is rounded to _____.

✔ When rounding money to the
nearest dollar, the rounded
number is written without a
decimal point, and without zeros
in the dimes and pennies places.
For example, $8.45 is rounded to
$8.

Mr. Sanchez will have to pay about _____ for

the wrapping paper, about _____ for the earrings

and about _____ for the bracelet.

Getting Started

Round to the nearest

1. ten. 38 _____   2. hundred. 316 _____   3. dollar. $3.81 _____

31

Practice

Round to the nearest ten.

1. 26 _____
2. 67 _____
3. 59¢ _____
4. 35 _____

5. 47¢ _____
6. 81 _____
7. 87 _____
8. 78¢ _____

9. 23 _____
10. 17 _____
11. 25¢ _____
12. 38 _____

13. 72 _____
14. 91¢ _____
15. 42 _____
16. 76 _____

Round to the nearest hundred.

17. 351 _____
18. 286 _____
19. 142 _____
20. $350 _____

21. $187 _____
22. 427 _____
23. 583 _____
24. 791 _____

25. 820 _____
26. $275 _____
27. 321 _____
28. 468 _____

Round to the nearest dollar.

29. $8.51 _____
30. $6.35 _____
31. $2.50 _____
32. $3.16 _____

33. $7.89 _____
34. $5.29 _____
35. $4.10 _____
36. $7.38 _____

EXCURSION

How many hidden numbers can you find in the meaning of these words? Write the numbers on the blanks.

double _____
dozen _____
baker's dozen _____

decade _____
score _____
octet _____

unit _____
quartet _____
gross _____

century _____
quintet _____
twins _____

ream _____
triple _____
quire _____

trio _____
duo _____
quadruplets _____

Rounding Greater Numbers

Theodore Roosevelt made his home in Oyster Bay, New York. His cousin Franklin D. Roosevelt made his home in Hyde Park, New York. About how many people live in each of these towns?

Small Towns in New York

Town	Population
Geneseo	6,746
Herkimer	8,383
Hyde Park	2,550
Larchmont	6,308
Oyster Bay	6,497

We want to estimate the population of Oyster Bay and Hyde Park.
We know the population of Oyster Bay is

_____ and that of Hyde Park is _____.
We can estimate these populations to thousands place, to hundreds or to tens.

	Population	Rounded to thousands	Rounded to hundreds	Rounded to tens
Oyster Bay	6,497	6,000	6,500	6,500
Hyde Park	_____	_____	_____	_____

About _____ people live in Oyster Bay.

About _____ people live in Hyde Park.

Getting Started

Round to the nearest ten.

1. 5,438 _____
2. 7,015 _____
3. 7,212 _____
4. 3,896 _____

Round to the nearest hundred.

5. 3,248 _____
6. 5,598 _____
7. 6,750 _____
8. 8,290 _____

Round to the nearest thousand.

9. 6,585 _____
10. 3,296 _____
11. 4,500 _____
12. 8,196 _____

Practice

Round to the nearest ten.

1. 3,276 _____   2. 4,391 _____   3. 7,549 _____   4. 4,212 _____

5. 6,831 _____   6. 4,287 _____   7. 6,375 _____   8. 7,126 _____

9. 5,650 _____   10. 8,296 _____   11. 9,632 _____   12. 5,864 _____

Round to the nearest hundred.

13. 2,975 _____   14. 3,710 _____   15. 6,823 _____   16. 7,879 _____

17. 4,176 _____   18. 5,275 _____   19. 8,048 _____   20. 3,119 _____

21. 8,225 _____   22. 6,867 _____   23. 5,500 _____   24. 3,271 _____

Round to the nearest thousand.

25. 2,659 _____   26. 8,960 _____   27. 7,016 _____   28. 6,400 _____

29. 4,867 _____   30. 3,450 _____   31. 6,650 _____   32. 2,905 _____

33. 7,221 _____   34. 8,949 _____   35. 3,738 _____   36. 5,615 _____

Small Towns in New York	
Town	**Population**
Bayport	9,282
Brockport	9,776
Delmar	8,423
Great Neck	9,168
Herricks	8,123

	Round each population to the nearest ten.	Round to the nearest hundred.
37. Bayport	_____	_____
38. Brockport	_____	_____
39. Delmar	_____	_____
40. Great Neck	_____	_____
41. Herricks	_____	_____

Understanding Ten Thousands and Hundred Thousands

Normal Heart Rates	
Beats	**Time**
72	minute
4,320	hour
103,680	day

A human heart normally beats 72 times every minute. How many times does a normal heart beat in one day?

We know that the normal heart will beat

_____ times in one day. To understand this number, study this place value chart.

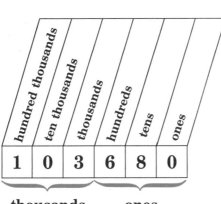

A comma separates the periods.

We say a normal heart beats **one hundred three thousand, six hundred eighty** times a day.

We write the number as _____.

Getting Started

Write the place value of the red digits.

1. 341,219

2. 120,210

3. 156,035

_____   _____   _____

Write the number.

4. two hundred forty-six thousand, five hundred fifteen _____

Write the missing word.

5. 470,050 four hundred seventy _____, fifty

35

Practice

Write the place value of the red digits.

1. 63,215

2. 139,073

3. 21,875

4. 370,150

_____   _____   _____   _____

5. 929,175

6. 836,207

7. 180,000

8. 57,329

_____   _____   _____   _____

Write the numbers.

9. four hundred twenty-seven thousand, three hundred twelve _____

10. two hundred nine thousand, one hundred fifty-six _____

11. eighty-seven thousand, nine hundred nine _____

12. ten thousand, two hundred eighty-three _____

Write the missing words.

13. 64,419 sixty-four _____, four hundred nineteen

14. 406,060 four _____ six thousand, sixty

15. 515,291 five hundred _____ thousand, two hundred ninety-one

Apply

Write the numbers.

16. The highest mountain in the world is Mt. Everest. It is twenty-nine thousand, twenty-eight feet high.

17. In 1962, Major Robert M. White flew an X-15 plane to the altitude of three hundred fourteen thousand, seven hundred fifty feet.

18. Earth is about two hundred thirty-eight thousand, eight hundred sixty miles from the moon.

19. The earth travels in orbit at about sixty-six thousand, six hundred miles per hour.

Understanding Millions

Chicago is the home of the world's busiest airport. Over 20 million passengers take off from O'Hare Airport each year. How many travellers have departed from O'Hare according to the meter?

PASSENGER DEPARTURES

2 5 6 3 6 4 8 3

We know the meter shows _____ passengers have departed from O'Hare Airport. To understand this number, study this place value chart.

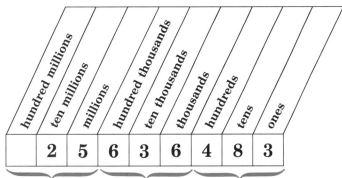

hundred millions	ten millions	millions	hundred thousands	ten thousands	thousands	hundreds	tens	ones
2	5	6	3	6	4	8	3

millions period , thousands period , ones period

Commas separate the periods.

We say that **twenty-five million, six hundred thirty-six thousand, four hundred eighty-three** travellers have departed from O'Hare Airport

this year. We write this number as _____ .

Getting Started

Write the numbers.

1. two hundred twelve million, four hundred sixty-five thousand, twenty-nine _____

Write the place value of the red digits.

2. 23,465,183   3. 706,341,212   4. 5,962,159

_____   _____   _____

Practice

Write the numbers.

1. three hundred seventy-five million, two hundred five thousand, sixty-seven _____

2. four hundred ten million, five hundred sixteen thousand, four hundred twenty _____

3. thirty-eight million, sixty-three thousand, eight hundred forty-nine _____

Write the place value of the red digits.

4. 6,241,573

_____

5. 14,903,124

_____

6. 136,248,796

_____

7. 828,297,159

_____

8. 16,274,302

_____

9. 460,760,858

_____

10. 3,926,575

_____

11. 47,239,105

_____

12. 906,400,000

_____

EXCURSION

Rearrange the letters in each word to help write these large numbers.

1. enevs   lloimni   hteer   nudrhde   tduhonas

_____   _____   _____   _____   _____

2. tyiff-wto   sdntuoha   owt   rddheun   iffneet

_____   _____   _____   _____   _____

3. thgie   dhernud   neo   nmliloi   inne   shudtoan

_____   _____   _____   _____   _____   _____

38

Guessing and Checking

Holly's age is 4 times Phillip's age.
Eric's age is twice Phillip's age. The sum of
all of their ages is 21. How old is each child?

★ **SEE**

We need to find each child's age.

We know:
Holly is _____ times older than Phillip.

Eric is _____ times older than Phillip.

The sum of all three ages is _____.

★ **PLAN**

We can make an **educated guess** of each child's
age using the given information. Since the facts
seem to show that Phillip is the youngest, we
should start with him. To know when we have
reached the solution, it is important to check
after each guess. We can also use guesses to
help us make a better guess on the next try.

★ **DO**

	Phillip's Age	Holly's Age	Eric's Age	Sum of Ages	
Guess 1	5	20	10	35	(too high)
Guess 2	2	8	_____	_____	(too low)
Guess 3	3	_____	6	_____	

Phillip is _____ years old. Holly is _____ and Eric is _____.

★ **CHECK**

We can check further by making sure our solution fits the problem.
Philip's age: 3
Holly's age: 12 (4 × 3 = 12)
Eric's age: 6 (2 × 3 = 6)   _____ + _____ + _____ = _____

Apply

Guess and check to help solve these problems.

1. Put each of the digits from 1 to 9 in a circle so each side of the triangle adds up to exactly 20.

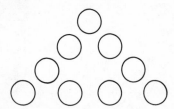

2. Put the digits 1 through 7 in the circles so that any 3 circles connected by a line have the same sum.

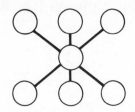

3. Use the digits 1 through 7 only once to make an addition problem that will have a sum of 100. Find 2 ways to solve this.

4. Complete this multiplication table.

×				
8				72
4		12		
				18
	25		35	

5. If the sum of two numbers is 8 and the product is 0, what are the two numbers?

6. How can a 6-digit number with 5 in the ten-thousands place be greater than a number with 9 in the ten-thousands place?

7. One of the digits in a seven-digit number is the digit 6. If the digit in the next place to the left has a value 10 times the value of the digit 6, what digit is to the left?

8. Write a guess-and-check problem about four numbers for a classmate to solve. Use information about the numbers shown below.

$$20 + 40 + 60 + 80 = 200$$

Write the place value of the red digits.

1. 6,508
2. 13,279
3. 8,111
4. 149,000,432

_____   _____   _____   _____

5. 3,406
6. 126,031,210
7. 2,479,036
8. 75,493,000

_____   _____   _____   _____

Write the numbers.

9. three hundred sixty-five   10. four thousand, two hundred twenty-four

_____   _____

11. three million, three hundred thousand, sixty-two

_____

Write the missing words.

12. 56,483 fifty-six _____, four _____ eighty-three

13. 216,050,000 two _____ sixteen _____, fifty _____

Compare these numbers.

14. 6,247 ◯ 4,396   15. 7,743 ◯ 7,748   16. 5,029 ◯ 5,039

Round to the nearest ten.

17. 1,463 _____   18. 3,555 _____   19. 4,096 _____

Round to the nearest hundred or dollar.

20. 398 _____   21. 456 _____   22. $7.48 _____

23. $8.21 _____   24. 1,612 _____   25. 550 _____

Circle the letter of the correct answer.

1 53 ◯ 35

a <
b >

2 4 + 8

a 4
b 10
c 12
d NG

3   8
    + 7

a 14
b 15
c 16
d NG

4   3
    2
  + 6

a 5
b 8
c 13
d NG

5 7 + (6 + 3)

a 2
b 9
c 16
d NG

6 14 − 8

a 6
b 7
c 8
d NG

7   12
    − 9

a 3
b 4
c 5
d NG

8   9
    − 0

a 0
b 9
c 10
d NG

9 $n + 6 = 13$
    $n = ?$

a 5
b 6
c 7
d NG

10 What is the value of the 5 in 4,256?

a ones
b tens
c hundreds
d NG

11 3,279 ◯ 3,289

a <
b >

12 Round 896 to the nearest hundred

a 800
b 900
c NG

13 Round 6,750 to the nearest thousand.

a 6,000
b 6,800
c 7,000
d NG

14 What is the value of the 9 in 29,067?

a tens
b hundreds
c thousands
d NG

 score

ADDITION OF WHOLE NUMBERS

Adding 2-digit Numbers

Carla eats fruit for breakfast each morning. This morning, she ate a peach and half a grapefruit. How many calories does Carla get in her fruit?

We want to know the total number of calories that Carla gets from the fruit.

We know a peach provides _____ calories

and half a grapefruit _____ calories.

To find the total, we add _____ and _____.

Add the ones.	Make a trade.	Add the tens.

  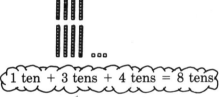

6 ones + 7 ones = 13 ones   13 ones = 1 ten + 3 ones   1 ten + 3 tens + 4 tens = 8 tens

$$\begin{array}{r} 3\,6 \\ +\,4\,7 \\ \hline \end{array}$$

$$\begin{array}{r} \overset{1}{3}\,6 \\ +\,4\,7 \\ \hline 3 \end{array}$$

$$\begin{array}{r} \overset{1}{3}\,6 \quad \text{addend} \\ +\,4\,7 \quad \text{addend} \\ \hline 8\,3 \quad \text{sum} \end{array}$$

Carla gets _____ calories from the fruit she eats.

Getting Started

Add.

1. $\begin{array}{r} 43 \\ +\,18 \\ \hline \end{array}$

2. $\begin{array}{r} 79 \\ +\,35 \\ \hline \end{array}$

3. $\begin{array}{r} 26 \\ +\,53 \\ \hline \end{array}$

4. $\begin{array}{r} 86 \\ +\,58 \\ \hline \end{array}$

Copy and add.

5. 17 + 59

6. 76 + 8

7. 61 + 48

8. 87 + 67

43

Practice

Add.

1. 38 +26	2. 49 + 8	3. 36 +81	4. 9 +86	5. 78 +57
6. 76 +43	7. 45 +55	8. 26 + 9	9. 59 +63	10. 71 +65
11. 6 +58	12. 67 +96	13. 80 +17	14. 46 +74	15. 98 +96

Copy and Do

16. 32 + 19   17. 75 + 48   18. 82 + 57   19. 25 + 96

20. 43 + 58   21. 22 + 67   22. 9 + 86   23. 82 + 53

24. 74 + 8   25. 82 + 48   26. 93 + 19   27. 57 + 70

Apply

Solve these problems.

28. Robert poured a cup of skim milk over his bowl of oatmeal. The oatmeal contained 68 calories and the skim milk had 85. How many calories did Robert eat?

29. Juanita ate a scrambled egg and a piece of toast. The egg contained 96 calories and the toast had 79. How many calories did Juanita eat?

Adding 3-digit Numbers

Jerry is the left tackle for Saratoga High School. Bill is the left guard. Jerry and Bill work well when they block together. What is their total weight?

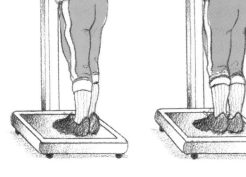

We want to know the total weight of the two players.

Jerry weighs _____ pounds and Bill

weighs _____.

To find their total weight, we add _____ and _____.

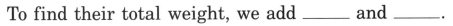

Add the ones and trade.	Add the tens and trade.	Add the hundreds.

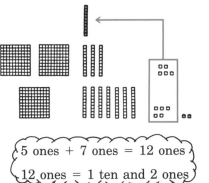 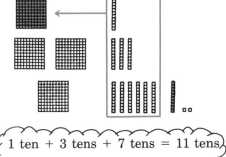 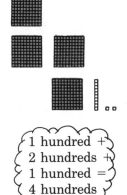

5 ones + 7 ones = 12 ones
12 ones = 1 ten and 2 ones

1 ten + 3 tens + 7 tens = 11 tens
11 tens = 1 hundred and 1 ten

1 hundred +
2 hundreds +
1 hundred =
4 hundreds

$$
\begin{array}{r}
{\overset{1}{2}}3\,5 \\
+\,1\,7\,7 \\
\hline
2
\end{array}
$$

$$
\begin{array}{r}
\overset{1}{2}\overset{1}{3}\,5 \\
+\,1\,7\,7 \\
\hline
1\,2
\end{array}
$$

$$
\begin{array}{r}
\overset{1}{2}\,3\,5 \\
+\,1\,7\,7 \\
\hline
4\,1\,2
\end{array}
$$

The total weight for both boys is _____ pounds.

Getting Started

Add.

1. $\begin{array}{r} 138 \\ +147 \end{array}$

2. $\begin{array}{r} 384 \\ +135 \end{array}$

3. $\begin{array}{r} 473 \\ +798 \end{array}$

4. $\begin{array}{r} 157 \\ +\ 60 \end{array}$

Copy and add.

5. $683 + 294$

6. $64 + 743$

7. $811 + 496$

8. $426 + 788$

45

Practice

Add.

1. 256
    + 129

2. 627
    + 438

3. 581
    + 276

4. 875
    + 89

5.   67
    + 483

6. 373
    + 876

7. 541
    + 212

8. 347
    + 96

9. 709
    + 584

10. 295
    + 99

11. 560
    + 348

12. 883
    + 910

13. 396
    + 264

14. 79
    + 389

15. 543
    + 377

Copy and Do

16. 386 + 409

17. 718 + 534

18. 475 + 221

19. 256 + 908

20. 415 + 344

21. 690 + 283

22. 596 + 19

23. 753 + 188

24. 93 + 815

25. 126 + 568

26. 836 + 684

27. 314 + 375

Apply

Solve these problems.

28. The Amelia Earhart School library contains 472 fiction books. The librarian is ordering 255 more. How many fiction books will the library have?

29. The boys at Clara Barton School collected 267 cans of food for the Thanksgiving food drive. The girls brought in 278 cans. Which group collected the greater number of cans?

Adding 4-digit Numbers

The Missouri-Mississippi River system is the third longest river in the world. The Missouri starts at Three Forks, Montana, and joins the lower Mississippi River just north of St. Louis. It empties into the Gulf of Mexico near New Orleans. How long is the Missouri-Mississippi River system?

Three Forks

3,726 km

St. Louis

2,295 km

New Orleans

We want to know the total length of the Missouri-Mississippi River system.

We know the Missouri River from Three Forks

to St. Louis measures _____ kilometers.

The Mississippi River from St. Louis to

New Orleans measures _____ kilometers.

To find the system's total length, we add _____ and _____.

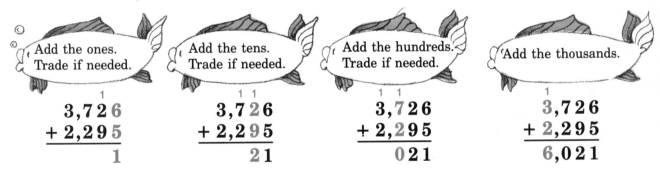

Add the ones. Trade if needed.

```
  1
3,726
+2,295
    1
```

Add the tens. Trade if needed.

```
 1 1
3,726
+2,295
   21
```

Add the hundreds. Trade if needed.

```
 1 1
3,726
+2,295
  021
```

Add the thousands.

```
  1
3,726
+2,295
6,021
```

The Missouri-Mississippi River system is _____ kilometers long.

Getting Started

Add.

1. 7,836
   + 1,193

2. 4,827
   + 9,162

3. 6,256
   + 3,498

Copy and add.

4. 4,275 + 907

5. 8,246 + 3,766

6. 659 + 5,941

47

Practice

Add.

1. $\begin{array}{r} 4{,}263 \\ +\,3{,}514 \\ \hline \end{array}$

2. $\begin{array}{r} 3{,}482 \\ +\,6{,}279 \\ \hline \end{array}$

3. $\begin{array}{r} 6{,}257 \\ +\,5{,}767 \\ \hline \end{array}$

4. $\begin{array}{r} 8{,}546 \\ +\,1{,}829 \\ \hline \end{array}$

5. $\begin{array}{r} 4{,}395 \\ +\,7{,}826 \\ \hline \end{array}$

6. $\begin{array}{r} 2{,}054 \\ +\,9{,}975 \\ \hline \end{array}$

7. $\begin{array}{r} 8{,}370 \\ +\,7{,}851 \\ \hline \end{array}$

8. $\begin{array}{r} 6{,}975 \\ +\,6{,}648 \\ \hline \end{array}$

Copy and Do

9. $5{,}483 + 807$

10. $4{,}563 + 8{,}789$

11. $7{,}625 + 9{,}498$

12. $3{,}748 + 6{,}943$

13. $673 + 4{,}287$

14. $8{,}496 + 7{,}827$

15. $5{,}356 + 7{,}409$

16. $4{,}358 + 97$

17. $2{,}195 + 3{,}284$

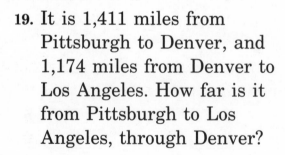

Apply

Solve these problems.

18. The enrollment of Colgate University in one year included 1,423 men and 1,127 women. What was the total number of students?

19. It is 1,411 miles from Pittsburgh to Denver, and 1,174 miles from Denver to Los Angeles. How far is it from Pittsburgh to Los Angeles, through Denver?

EXCURSION

Fill in the blanks on this magic square so that the sum of each row down, across and diagonally equals 65. You may use the numbers 1 through 25 only once.

17		1		15
23	5		14	
	6	13		22
10				3
	18	25	2	

Estimating Sums

Sometimes we don't need an exact answer to a problem. We only need to estimate the answer. For example, approximately how many gallons of gasoline are stored in these two tanks?

We want an estimate of the total number of gallons in both tanks.

Tank number 1 contains _____ gallons of gasoline.

Tank number 2 contains _____ gallons. To estimate the sum, we can round each addend to the nearest thousand, and add these rounded numbers.

1,934 is rounded to _____.

3,587 is rounded to _____.

There are about _____ gallons of gasoline stored in the two tanks.

Getting Started

Estimate the sum after rounding each addend to the nearest ten.

1.	56 + 87	2.	34 + 415	3.	163 + 589	4.	3,019 + 2,936

Estimate the sum after rounding each addend to the nearest hundred.

5.	368 + 526	6.	1,946 + 758	7.	968 + 412	8.	3,750 + 1,895

Estimate the sum after rounding each addend to the nearest thousand.

9.	5,260 + 1,680	10.	8,576 + 2,750	11.	6,749 + 7,284	12.	8,500 + 3,850

Practice

Estimate the sum after rounding each addend to the nearest ten.

1. 23
   + 58

2. 59
   + 16

3. 275
   + 88

4. 546
   + 682

5. 7,367
   + 4,431

Estimate the sum after rounding each addend to the nearest hundred.

6. 393
   + 167

7. 485
   + 836

8. 1,941
   +   287

9. 1,755
   + 4,628

10. 2,808
    + 1,576

Estimate the sum after rounding each addend to the nearest thousand.

11. 3,965
    + 2,646

12. 8,397
    + 6,845

13. 5,545
    + 7,851

14. 4,096
    + 9,850

Copy and Do

15. 73 + 86

16. 93 + 18

17. 27 + 76

18. 41 + 88

19. 375 + 916

20. 876 + 652

21. 248 + 796

22. 850 + 525

23. 5,964 + 8,572

24. 8,863 + 1,650

25. 9,452 + 3,925

26. 229 + 4,076

Apply

Solve these problems.

27. One storage tank can hold 4,246 gallons of gasoline. Another tank can hold 3,575 gallons. About how many gallons of gasoline can both tanks hold?

28. It is 1,717 miles from Albany, New York to Dallas, Texas. Dallas is another 2,151 miles from Seattle, Washington. About how far is it from Albany to Seattle, if you drive through Dallas?

Adding 5-digit Numbers

The Dallas Cowboys and the Washington Redskins play each other twice each year. What was the total attendance for this year's games?

We want to know the total number of fans who attended both games.

We know that _____ fans attended the game in Dallas.

The Washington game drew _____ fans.

To find the sum, we add _____ and _____.

ADMIT ONE

To add two 5-digit numbers, begin by adding the ones. Then add each column to the left. Trade if needed.

$$
\begin{array}{r}
1 \\
78,475 \\
+\,76,386 \\
\hline
1
\end{array}
\qquad
\begin{array}{r}
1\ 1 \\
78,475 \\
+\,76,386 \\
\hline
61
\end{array}
\qquad
\begin{array}{r}
1 \\
78,475 \\
+\,76,386 \\
\hline
861
\end{array}
\qquad
\begin{array}{r}
1 \\
78,475 \\
+\,76,386 \\
\hline
4,861
\end{array}
\qquad
\begin{array}{r}
1 \\
78,475 \\
+\,76,386 \\
\hline
154,861
\end{array}
$$

The total attendance for both games was _____.

Getting Started

Add.

1. $\begin{array}{r} 17,836 \\ +\ \ 1,295 \\ \hline \end{array}$

2. $\begin{array}{r} 4,827 \\ +\,19,254 \\ \hline \end{array}$

3. $\begin{array}{r} 16,875 \\ +\,58,596 \\ \hline \end{array}$

4. $\begin{array}{r} 39,454 \\ +\,12,926 \\ \hline \end{array}$

5. $\begin{array}{r} 49,025 \\ +\,38,484 \\ \hline \end{array}$

6. $\begin{array}{r} 22,456 \\ +\,67,381 \\ \hline \end{array}$

Copy and add.

7. $16,214 + 8,295$

8. $2,897 + 56,850$

9. $37,488 + 55,746$

Practice

Add.

1. 16,354
   + 2,865

2. 4,967
   + 15,096

3. 17,858
   + 8,392

4. 11,456
   + 56,729

5. 96,254
   + 39,687

6. 9,560
   + 83,785

7. 26,586
   + 76,253

8. 18,609
   + 25,996

9. 35,694
   + 47,828

10. 83,467
    + 25,704

11. 75,496
    + 86,894

12. 48,182
    + 69,778

Copy and Do

13. 56,965 + 38,758

14. 41,853 + 26,348

15. 77,486 + 67,398

16. 47,836 + 9,548

17. 64,495 + 40,867

18. 87,187 + 56,838

19. 14,390 + 78,956

20. 60,086 + 88,956

21. 47,539 + 26,211

EXCURSION

Write the missing numbers in these problems.

1. ☐ 6 , 5 0 ☐
   + 1 ☐ , 9 ☐ 4
   ─────────────
   5 9 , ☐ 3 1

2. ☐ 3 , ☐ 7 4
   + 2 5 , 4 2 ☐
   ─────────────
   4 ☐ , 3 ☐ 3

3. 3 8 , ☐ 5 ☐
   + ☐ 6 , 1 ☐ 7
   ─────────────
   6 ☐ , 2 5 0

4. ☐ 7 , 0 ☐ 3
   + 5 ☐ , 2 1 8
   ─────────────
   7 1 , ☐ 6 ☐

Column Addition

The Metro All-Stars celebrated their tournament win by going out for pizza. They ordered one large Supreme, one family-sized Special and one large Vegetable. How much was their bill?

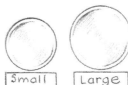

Pizza			
	Supreme	**Special**	**Vegetable**
Family	$12.95	$11.59	$10.29
Large	$9.95	$8.59	$7.29
Small	$6.95	$5.59	$4.29

We want to know the total bill.

We know that a large Supreme pizza costs _____.

A family-sized Special costs _____.

A large Vegetable pizza costs _____.

To find the sum of all the prices, we add

_____, _____ and _____.

✔ When adding numbers in a column, add two digits at a time, and then add that sum to the next digit.

✔ When adding amounts of money, remember to line up the decimal points. Include the dollar sign and decimal point in the sum.

$$
\begin{array}{r}
^2 \\
\$\ \ 9.95 \\
11.59 \\
+\ \ \ 7.29 \\
\hline
3
\end{array}
\qquad
\begin{array}{l}
5 + 9 = 14 \\
\\
14 + 9 = 23
\end{array}
\qquad
\begin{array}{r}
^{1\ 2} \\
\$\ \ 9.95 \\
11.59 \\
+\ \ \ 7.29 \\
\hline
.83
\end{array}
\qquad
\begin{array}{r}
^{1\ 1} \\
\$\ \ 9.95 \\
11.59 \\
+\ \ \ 7.29 \\
\hline
8.83
\end{array}
\qquad
\begin{array}{r}
^1 \\
\$\ \ 9.95 \\
11.59 \\
+\ \ \ 7.29 \\
\hline
\$28.83
\end{array}
$$

The total pizza bill was _____.

Getting Started

Add.

1.
```
   43
   96
+ 83
```

2.
```
$  37.46
  158.49
+  65.53
```

Copy and add.

3. 756 + 4,096 + 8,749

4. $52.46 + $96.75 + $43.38

Practice

Add.

1.
```
    86
    94
  + 27
```

2.
```
   215
    48
  +135
```

3.
```
  $2.47
   6.29
  + 5.15
```

4.
```
  $8.37
   0.96
  + 4.15
```

5.
```
   168
   457
  +816
```

6.
```
  $4.86
   2.95
  + 6.18
```

7.
```
    738
    915
  +2,316
```

8.
```
  $25.10
    6.15
  +  8.85
```

9.
```
  1,643
    851
  +1,175
```

10.
```
  $126.21
    27.39
  + 436.51
```

11.
```
  $ 16.43
   537.82
     4.57
  +  89.75
```

12.
```
   37,265
   15,586
   39,509
  + 4,228
```

Copy and Do

13. 48 + 87

14. 64 + 168 + 452

15. 869 + 47 + 1,750

16. 984 + 5,465 + 3,750

17. $41.56 + $1.97 + $562.27

18. $39.75 + $18.56 + $27.38

19. $50.37 + $392.47 + $88.50

20. $65.46 + $39.75 + $132.59 + $3.40

21. 13,750 + 27,967 + 37,875

22. 27,296 + 8,275 + 11,750 + 2,068

Apply

Use the pizza order board on page 53 to find
the total cost of these orders.

23. 1 family Vegetable
    1 large Vegetable
    1 small Vegetable

24. 1 family Supreme
    1 family Special
    1 large Special
    1 small Vegetable

Making a Systematic Listing or Table

Peanuts are packaged in 1-pound and 2-pound cans. List all the different ways you could buy 10 pounds of peanuts.

★ **SEE**

We need to find:
    all possible arrangements for purchasing 10 pounds of peanuts.
We know:
    peanuts come in _____-pound and _____-pound cans.

    A total of _____ pounds are being purchased.

★ **PLAN**

We can make an organized list of all the possibilities.

★ **DO**

Number of 1-lb Cans	10	9	8	7	6	5	4	3	2	1	0
Number of 2-lb Cans	0	0	1	1	2	2	3	3	4	4	5
Total Weight	10	9	10	9	10	9	10	9	10	9	10
Possible Solution	Yes	No									

★ **CHECK**

The total weight of the 1-pound cans plus the total weight of the 2-pound cans should equal 10 pounds.

$10 + \underline{} = \underline{}$ $8 + \underline{} = \underline{}$ $6 + \underline{} = \underline{}$

$4 + \underline{} = \underline{}$ $2 + \underline{} = \underline{}$ $0 + \underline{} = \underline{}$

Apply

Make a systematic listing or table to help solve these problems.

1. A snail crawls five inches up a wall the first minute and then slides back two inches during the second minute. It moves five inches forward the third minute and slides back two inches the fourth minute. If the snail continues in this manner, how far will the snail have traveled in five minutes?

2. The three numbered marbles shown below are placed in a bag.

   ③ ⑤ ①

   Without looking at the numbers pick two marbles from the bag. Your score is the sum of the numbers on the two marbles. What are all possible scores?

3. The four numbered marbles shown below are placed in a bag.

   ① ② ④ ⑧

   Without looking at the numbers, draw two marbles from the bag and find the sum of their numbers. What scores are possible?

4. Two cuckoo clocks are hanging on the wall. The cuckoo from the first clock comes out every 6 minutes, while the cuckoo from the second clock comes out every 8 minutes. If both cuckoos come out at noon, when will they come out together again?

5. Marcy is making a list to solve a problem. She has written 21, 32, 43, and 54. Tell what number you think she will write next and explain why.

6. Read Exercise 1 again. If the snail has traveled 1 foot up the wall, how many minutes has it been crawling? (Remember: 1 foot = 12 inches.)

7. Read Exercise 2 again. What if the digits on the marbles were 4, 6, and 2. How would this affect the scores you listed?

8. If you increase each addend in an addition problem by 100, by how much would you increase the sum?

Calculator Codes

A calculator has **number keys, operation keys** and **special keys** on its **keyboard.** The calculator also has an **on/off key.** When you turn your calculator on, a zero should show on the screen. When you press a number key or operation key, an **entry** is made in the calculator and shows on the screen. When you press the [C] key, all entries are cleared from the calculator. When you press the [CE] key, the last entry is cancelled, but the previous entries are remembered.

Number Keys	**Operation Keys**	**Special Keys**
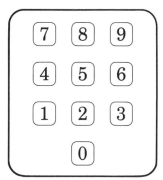	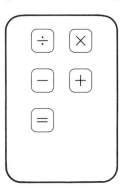	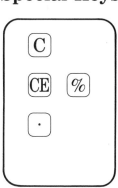

A **calculator code** gives the order for pressing the keys on your calculator. Try these codes and write the results on the screen.

127 [+] 326 [=] ( )

5162 [+] 463 [+] 2000 [=] ( )

18036 [+] 6259 [+] 2475 [+] 72405 [=] ( )

✔ When you enter an amount of money into the calculator, the zeros to the far right of the decimal point do not have to be entered. The calculator will not print them, or a dollar sign, in the answer.

$9.20 will be entered as and appear as (9.2).

Enter this code and write the answer on the screen:

65 [·] 45 [+] 72 [·] 05 [+] 6 [·] 4 [=] ( )

Practice

Complete these codes. Write the answers on the screens.

1. 5 $\cdot$ 16 $+$ 9 $\cdot$ 84 = ⬭
2. 7691 $+$ 12465 $=$ ⬭
3. 36615 $+$ 9475 $=$ ⬭
4. 6458 $+$ 605 $+$ 11927 $=$ ⬭

Use a calculator to find the sum.
Use estimation to be sure the answer seems correct.

5.
```
   247
   629
 + 515
```

6.
```
  1,643
    851
+ 1,175
```

7.
```
  42,621
  27,436
  16,948
+ 11,753
```

8.
```
  16,941
  40,432
     895
 + 6,748
```

Copy and Do

9. $3.57 + $2.96 + $8.38

10. $7.95 + $24.63 + $87.51

11. 8,207 + 28,416 + 3,796

12. 6,240 + 14,256 + 3,901

Apply

Use a calculator to solve this problem.

13. The three tallest mountains in the United States are Mt. McKinley, St. Elias and Mt. Foraker. These mountains are all in Alaska. If you climbed all 3 mountains, how many feet of mountain have you scaled?

Mountain	Height
Mt. McKinley	20,320 ft
St. Elias	18,008 ft
Mt. Foraker	17,400 ft

EXCURSION

What does Sally do at the seashore?

To figure out this mystery, complete each code on the calculator. Then turn the calculator upside down and print each word that shows on the screen.

1. 113 $+$ 96 $+$ 136 $=$ ___ ___ ___

2. 44772 $+$ 12963 $=$ ___ ___ ___ ___ ___

3. 175596 $+$ 39501 $+$ 362248 $=$ ___ ___ ___ ___ ___ ___ ___.

3 CHAPTER TEST

Add.

1. 63
   + 31

2. 52
   + 26

3. 84
   + 29

4. 75
   + 86

5. 225
   + 134

6. 604
   + 138

7. 541
   + 183

8. 958
   + 476

9. 2,426
   + 1,273

10. 4,625
    + 2,419

11. 7,219
    + 5,825

12. 4,926
    + 8,286

13. 4,952
    + 6,098

14. 7,846
    + 9,752

15. 9,476
    + 3,697

16. 6,543
    + 9,758

Estimate the sum after rounding to the
nearest hundred or dollar.

17. 459
    + 675

18. 352
    + 687

19. 5,290
    + 7,500

20. $18.96
    + 37.25

Estimate the sum after rounding to the
nearest thousand.

21. 5,296
    + 3,475

22. 1,256
    + 7,185

23. 6,295
    + 8,921

24. 8,377
    + 2,934

Add.

25. 892
     437
    + 186

26. 7,275
     4,687
    + 2,651

27. 11,751
      2,627
    + 37,583

28. $29.47
      7.55
    + 58.43

Circle the letter of the correct answer.

1 5 + 9

a 13
b 14
c 15
d NG

2   4
    + 8

a 12
b 13
c 14
d NG

3   4
      3
    + 8

a 7
b 11
c 15
d NG

4 16 − 9

a 8
b 7
c 6
d NG

5   1 1
    −   8

a 4
b 5
c 6
d NG

6 7 + n = 9
      n = ?

a 2
b 5
c 16
d NG

7 What is the value of the 3
in 2,436?

a tens
b hundreds
c thousands
d NG

8 2,358 $\bigcirc$ 2,538

a <
b >

9 Round 750 to the nearest
hundred.

a 600
b 700
c NG

10 Round 5,285 to the
nearest thousand.

a 5,000
b 6,000
c NG

11 What is the value of the 5
in 357,286?

a ten
    thousands
b thousands
c hundreds
d NG

12 54 + 87

a 131
b 141
c 1,311
d NG

13 257 + 189

a 336
b 346
c 446
d NG

14   3,279
     + 5,726

a 9,005
b 9,015
c 9,105
d NG

☐ score

SUBTRACTION OF WHOLE NUMBERS

Subtracting 2-digit Numbers

Abby, who is on the swim team, has saved $50 to buy a waterproof watch. How much will she have left after she buys the watch?

We want to know how much Abby will have left after her purchase.
We know that Abby has saved _____.

The watch costs _____.
To find the amount left, we subtract _____

from _____.

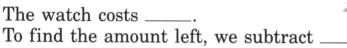

Trade if needed.	Subtract the ones.	Subtract the tens.

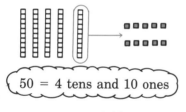

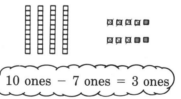

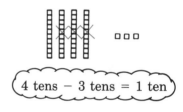

50 = 4 tens and 10 ones

10 ones − 7 ones = 3 ones

4 tens − 3 tens = 1 ten

$$\begin{array}{r} \overset{4\ 10}{\$\cancel{5}0} \\ -\ 37 \\ \hline \end{array}$$

$$\begin{array}{r} \overset{4\ 10}{\$\cancel{5}0} \\ -\ 37 \\ \hline 3 \end{array}$$

$$\begin{array}{r} \overset{4}{\$\cancel{5}0} \\ -\ 37 \\ \hline \$13 \end{array}$$

Abby will have _____ left.

Getting Started

Subtract.

1. $\begin{array}{r} 79 \\ -16 \\ \hline \end{array}$

2. $\begin{array}{r} 25 \\ -\ 9 \\ \hline \end{array}$

3. $\begin{array}{r} 97 \\ -28 \\ \hline \end{array}$

4. $\begin{array}{r} 52 \\ -14 \\ \hline \end{array}$

Copy and subtract.

5. $80 - 14$

6. $57 - 20$

7. $63 - 61$

8. $84 - 27$

Practice

Subtract.

1. 43
    − 13

2. 72
    − 34

3. 58
    − 36

4. 84
    − 29

5. 29
    − 5

6. 74
    − 25

7. 60
    − 28

8. 37
    − 18

9. 82
    − 26

10. 94
    − 67

11. 39
    − 17

12. 76
    − 9

13. 41
    − 38

14. 57
    − 14

15. 63
    − 45

Copy and Do

16. 19 − 12

17. 43 − 16

18. 70 − 15

19. 47 − 17

20. 37 − 20

21. 61 − 43

22. 58 − 17

23. 30 − 19

24. 72 − 36

25. 15 − 12

26. 82 − 37

27. 96 − 58

Apply

Solve these problems.

28. Marge spent $24 on a new blouse. Alice spent $38 on a new outfit. How much more did Alice spend for clothes?

29. Chen earned $53 in one month. He spent $38 on birthday gifts for 3 friends. How much did Chen have left?

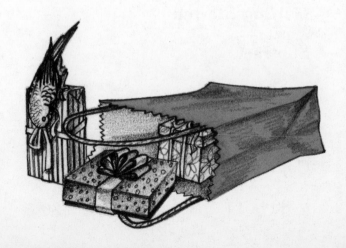

Subtracting 3-digit Numbers

The Lopez family drove from Phoenix to the Grand Canyon for a vacation. Their California relatives, the Ruiz family, drove from San Francisco to Yosemite National Park. How much farther did the Lopez family drive than the Ruiz family?

Driving Distances to Parks

Denver—Pikes Peak	134 kilometers
Los Angeles—Death Valley	416 kilometers
Phoenix—Grand Canyon	351 kilometers
Portland—Crater Lake	394 kilometers
San Francisco—Yosemite	293 kilometers

We want to compare the distances to find how much farther the Lopez family drove.

We know that Phoenix is _____ kilometers from the Grand Canyon.

San Francisco is _____ kilometers from Yosemite.

To compare these distances, we subtract _____ from _____.

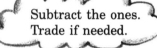

Subtract the ones. Trade if needed.

Subtract the tens. Trade if needed.

Subtract the hundreds.

$$\begin{array}{r} {}^{4}\,{}^{11} \\ 3\,5\,1 \\ -\,2\,9\,3 \\ \hline 8 \end{array}$$

$$\begin{array}{r} {}^{14} \\ {}^{2}\,\cancel{4} \\ 3\,5\,1 \\ -\,2\,9\,3 \\ \hline 5\,8 \end{array}$$

$$\begin{array}{r} {}^{2} \\ \cancel{3}\,5\,1 \\ -\,2\,9\,3 \\ \hline 5\,8 \end{array}$$

The Lopez family drove _____ kilometers farther than the Ruiz family.

Getting Started

Subtract.

1. $\begin{array}{r} 836 \\ -275 \\ \hline \end{array}$

2. $\begin{array}{r} \$4.57 \\ -\ 1.39 \\ \hline \end{array}$

3. $\begin{array}{r} 983 \\ -259 \\ \hline \end{array}$

4. $\begin{array}{r} 821 \\ -637 \\ \hline \end{array}$

5. $\begin{array}{r} 654 \\ -406 \\ \hline \end{array}$

6. $\begin{array}{r} \$7.93 \\ -\ 1.87 \\ \hline \end{array}$

7. $\begin{array}{r} 519 \\ -483 \\ \hline \end{array}$

8. $\begin{array}{r} \$9.42 \\ -\ 0.96 \\ \hline \end{array}$

Copy and subtract.

9. $341 - 170$

10. $523 - 487$

11. $\$8.51 - \$3.75$

12. $\$7.12 - \$6.88$

Practice

Subtract.

1.   645
  − 437
	2. 592
	  − 358
		3. 728
		  − 283
			4. $4.16
			  − 1.53

5.   721
  − 258
	6. 926
	  − 305
		7. 823
		  − 647
			8. 615
			  − 339

9.   752
  − 283
	10. $4.35
	  − 0.97
		11. 632
		  − 108
			12. 723
			  − 659

Copy and Do

13. 275 − 88

14. 732 − 486

15. $6.26 − $1.54

16. 924 − 808

17. 437 − 158

18. 821 − 480

19. 515 − 326

20. 740 − 196

21. 527 − 83

22. $4.73 − $1.29

23. 752 − 481

24. 916 − 548

25. 626 − 206

26. 816 − 539

27. 420 − 396

28. $9.38 − $8.42

Apply

Use the chart on page 63 to solve these problems.

29. The Peterson family is driving from San Francisco to Yosemite. They stop for lunch after driving 157 kilometers. How much farther do the Petersons have to drive?

30. How far is it from Portland to Crater Lake and back again?

Subtracting, Minuends with Zeros

The Mayflower landed at Plymouth Rock in 1620. There were 87 Pilgrims among the passengers. How many passengers were not Pilgrims?

We want to know how many of the passengers were not Pilgrims.

We know there were _____ people aboard the Mayflower when it landed at Plymouth Rock.

Of all the people on the ship, only _____ were Pilgrims.

To find the number of non-Pilgrims we subtract

_____ from _____.

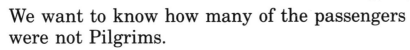

Subtract the ones. Trade if needed.	Subtract the tens.	Subtract the hundreds.
100 = 0 hundreds and 10 tens 10 tens = 9 tens and 10 ones	9 tens − 8 tens = 1 ten	0 hundreds − 0 hundreds = 0 hundreds

$$\begin{array}{r} \overset{9}{\cancel{10}11} \\ \cancel{1}\cancel{0}\cancel{1} \\ -\ 87 \\ \hline 4 \end{array}$$

$$\begin{array}{r} 9 \\ 1\cancel{0}1 \\ -\ 87 \\ \hline 14 \end{array}$$

$$\begin{array}{r} 101 \\ -\ 87 \\ \hline 14 \end{array}$$

There were _____ passengers on the Mayflower who were not Pilgrims.

Getting Started

Subtract.

1. $\begin{array}{r} 503 \\ -231 \\ \hline \end{array}$

2. $\begin{array}{r} 706 \\ -\ 88 \\ \hline \end{array}$

3. $\begin{array}{r} 521 \\ -126 \\ \hline \end{array}$

4. $\begin{array}{r} \$4.06 \\ -\ 1.85 \\ \hline \end{array}$

Copy and subtract.

5. $3.05 − $2.95

6. 603 − 245

7. 905 − 728

8. $7.04 − $5.28

Practice

Subtract.

1.	604 − 136	2.	502 − 185	3.	988 − 358	4.	$6.05 − 4.83
5.	408 − 391	6.	$6.00 − 4.75	7.	201 − 128	8.	708 − 220
9.	$3.05 − 2.95	10.	613 − 245	11.	905 − 728	12.	$7.04 − 5.28

Copy and Do

13. 307 − 184   14. 509 − 436   15. 802 − 656   16. $9.05 − $6.47

17. 408 − 227   18. 506 − 309   19. 328 − 253   20. $4.07 − $2.28

21. 107 − 98   22. $8.00 − $5.53   23. 604 − 586   24. 705 − 489

Apply

Solve these problems.

25. There are 206 bones in the human body. Of these, 29 bones are in the head. How many bones are there in the rest of the body?

26. A bunch of daisies costs $3.79. If you give the clerk a $5 bill, how much change will you receive?

EXCURSION

Build two more magic word squares like the first one. Use the same words on the horizontal as you do on the vertical.

T	A	P
A	R	E
P	E	T

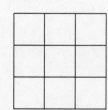

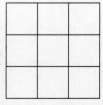

Subtracting Multi-digit Numbers

Craters of the Moon National Monument, in Idaho, was dedicated in 1924. Dinosaur National Monument, in Colorado and Utah, is an older and larger park. It was dedicated in 1915. How much larger is Dinosaur than Craters of the Moon?

National Monuments		
Name	**Opened**	**Size**
Craters of the Moon	1924	53,440 acres
Dinosaur	1915	210,844 acres
Organ Pipe Cactus	1937	330,689 acres
Sunset Crater	1930	3,040 acres
Walnut Canyon	1915	3,541 acres

We want to know how much larger Dinosaur is than Craters of the Moon. We know that Craters of the Moon is _____ acres large.
Dinosaur National Monument measures _____ acres.
To find the difference in size between the

two parks, we subtract _____ from _____.

To subtract multi-digit numbers, begin by subtracting the ones. Trade if needed. Continue subtracting each column to the left.

✔ Remember to trade from one place value at a time. Sometimes you will need to trade from a trade.

$$\begin{array}{r} \overset{\scriptstyle 10}{\underset{}{\cancel{2}}}\overset{\scriptstyle 1\ \cancel{0}\ 10}{10,844} \\ 210,844 \\ -\ 53,440 \\ \hline 157,404 \end{array}$$

Dinosaur is _____ acres larger than Craters of the Moon.

Getting Started

Subtract.

1. 8,475
    − 2,243

2. $123.27
    −   86.43

3. 176,043
    − 29,228

Copy and subtract.

4. 48,758 − 21,475

5. 192,175 − 39,857

6. $436.25 − $348.99

67

Practice

Subtract.

1.   6,456
  − 2,329
	2. 7,502
	  − 3,296
		3. $57.43
		  − 18.59
			4. 18,275
			  − 3,596

5.   4,253
  − 1,327
	6. 6,851
	  − 5,926
		7. $91.15
		  − 63.75
			8. 8,273
			  − 4,829

9. 127,243
  − 16,158
	10. 40,871
	  − 29,137
		11. 281,275
		  − 29,469
			12. $173.84
			  − 86.96

Copy and Do

13. 7,243 − 1,165

14. $24.75 − $13.72

15. 8,527 − 695

16. 36,741 − 5,196

17. 20,275 − 6,889

18. $543.78 − $275.81

19. 296,258 − 26,579

20. $877.73 − $639.86

21. 47,868 − 21,975

22. 79,246 − 37,865

23. 430,173 − 14,688

24. 93,182 − 81,996

Apply

Use the chart on page 67 to help solve these problems.

25. How many acres larger is Organ Pipe Cactus National Monument than Dinosaur?

26. Is Organ Pipe Cactus National Monument larger than the other four listed national parks combined?

Subtracting, More Minuends with Zeros

The Susan B. Anthony School held
its annual fall Read-a-Thon.
How many more pages did the fifth
grade read than the second-place class?

We want to know how many more pages the
fifth grade read than the second-place class.

We know the fifth grade read _____ pages.

The second-place class is the _____ grade.

It read _____ pages.
To find the difference between the number

of pages, we subtract _____ from _____.

✔ Remember to trade from one place value
at a time.

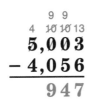

```
        9 9
   4  10 10 13
   5,003
 − 4,056
     947
```

The fifth grade read _____ more pages than
the sixth grade.

Class Reading Records

Fourth Grade	3,795 pages
Fifth Grade	5,003 pages
Sixth Grade	4,056 pages

Getting Started

Subtract.

1.	3,005	2.	$40.09	3.	3,300
	− 1,348		− 9.75		− 1,856

4.	$50.00	5.	8,512	6.	$90.17
	− 27.26		− 7,968		− 20.87

Copy and subtract.

7. 26,007 − 18,759   8. 70,026 − 23,576   9. $900.05 − $267.83

Practice

Subtract.

1.   3,004
    − 2,356
	2. 8,002
	    − 5,096
		3. 3,891
		    − 1,750
			4. $20.08
			    − 15.99

5.   4,020
    − 1,865
	6. $87.00
	    − 28.59
		7. 3,007
		    − 2,090
			8. $50.06
			    − 37.08

9.   19,006
    − 8,275
	10. 20,006
	    − 14,758
		11. $400.26
		    − 236.58
			12. $793.42
			    − 253.87

Copy and Do

13. 4,001 − 2,756
14. $70.05 − $26.59
15. 8,060 − 7,948

16. 7,007 − 2,468
17. 21,316 − 12,479
18. 14,000 − 8,396

19. $100.21 − $93.50
20. 60,004 − 51,476
21. 52,006 − 9,037

22. $800.00 − $275.67
23. 34,612 − 29,965
24. 50,010 − 36,754

Apply

Use the chart on page 69 to help solve these problems.

25. How many pages did the three classes read all together?

26. How many more pages did the sixth grade read than the fourth grade?

Estimating Differences

Dominic earned $46.75
as a baker's helper. He
wants to buy his own stereo.
About how much more money
does Dominic need to earn?

We want to estimate how much money
Dominic still needs to earn.
We know the stereo costs _____.

So far, Dominic has earned _____.
To estimate what he still needs, we round
both amounts of money to the nearest dollar,
and find the difference between the two.

$$\$89.29 \longrightarrow \quad \mathbf{\$89}$$
$$\$46.75 \longrightarrow \quad \mathbf{-\ 47}$$

Dominic still needs about _____ to buy
the stereo.

Getting Started

Estimate each difference.

Round to the nearest hundred.

1. 845
  − 236
	2. 906
	  − 483
		3. 726
		  − 413
			4. 586
			  − 275

Round to the nearest thousand.

5. 4,796
  − 1,926
	5. 6,500
	  − 2,375
		7. 4,975
		  − 1,610
			8. 8,279
			  − 3,758

Round to the nearest dollar.

9. $29.35
  − 12.50
	10. $76.21
	  − 48.76
		11. $94.39
		  − 81.56
			12. $62.83
			  − 46.15

Practice

Estimate each difference.
Round to the nearest hundred.

1. 579
   − 346

2. 481
   − 276

3. 825
   − 279

4. 921
   − 735

5. 791
   − 347

6. 426
   − 139

7. 776
   − 438

8. 861
   − 475

Round to the nearest thousand.

9.   7,351
    − 2,686

10. 9,251
    − 4,460

11. 6,865
    − 4,956

12. 8,753
    − 1,829

13. 4,629
    − 1,510

14. 8,475
    − 6,832

15. 4,500
    − 3,723

16. 8,216
    − 5,006

Round to the nearest dollar.

17. $43.27
    − 21.95

18. $71.38
    − 18.46

19. $92.50
    − 46.89

20. $52.89
    − 46.75

21. $38.27
    − 14.58

22. $86.89
    − 71.76

23. $97.17
    − 42.45

24. $66.12
    − 51.87

Apply

Solve. Use the ad on page 71 to help solve these problems.

25. About how much money would you have left if you bought the camera with a $100 bill?

26. About how much do the stereo and camera cost together?

Checking Subtraction

Start with a number like 628. Subtract any number from it. Then add that same number to your answer. What do you find? Try this using several different subtrahends. Does the sum always equal the minuend?

We start with a minuend of _____.
Then, for example, we subtract the subtrahend 216.
We want to see what happens when we add 216 to the difference between 628 and 216.

$$
\begin{array}{r} 628 \\ -216 \\ \hline \end{array}
\qquad
\begin{array}{r} \boxed{} \\ +216 \\ \hline \end{array}
$$

When we add the subtrahend to the difference,

we must always get the _____.

✔ We say that we can check subtraction by addition.

minuend	difference
− subtrahend	+ subtrahend
difference	minuend

Did your sum always equal the minuend? _____

Getting Started

Subtract and check.

1.	639	2.	427	3.	708
	− 156		− 359		− 519

4.	4,265	5.	8,056	6.	9,125
	− 2,458		− 3,683		− 8,136

Copy, subtract and check.

7. 14,006 − 9,378
8. $36.86 − $12.97
9. 37,850 − 19,873

Practice

Subtract and check.

1.   896
    − 257

2.   4,081
    − 3,795

3.   5,279
    − 875

4.   8,465
    − 7,689

5.   11,256
    − 7,587

6. $85.40
    − 19.73

7.   60,053
    − 36,285

8. $423.50
    − 176.48

9.   42,000
    − 18,732

Copy and Do

10. 9,675 − 2,487

11. 5,001 − 3,974

12. 27,681 − 8,854

13. 63,451 − 45,787

14. $86.53 − $52.45

15. 82,741 − 76,857

Apply

Solve these problems.

16. Queen Victoria ruled Great Britain for 64 years. She was born in 1819 and died in 1901. How old was she when she died?

17. The United States admitted 398,613 immigrants in 1976, and 596,600 in 1981. How many more immigrants entered America in 1981 than in 1976?

EXCURSION

Draw the next figure in this geometrical sequence.

 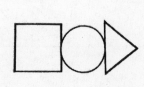  

Acting It Out

The five boys sitting on the bench are Bob, Doug, George, John and Ted. They are not sitting in that order. Neither Bob nor Doug is next to John. Neither Doug nor Bob is next to Ted. Neither John nor Doug is next to George. Ted is just to the right of George. Tell the order in which the boys are sitting.

★ **SEE**

We need to find:
    the order of the 5 boys in the picture.

★ **PLAN**

We can act this problem out by following the clues using 5 students and 5 empty chairs.

★ **DO**

1. We know Ted is just to the right of George.

?	?	George		?

2. We know Ted is not next to Doug or Bob, which leaves only John to sit there.

?	?	George	Ted	

3. Of the two boys who are left, Doug is not next to George, so we can sit Bob there.

?		George	Ted	John

4. Doug is the only one left.

	Bob	George	Ted	John

★ **CHECK**

Neither Bob nor Doug is next to John.
Neither Doug nor Bob is next to Ted.
Neither John nor Doug is next to George.
Ted is just to the right of George.

Apply

Act out the problems to help you solve them.

1. There are 8 tables in the school cafeteria. If 56 students are eating lunch, how many students are seated at each table?

2. Start with 20 pennies. Make stacks of 7, 2, 6 and 5 pennies. A move is taking one or more pennies from a stack and placing them on another stack. How many moves are needed to make the four stacks the same height?

3. The 8 members of the chess club are planning a chess tournament. Each member will play one game against each other member. The player who wins the most games will be the champion. How many chess games will be played all together?

4. Choose 4 pieces of colored paper and cut 4 small circles from each. Arrange them in the squares below so that there is a circle in each square, and there are no circles of like color in the same row, column, or in either of the main diagonals.

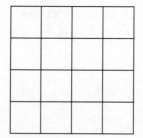

5. Mario Mouse can run at a rate of 2 feet a second. Miranda Mouse can run at a rate of 100 feet a minute. If both run at these rates for 5 minutes, who will run the greater distance?

6. Eight mice are equally spaced around a circle of cheese. If every third mouse takes a bite, will all 8 mice get some cheese? Prove your answer.

76

Calculators, Data from an Ad

Cecily has $25 to spend on
her mother's birthday present.
She has decided to buy the camera
and the wallet. How much
money will Cecily have left?

We want to find how much money Cecily
will have left after buying the present.
We know the cost of the wallet is _____

and the camera costs _____.

Cecily has _____ to spend.
To find the amount Cecily will have left, add _____

to _____, and subtract that sum from _____.
Enter these codes into your calculator and record
the answers on the screens.

Cost of the Camera   Cost of the Wallet   Total Cost

  15 ⟨·⟩ 39   ⟨+⟩   8 ⟨·⟩ 97   ⟨=⟩ ⟨____⟩

Amount Given   Cost of Items   Change

  25   ⟨−⟩   _____   ⟨=⟩ ⟨____⟩

Cecily will have _____ left.

✔ Remember, the calculator will not print
zeros to the far right of the decimal point.
You do not have to enter these zeros when
you enter an amount of money.

⟨   13⟩ means $13

⟨ 6.1⟩ means $6.10

Enter these codes. Write the differences on the screens.

1. 16 ⟨−⟩ 14 ⟨·⟩ 25 ⟨=⟩ ⟨____⟩

2. 240 ⟨·⟩ 15 ⟨−⟩ 168 ⟨·⟩ 20 ⟨=⟩ ⟨____⟩

3. 7500 ⟨−⟩ 5000 ⟨=⟩ ⟨____⟩

Practice

Complete these codes. Write the differences on the screens.

1. 9 $\cdot$ 83 $-$ 8 $\cdot$ 15 $=$ ⬭

2. 324 $\cdot$ 60 $+$ 14 $\cdot$ 68 $-$ 43 $\cdot$ 76 $=$ ⬭

3. 167 $\cdot$ 46 $-$ 112 $\cdot$ 48 $-$ 54 $\cdot$ 85 $=$ ⬭

4. 11 $\cdot$ 15 $+$ 7 $\cdot$ 30 $-$ 15 $=$ ⬭

Use a calculator to find these differences.
Use estimation to make sure the answers seem correct.

5. $\quad$ $9.86
$\quad$ $-$ $\quad$ 4.98

6. $\quad$ $41.38
$\quad$ $-$ $\quad$ 16.59

7. $\quad$ $397.58
$\quad$ $-$ $\quad$ 169.59

8. $\quad$ $426.37
$\quad$ $-$ $\quad$ 85.67

9. $13.79 $-$ $8.50

10. $36.84 $-$ $9.95

11. $18,475 $-$ $15,989

12. $860.05 $-$ $276.48

13. $175 $+$ $68.37 $-$ $115.37

14. $439.20 $+$ $179.56 $-$ $218.73

Apply

Use the ad to solve these problems.

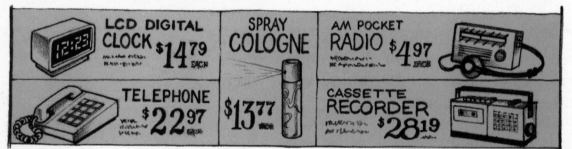

15. Is the cost of the spray cologne and the clock more or less than $28.50?

16. How much more is the digital clock than the radio?

17. Which three items added together cost exactly $51.53?

18. Which costs more, the telephone and the spray cologne, or the cassette recorder and the clock?

Subtract and check.

1.	68 − 34	2.	96 − 21	3.	61 − 37	4.	85 − 19
5.	375 − 123	6.	485 − 149	7.	718 − 253	8.	826 − 198
9.	503 − 322	10.	601 − 427	11.	$9.03 − 5.27	12.	$4.00 − 3.72
13.	7,294 − 3,485	14.	$85.37 − 29.18	15.	16,375 − 9,887	16.	$483.29 − 136.84
17.	4,006 − 2,988	18.	$30.00 − 11.76	19.	70,004 − 27,268	20.	$300.25 − 129.37

Estimate each difference.

Round to the nearest thousand.

21.	8,275 − 3,927	22.	8,069 − 4,275	23.	7,523 − 2,130	24.	6,135 − 1,852

Round to the nearest hundred.

25.	796 − 249	26.	816 − 257	27.	923 − 375	28.	695 − 96

CUMULATIVE REVIEW

Circle the letter of the correct answer.

1 6 + 7

a 1
b 11
c 14
d NG

2   5
   3
+ 6

a 8
b 9
c 14
d NG

3 12 − 4

a 4
b 8
c 16
d NG

4 What is the value of the 0 in 3,076?

a ones
b tens
c hundreds
d NG

5 5,265 ◯ 4,265

a <
b >

6 Round 873 to the nearest hundred.

a 700
b 800
c NG

7 Round 6,750 to the nearest thousand.

a 6,000
b 7,000
c NG

8 What is the value of the 8 in 823,075?

a hundred thousands
b ten thousands
c thousands
d NG

9 62 + 49

a 27
b 111
c 1,011
d NG

10   456
  + 324

a 770
b 780
c 880
d NG

11   4,327
  + 1,495

a 5,722
b 5,812
c 6,822
d NG

12   41,615
  + 29,256

a 70,871
b 70,881
c 71,871
d NG

13   626
  − 359

a 267
b 333
c 367
d NG

 score

Understanding Multiplication

Charlie packs groceries after school at the Food Mart. How many soup cans can he fit into a box?

We want to know how many cans fit into the box.
We know there are _____ rows with _____ cans in each row.

We can add the number of cans in each row.

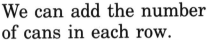

3
3
3
+ 3

We can add the number of cans in each column.

4 + 4 + 4 = ___

We can multiply the number of rows by the number of cans in each.

4 threes = ___

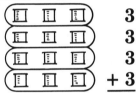

factor × factor = product

We can multiply the number of columns by the number of cans in each.

3 fours = ___

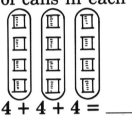

factor × factor = product

Charlie can fit _____ cans into one box.

Getting Started

Use both addition and multiplication to show how many are in each picture.

1. 🥫 🥫 🥫 🥫
   🥫 🥫 🥫 🥫

   2 + 2 + 2 + 2 = ___

   4 × 2 = ___

   2 × 4 = ___

2. 🥫🥫🥫🥫🥫 5
   🥫🥫🥫🥫🥫 5
   🥫🥫🥫🥫🥫 + 5

   3 × 5 = ___

   5 × 3 = ___

3. 🥫 🥫 🥫 🥫
   🥫 🥫 🥫 🥫
   🥫 🥫 🥫 🥫
   🥫 🥫 🥫 🥫

   4 + 4 + 4 + 4 = ___

   4 × 4 = ___

Practice

Use both addition and multiplication to show how many are in each picture.

1.
3 + 3 + 3 + 3 + 3 + 3 = ___

6 × 3 = ___

3 × 6 = ___

2.
5
+ 5

2 × 5 = ___

5 × 2 = ___

3.
1 + 1 + 1 + 1 + 1 + 1 + 1 = ___

7 × 1 = ___

1 × 7 = ___

4.
6
6
6
+ 6

4 × 6 = ___

6 × 4 = ___

5.
9
+ 9

2 × 9 = ___

9 × 2 = ___

6.
4 + 4 + 4 + 4 + 4 + 4 + 4 = ___

7 × 4 = ___

4 × 7 = ___

7.
7 + 7 + 7 = ___

3 × 7 = ___

7 × 3 = ___

8.
5
5
5
5
+ 5

5 × 5 = ___

Multiplying, the Factors 2 and 3

Rose helped her uncle pick cherries. She saved some of the fruit for her lunch. How many cherries did Rose have for lunch?

We want to know how many cherries Rose ate for lunch.

We know there are _____ bunches of _____ cherries each.

To find out how many cherries she ate, we

multiply _____ by _____.

$4 \times 3 =$ _____

$$\begin{array}{r} 3 \\ \times\ 4 \\ \hline \end{array}$$

We say: **four times three equals twelve.**

Rose saved _____ cherries for lunch.

Getting Started

Complete the table.

1.　　　　The Facts of 2

1	2	3	4	5	6	7	8	9
2	4							

Multiply.

2. $5 \times 3 =$ _____

3. $4 \times 2 =$ _____

4. $\begin{array}{r} 2 \\ \times\ 9 \\ \hline \end{array}$

5. $\begin{array}{r} 3 \\ \times\ 7 \\ \hline \end{array}$

Practice

Complete the table.

The Facts of 3

1.

1	2	3	4	5	6	7	8	9
3	6							

Multiply.

2. $2 \times 3 =$ ___　　　3. $3 \times 4 =$ ___　　　4. $3 \times 5 =$ ___　　　5. $2 \times 6 =$ ___

6. $2 \times 2 =$ ___　　　7. $3 \times 9 =$ ___　　　8. $2 \times 8 =$ ___　　　9. $2 \times 7 =$ ___

10. $3 \times 8 =$ ___　　11. $3 \times 2 =$ ___　　12. $2 \times 5 =$ ___　　13. $3 \times 3 =$ ___

14. $2 \times 9 =$ ___　　15. $3 \times 7 =$ ___　　16. $3 \times 6 =$ ___　　17. $2 \times 4 =$ ___

18. $\begin{array}{r} 2 \\ \times 8 \\ \hline \end{array}$　　19. $\begin{array}{r} 3 \\ \times 9 \\ \hline \end{array}$　　20. $\begin{array}{r} 2 \\ \times 4 \\ \hline \end{array}$　　21. $\begin{array}{r} 2 \\ \times 5 \\ \hline \end{array}$　　22. $\begin{array}{r} 3 \\ \times 6 \\ \hline \end{array}$　　23. $\begin{array}{r} 3 \\ \times 7 \\ \hline \end{array}$

24. $\begin{array}{r} 3 \\ \times 8 \\ \hline \end{array}$　　25. $\begin{array}{r} 2 \\ \times 9 \\ \hline \end{array}$　　26. $\begin{array}{r} 2 \\ \times 5 \\ \hline \end{array}$　　27. $\begin{array}{r} 3 \\ \times 5 \\ \hline \end{array}$　　28. $\begin{array}{r} 3 \\ \times 4 \\ \hline \end{array}$　　29. $\begin{array}{r} 2 \\ \times 7 \\ \hline \end{array}$

Apply

Solve these problems.

30. Fred has outgrown 4 pairs of tennis shoes in one year. How many shoes has he outgrown?

31. There are 9 vases, each containing 3 daisies. How many daisies are there altogether?

32. There are 5 study tables in the library. Each table has 2 chairs. How many chairs are there?

33. Bill has 9 model cars to build. Don has 3 cars. How many more cars does Bill have?

34. Betty has 2 records. Each record has 8 songs. How many songs can Betty listen to if she plays both records?

35. Ilonda ate 3 apples on Tuesday, 5 apples on Wednesday and 2 apples on Friday. How many apples did she eat altogether?

84

Multiplying, the Factors 4 and 5

Kerry's mother is making pickles.
How many quart canning jars
did Kerry buy for her?

We want to know how many jars
Kerry bought.

We know Kerry bought _____ boxes

of _____ quart jars each.

To find out how many jars there
are in the boxes, we think of 5 sets

of 4 each. We multiply _____ by _____.

| 4 | 8 | 12 | 16 | 20 |

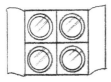 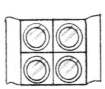

$1 \times 4 =$ ___ $2 \times 4 =$ ___ $3 \times 4 =$ ___ $4 \times 4 =$ ___ $5 \times 4 =$ ___

Kerry bought __20__ jars for his mother.

Getting Started

Complete the table.

1.   The Facts of 4

1	2	3	4	5	6	7	8	9
4	8							

Multiply.

2. $6 \times 4 =$ ___

3. $9 \times 5 =$ ___

4. $\begin{array}{r} 5 \\ \times 2 \\ \hline \end{array}$

5. $\begin{array}{r} 4 \\ \times 7 \\ \hline \end{array}$

85

Practice

Complete the table.

1. The Facts of 5

1	2	3	4	5	6	7	8	9
5	10							

Multiply.

2. $2 \times 4 = \underline{\hphantom{00}}$ 3. $4 \times 5 = \underline{\hphantom{00}}$ 4. $5 \times 5 = \underline{\hphantom{00}}$ 5. $7 \times 4 = \underline{\hphantom{00}}$

6. $5 \times 4 = \underline{\hphantom{00}}$ 7. $6 \times 5 = \underline{\hphantom{00}}$ 8. $8 \times 5 = \underline{\hphantom{00}}$ 9. $3 \times 4 = \underline{\hphantom{00}}$

10. $4 \times 4 = \underline{\hphantom{00}}$ 11. $2 \times 5 = \underline{\hphantom{00}}$ 12. $3 \times 5 = \underline{\hphantom{00}}$ 13. $6 \times 4 = \underline{\hphantom{00}}$

14. $9 \times 4 = \underline{\hphantom{00}}$ 15. $7 \times 5 = \underline{\hphantom{00}}$ 16. $9 \times 5 = \underline{\hphantom{00}}$ 17. $8 \times 4 = \underline{\hphantom{00}}$

18. $\begin{array}{r} 5 \\ \times\,5 \\ \hline \end{array}$ 19. $\begin{array}{r} 5 \\ \times\,8 \\ \hline \end{array}$ 20. $\begin{array}{r} 2 \\ \times\,2 \\ \hline \end{array}$ 21. $\begin{array}{r} 4 \\ \times\,7 \\ \hline \end{array}$ 22. $\begin{array}{r} 3 \\ \times\,4 \\ \hline \end{array}$ 23. $\begin{array}{r} 2 \\ \times\,9 \\ \hline \end{array}$

24. $\begin{array}{r} 4 \\ \times\,9 \\ \hline \end{array}$ 25. $\begin{array}{r} 5 \\ \times\,4 \\ \hline \end{array}$ 26. $\begin{array}{r} 3 \\ \times\,6 \\ \hline \end{array}$ 27. $\begin{array}{r} 5 \\ \times\,7 \\ \hline \end{array}$ 28. $\begin{array}{r} 5 \\ \times\,2 \\ \hline \end{array}$ 29. $\begin{array}{r} 4 \\ \times\,6 \\ \hline \end{array}$

30. $\begin{array}{r} 5 \\ \times\,9 \\ \hline \end{array}$ 31. $\begin{array}{r} 3 \\ \times\,3 \\ \hline \end{array}$ 32. $\begin{array}{r} 4 \\ \times\,8 \\ \hline \end{array}$ 33. $\begin{array}{r} 3 \\ \times\,7 \\ \hline \end{array}$ 34. $\begin{array}{r} 2 \\ \times\,3 \\ \hline \end{array}$ 35. $\begin{array}{r} 4 \\ \times\,5 \\ \hline \end{array}$

Apply

Solve these problems.

36. Each package holds 5 sticks of gum. How many sticks of gum are in 8 packages?

37. Pamela has 8 seedlings. She bought 5 more at the florist. How many seedlings does Pamela have?

38. Louis had $5. He spent $4 at the movies. How much does Louis have left?

39. Robert and Mike each bought 4 cans of apple juice. How many cans of juice did they buy together?

Understanding Multiplication Properties

Besides the multiplication facts, we need to understand other ideas related to multiplication. These ideas are called the **multiplication properties.**

The Order Property
We can multiply factors in any order.

$6 \times 4 = 24$

$4 \times 6 = 24$

The Zero Property
The product of a number and 0 is 0.

$4 \times 0 = 0$

The One Property
The product of a number and 1 is that number.

$4 \times 1 = 4$

Getting Started

Answer yes or no.

1. Does a number times zero equal that number? _____

2. Is a number times 5 the same as 5 times the number? _____

Multiply.

3. $1 \times 7 =$ ___   4. $7 \times 1 =$ ___   5. $0 \times 8 =$ ___   6. $8 \times 0 =$ ___

Practice

Answer yes or no.

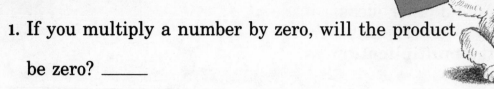

1. If you multiply a number by zero, will the product

   be zero? _____

2. Is 6 times a number the same as the number times 6? _____

3. If you multiply 1 by 0, is the answer 1? _____

4. If you multiply a number by 1, is the product

   always the same as the other factor? _____

5. If you multiply 1 by 1, is the product 2? _____

Multiply.

6. $3 \times 3 =$ ___   7. $8 \times 2 =$ ___   8. $3 \times 1 =$ ___   9. $9 \times 0 =$ ___

10. $6 \times 5 =$ ___   11. $5 \times 6 =$ ___   12. $0 \times 2 =$ ___   13. $4 \times 4 =$ ___

14. $8 \times 3 =$ ___   15. $3 \times 8 =$ ___   16. $1 \times 7 =$ ___   17. $7 \times 1 =$ ___

18. $\begin{array}{r} 5 \\ \times 3 \\ \hline \end{array}$	19. $\begin{array}{r} 3 \\ \times 4 \\ \hline \end{array}$	20. $\begin{array}{r} 9 \\ \times 5 \\ \hline \end{array}$	21. $\begin{array}{r} 1 \\ \times 7 \\ \hline \end{array}$	22. $\begin{array}{r} 0 \\ \times 8 \\ \hline \end{array}$	23. $\begin{array}{r} 2 \\ \times 5 \\ \hline \end{array}$
24. $\begin{array}{r} 3 \\ \times 7 \\ \hline \end{array}$	25. $\begin{array}{r} 1 \\ \times 9 \\ \hline \end{array}$	26. $\begin{array}{r} 8 \\ 5 \\ \hline \end{array}$	27. $\begin{array}{r} 0 \\ \times 4 \\ \hline \end{array}$	28. $\begin{array}{r} 4 \\ \times 6 \\ \hline \end{array}$	29. $\begin{array}{r} 1 \\ \times 2 \\ \hline \end{array}$
30. $\begin{array}{r} 0 \\ \times 0 \\ \hline \end{array}$	31. $\begin{array}{r} 4 \\ \times 5 \\ \hline \end{array}$	32. $\begin{array}{r} 7 \\ \times 4 \\ \hline \end{array}$	33. $\begin{array}{r} 2 \\ \times 4 \\ \hline \end{array}$	34. $\begin{array}{r} 1 \\ \times 5 \\ \hline \end{array}$	35. $\begin{array}{r} 8 \\ \times 5 \\ \hline \end{array}$
36. $\begin{array}{r} 3 \\ \times 2 \\ \hline \end{array}$	37. $\begin{array}{r} 5 \\ \times 9 \\ \hline \end{array}$	38. $\begin{array}{r} 2 \\ \times 9 \\ \hline \end{array}$	39. $\begin{array}{r} 3 \\ \times 6 \\ \hline \end{array}$	40. $\begin{array}{r} 5 \\ \times 6 \\ \hline \end{array}$	41. $\begin{array}{r} 9 \\ \times 4 \\ \hline \end{array}$

Understanding Rule of Order

Working an operation in a mathematical sentence to find the value of n is called **solving for n.** Solve for n in the sentence on the chalkboard.

$$9 - 4 \times 2 = n$$

If we subtract and then multiply, the value of n is _____.

If we multiply and then subtract, the value of n is _____.

Both answers can't be correct. We must follow **rule of order** to know how to solve this sentence correctly.

✔ First, work all multiplications left to right.

✔ Then, work all additions and subtractions left to right.

$$9 - 4 \times 2 = n$$

$$9 - \underline{} = n$$

$$\underline{} = n$$

✔ In rule of order, operations within parentheses should be worked before multiplications.

$$(9 - 2) \times 4 = n$$

$$\underline{} \times 4 = n$$

$$\underline{} = n$$

Rule of order has been followed in these three mathematical sentences. Solve for n.

$3 \times 4 - 3 = n$

$\underline{} - 3 = n$

$\underline{} = n$

$(3 \times 4) - 3 = n$

$\underline{} - 3 = n$

$\underline{} = n$

$3 \times (4 - 3) = n$

$3 \times \underline{} = n$

$\underline{} = n$

The correct answer for the sentence on the chalkboard is _____.

Getting Started

Solve for n. Follow rule of order.

1. $5 + (3 \times 4) = n$

$\underline{} = n$

2. $3 + 4 \times 5 = n$

$\underline{} = n$

3. $(6 - 0) \times 4 = n$

$\underline{} = n$

89

Practice

Solve for n. Follow rule of order.

1. $(2 \times 5) + 3 = n$

___ $= n$

2. $8 + (3 \times 4) = n$

___ $= n$

3. $(7 \times 3) - 9 = n$

___ $= n$

4. $4 \times 3 + 7 = n$

___ $= n$

5. $(7 \times 4) + 15 = n$

___ $= n$

6. $(6 \times 5) - 18 = n$

___ $= n$

7. $(24 - 16) \times 4 = n$

___ $= n$

8. $(2 \times 3) \times 4 = n$

___ $= n$

9. $(5 - 3) \times 7 = n$

___ $= n$

10. $8 - (6 \times 1) = n$

___ $= n$

11. $5 + 3 \times 6 = n$

___ $= n$

12. $9 \times (8 - 8) = n$

___ $= n$

13. $(7 - 6) \times 4 = n$

___ $= n$

14. $(7 \times 5) + 26 = n$

___ $= n$

15. $56 - (4 \times 8) = n$

___ $= n$

16. $46 + (9 \times 0) = n$

___ $= n$

17. $(3 \times 9) + 46 = n$

___ $= n$

18. $(5 \times 2) + 30 = n$

___ $= n$

19. $7 \times 2 - 8 = n$

___ $= n$

20. $72 + (8 \times 4) = n$

___ $= n$

21. $(95 - 95) \times 4 = n$

___ $= n$

EXCURSION

How many numbers can you make using four 4's?

$(4 + 4 + 4) \times 4 = 48$

$( ) + - = \times \ 4 \ 4 \ 4 \ ( )$

Multiplying, the Factors 6 and 7

It is exactly 8 weeks from New Year's Day to Opal's birthday. How many days does Opal have to wait to celebrate her birthday?

We want to find the number of days before Opal's birthday.

We know that Opal's birthday is _____ weeks from New Year's Day.

There are _____ days in one week.

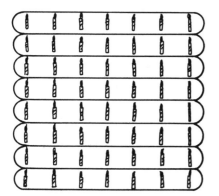

$7 \times 8 =$ ___

$8 \times 7 =$ ___

Opal's birthday is _____ days away.

Getting Started

Complete the table.

1.   The Facts of 6

0	1	2	3	4	5	6	7	8	9
0	6	12							

Multiply.

2. $3 \times 6 =$ ___

3. $5 \times 6 =$ ___

4. $4 \times 6 =$ ___

5. $2 \times 6 =$ ___

6. $\begin{array}{r} 6 \\ \times 9 \\ \hline \end{array}$

7. $\begin{array}{r} 7 \\ \times 6 \\ \hline \end{array}$

8. $\begin{array}{r} 6 \\ \times 6 \\ \hline \end{array}$

9. $\begin{array}{r} 6 \\ \times 8 \\ \hline \end{array}$

91

Practice

Complete the table.

1.

The Facts of 7

0	1	2	3	4	5	6	7	8	9
0	7	14							

Multiply.

2. $5 \times 6 =$ _____

3. $1 \times 7 =$ _____

4. $2 \times 6 =$ _____

5. $7 \times 7 =$ _____

6. $3 \times 7 =$ _____

7. $9 \times 7 =$ _____

8. $0 \times 6 =$ _____

9. $4 \times 6 =$ _____

10. $6 \times 7 =$ _____

11. $7 \times 6 =$ _____

12. $4 \times 7 =$ _____

13. $1 \times 6 =$ _____

14. $3 \times 6 =$ _____

15. $9 \times 6 =$ _____

16. $8 \times 7 =$ _____

17. $0 \times 7 =$ _____

18.
$$\begin{array}{r} 6 \\ \times\, 6 \\ \hline \end{array}$$

19.
$$\begin{array}{r} 7 \\ \times\, 5 \\ \hline \end{array}$$

20.
$$\begin{array}{r} 7 \\ \times\, 2 \\ \hline \end{array}$$

21.
$$\begin{array}{r} 6 \\ \times\, 8 \\ \hline \end{array}$$

22.
$$\begin{array}{r} 6 \\ \times\, 1 \\ \hline \end{array}$$

23.
$$\begin{array}{r} 7 \\ \times\, 4 \\ \hline \end{array}$$

24.
$$\begin{array}{r} 7 \\ \times\, 5 \\ \hline \end{array}$$

25.
$$\begin{array}{r} 6 \\ \times\, 0 \\ \hline \end{array}$$

26.
$$\begin{array}{r} 6 \\ \times\, 4 \\ \hline \end{array}$$

27.
$$\begin{array}{r} 7 \\ \times\, 0 \\ \hline \end{array}$$

28.
$$\begin{array}{r} 6 \\ \times\, 5 \\ \hline \end{array}$$

29.
$$\begin{array}{r} 6 \\ \times\, 6 \\ \hline \end{array}$$

30.
$$\begin{array}{r} 7 \\ \times\, 1 \\ \hline \end{array}$$

31.
$$\begin{array}{r} 7 \\ \times\, 7 \\ \hline \end{array}$$

32.
$$\begin{array}{r} 7 \\ \times\, 9 \\ \hline \end{array}$$

33.
$$\begin{array}{r} 6 \\ \times\, 2 \\ \hline \end{array}$$

34.
$$\begin{array}{r} 7 \\ \times\, 3 \\ \hline \end{array}$$

35.
$$\begin{array}{r} 6 \\ \times\, 7 \\ \hline \end{array}$$

Apply

Solve these problems.

36. I have 9 key rings. Each key ring holds 6 keys. How many keys do I have?

37. There are 15 apples in a bag. 7 apples are rotten. How many apples are not rotten?

38. One ticket for the ring-toss game costs 5¢. How much do 7 tickets cost?

39. Brenda waters 6 of her plants each day, in rotation. By the end of the week she has watered all her plants. How many plants does Brenda have?

Multiplying, the Factors 8 and 9

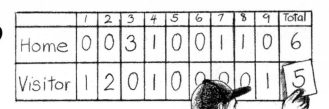

	1	2	3	4	5	6	7	8	9	Total
Home	0	0	3	1	0	0	1	1	0	6
Visitor	1	2	0	1	0	0	0	0	1	5

The Crosby County baseball team plays 8 games each summer. If all the games are complete, how many innings does the team play?

We want to know the number of innings Crosby County plays over the summer.

We know that Crosby County plays _____ games.

A regular baseball game lasts for _____ innings.

To find the total number of innings

we multiply _____ by _____.

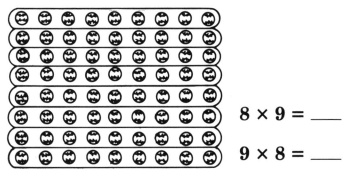

$8 \times 9 =$ ___

$9 \times 8 =$ ___

The Crosby County baseball team plays _____ innings.

Getting Started

Complete the table.

1.   The Facts of 8

0	1	2	3	4	5	6	7	8	9
0	8								

Multiply.

2. $3 \times 8 =$ ___   3. $7 \times 8 =$ ___   4. $0 \times 8 =$ ___   5. $5 \times 8 =$ ___

6. $\begin{array}{r} 8 \\ \times 9 \\ \hline \end{array}$ 7. $\begin{array}{r} 8 \\ \times 8 \\ \hline \end{array}$ 8. $\begin{array}{r} 8 \\ \times 7 \\ \hline \end{array}$ 9. $\begin{array}{r} 6 \\ \times 8 \\ \hline \end{array}$

93

Practice

Complete the table.

1.   The Facts of 9

0	1	2	3	4	5	6	7	8	9
0	9								

Multiply.

2. $0 \times 9 = $ _____   3. $8 \times 9 = $ _____   4. $1 \times 8 = $ _____   5. $3 \times 8 = $ _____

6. $7 \times 8 = $ _____   7. $4 \times 9 = $ _____   8. $9 \times 8 = $ _____   9. $6 \times 9 = $ _____

10. $4 \times 8 = $ _____   11. $0 \times 8 = $ _____   12. $7 \times 9 = $ _____   13. $3 \times 9 = $ _____

14. $\begin{array}{r} 9 \\ \times\, 5 \\ \hline \end{array}$ 15. $\begin{array}{r} 8 \\ \times\, 6 \\ \hline \end{array}$ 16. $\begin{array}{r} 9 \\ \times\, 9 \\ \hline \end{array}$ 17. $\begin{array}{r} 8 \\ \times\, 2 \\ \hline \end{array}$ 18. $\begin{array}{r} 8 \\ \times\, 9 \\ \hline \end{array}$ 19. $\begin{array}{r} 8 \\ \times\, 8 \\ \hline \end{array}$

20. $\begin{array}{r} 8 \\ \times\, 0 \\ \hline \end{array}$ 21. $\begin{array}{r} 8 \\ \times\, 5 \\ \hline \end{array}$ 22. $\begin{array}{r} 9 \\ \times\, 6 \\ \hline \end{array}$ 23. $\begin{array}{r} 9 \\ \times\, 1 \\ \hline \end{array}$ 24. $\begin{array}{r} 8 \\ \times\, 2 \\ \hline \end{array}$ 25. $\begin{array}{r} 9 \\ \times\, 7 \\ \hline \end{array}$

26. $\begin{array}{r} 8 \\ \times\, 4 \\ \hline \end{array}$ 27. $\begin{array}{r} 8 \\ \times\, 7 \\ \hline \end{array}$ 28. $\begin{array}{r} 9 \\ \times\, 4 \\ \hline \end{array}$ 29. $\begin{array}{r} 9 \\ \times\, 0 \\ \hline \end{array}$ 30. $\begin{array}{r} 8 \\ \times\, 1 \\ \hline \end{array}$ 31. $\begin{array}{r} 8 \\ \times\, 3 \\ \hline \end{array}$

Apply

Solve these problems.

32. Walter practiced his drums for 9 hours each week. How many hours did he practice in 6 weeks?

33. Mary bought 8 vases. Each vase cost $8. How much did the vases cost Mary?

34. It costs $8 for a ticket to see Bill's favorite musical group. He has saved $5. How much more does he need for a ticket?

35. Paper plates for a picnic are packed in packages of 8 each. How many plates are there in 7 packages?

Finding Missing Factors

Mike and his sister caught 63 fish on Saturday. Mike will clean the fish and put 7 of them into each freezer bag. Help Mike decide how many freezer bags he will need.

We want to know the number of bags Mike will need to freeze all the fish.

We know he and his sister caught _____ fish.

He is putting _____ fish in each freezer bag.

To find the total number of bags needed, we can write a multiplication sentence.

We have n stand for the number of bags.

$$7 \times n = 63$$

We think: 7 times what number equals 63?

$$7 \times \underline{\quad} = 63$$

$$n = \underline{\quad}$$

Mike needs _____ freezer bags.

Getting Started

Solve for n.

1. $n \times 3 = 15$

    $n = \underline{\quad}$

2. $4 \times n = 28$

    $n = \underline{\quad}$

3. $9 \times n = 0$

    $n = \underline{\quad}$

4. $n \times 7 = 42$

    $n = \underline{\quad}$

5. $8 \times n = 56$

    $n = \underline{\quad}$

6. $n \times 2 = 16$

    $n = \underline{\quad}$

Practice

Solve for n.

1. $7 \times n = 56$

   $n =$ ___

2. $5 \times n = 30$

   $n =$ ___

3. $n \times 4 = 8$

   $n =$ ___

4. $5 \times n = 45$

   $n =$ ___

5. $n \times 8 = 64$

   $n =$ ___

6. $n \times 7 = 35$

   $n =$ ___

7. $8 \times n = 40$

   $n =$ ___

8. $9 \times n = 54$

   $n =$ ___

9. $7 \times n = 42$

   $n =$ ___

10. $n \times 4 = 36$

    $n =$ ___

11. $4 \times n = 36$

    $n =$ ___

12. $4 \times n = 0$

    $n =$ ___

13. $n \times 8 = 48$

    $n =$ ___

14. $4 \times n = 12$

    $n =$ ___

15. $n \times 1 = 8$

    $n =$ ___

16. $9 \times n = 45$

    $n =$ ___

17. $8 \times n = 16$

    $n =$ ___

18. $n \times 4 = 32$

    $n =$ ___

19. $8 \times n = 56$

    $n =$ ___

20. $9 \times n = 27$

    $n =$ ___

21. $n \times 5 = 0$

    $n =$ ___

EXCURSION

Make the following sentences true by filling in the circle with either an addition symbol or a subtraction symbol.

Example: $8 \; \boxed{+} \; 3 \; \boxed{-} \; 1 = 10$

1. $9 \; \bigcirc \; 6 \; \bigcirc \; 2 = 5$

2. $15 \; \bigcirc \; 7 \; \bigcirc \; 2 = 6$

3. $8 \; \bigcirc \; 9 \; \bigcirc \; 4 = 13$

4. $6 \; \bigcirc \; 0 = 0 \; \bigcirc \; 6$

5. $12 \; \bigcirc \; 7 = 3 \; \bigcirc \; 2$

6. $14 \; \bigcirc \; 9 = 11 \; \bigcirc \; 7 \; \bigcirc \; 1$

Looking for a Pattern

This arrangement of numbers is called Pascal's triangle. What are the numbers in the next 3 rows?

```
            1
          1   1
        1   2   1
      1   3   3   1
    1   4   6   4   1
```

★ SEE

We need to find the patterns in Pascal's triangle.
We know:
   the end number in each row is _____;
   the other numbers in the row are the sum of the two closest numbers in the row

   above; and each row has _____ more number in it than the row above it.

★ PLAN

We predict the numbers there are in the next 3 rows by extending the patterns.

★ DO

```
                    1
                1       1
            1       2       1
        1       3       3       1
    1       4       6       4       1

  ___   ___   ___   ___   ___   ___

___   ___   ___   ___   ___   ___   ___

___   ___   ___   ___   ___   ___   ___   ___
```

★ CHECK

We check to see if the numbers continue the patterns.

Apply

Look for a pattern.

1. How many numbers are needed for the fiftieth row of Pascal's triangle?

2. Complete the last picture.

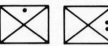

3. If two 6's are multiplied together the product is 36. If twelve 6's are multiplied together, what is the number in the ones place?

4. What number is missing?
1, 2, 4, 7, 11, ___, 22, 29, 37

5. The first three rows of Pascal's triangle use six numbers.

$$1$$
$$1 \quad 1$$
$$1 \quad 2 \quad 1$$

The first four rows use 10 numbers. How many numbers are needed for the first 10 rows? How can you prove that your answer is correct?

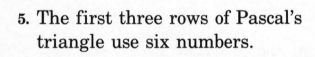

6. Think of each row in Pascal's triangle as one number. You can get the number in row two by multiplying 11×1. You can get row three by multiplying 11×11. Explain how to use 11 as a factor to get more rows.

7. Make five rows of another triangle by multiplying each digit in five rows of Pascal's triangle by 3. How is the pattern in your new triangle like that in Pascal's triangle? How is it different?

8. The sequence of numbers shown below is known as the Fibonacci sequence.
1, 1, 2, 3, 5, 8, 13, . . .
Tell what the next number in the sequence is and explain how you found it.

98

Calculators and Bank Accounts

Lorie is the student body treasurer. She writes **checks, deposits** money, and keeps the records for **expenses**. After a check is written, Lorie **balances the account.** How much does the student body have in its account?

We want to find the amount of money in the account. The amount after the last check was written

is _____. The check is written for _____.

To find the balance, we subtract _____ from

_____. Enter this code into your calculator and write the answer on the screen.

$$85 \; \boxed{\cdot} \; 35 \; \boxed{-} \; 17 \; \boxed{\cdot} \; 80 \; \boxed{=} \; \boxed{}$$

The student body has _____ in its account.

Some checkbooks have a **register** to keep records. How much is in the student body account after the $45.50 deposit? Remember to add deposits and subtract amounts of checks. Write the answer in the balance column.

No. 102		
19 __		
To Ace Ice Cream store		
	DOLLARS	CENTS
Balance Forward	85	35
Deposits		
Total	85	35
This Check	17	80
Balance		
Deductions		
Balance Forward		

CHECK NO.	DATE	CHECKS ISSUED TO OR DESCRIPTION OF DEPOSIT	AMOUNT OF CHECK		✔	AMOUNT OF DEPOSIT		BALANCE 85	35
102	NOV 1	Ace Ice Cream Store	17	80				67	55
	NOV 2	Deposit				45	50		

Use the register to show the balance after each of the following:

1. Check 103 on November 7, to Paul's Paper Company, for $13.68

2. Deposit on November 8 of $23.58

Practice

Complete the register using the information below.
Find each new balance.

Check Number	Date	Check or Deposit	Amount
201	Dec. 1	Bi/More Grocery Store	$36.18
202	Dec. 3	United Gas and Electrical	$45.73
203	Dec. 5	Sam's Shoes	$39.88
	Dec. 8	Deposit	$215.75
204	Dec. 8	Savings Account	$80.00
205	Dec. 9	Home Insurance Co.	$135.05
206	Dec. 16	Paul's Pizza Parlor	$16.50
207	Dec. 17	Dr. E. J. Goode	$49.78
	Dec. 22	Deposit	$205.75
208	Dec. 23	Alice Carson (rent)	$150.00

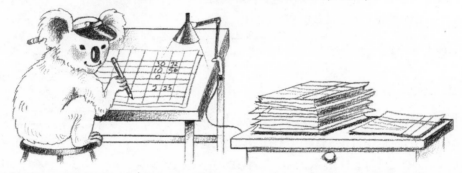

CHECK NO.	DATE	CHECKS ISSUED TO OR DESCRIPTION OF DEPOSIT	AMOUNT OF CHECK	✔	AMOUNT OF DEPOSIT	BALANCE	
						306	75

Multiply.

1. $\begin{array}{r} 3 \\ \times 2 \\ \hline \end{array}$	2. $\begin{array}{r} 8 \\ \times 5 \\ \hline \end{array}$	3. $\begin{array}{r} 7 \\ \times 9 \\ \hline \end{array}$	4. $\begin{array}{r} 4 \\ \times 3 \\ \hline \end{array}$	5. $\begin{array}{r} 2 \\ \times 8 \\ \hline \end{array}$	6. $\begin{array}{r} 9 \\ \times 6 \\ \hline \end{array}$	7. $\begin{array}{r} 5 \\ \times 8 \\ \hline \end{array}$
8. $\begin{array}{r} 5 \\ \times 5 \\ \hline \end{array}$	9. $\begin{array}{r} 6 \\ \times 7 \\ \hline \end{array}$	10. $\begin{array}{r} 5 \\ \times 9 \\ \hline \end{array}$	11. $\begin{array}{r} 8 \\ \times 7 \\ \hline \end{array}$	12. $\begin{array}{r} 6 \\ \times 0 \\ \hline \end{array}$	13. $\begin{array}{r} 6 \\ \times 5 \\ \hline \end{array}$	14. $\begin{array}{r} 8 \\ \times 9 \\ \hline \end{array}$
15. $\begin{array}{r} 7 \\ \times 8 \\ \hline \end{array}$	16. $\begin{array}{r} 3 \\ \times 9 \\ \hline \end{array}$	17. $\begin{array}{r} 9 \\ \times 7 \\ \hline \end{array}$	18. $\begin{array}{r} 6 \\ \times 6 \\ \hline \end{array}$	19. $\begin{array}{r} 8 \\ \times 6 \\ \hline \end{array}$	20. $\begin{array}{r} 4 \\ \times 5 \\ \hline \end{array}$	21. $\begin{array}{r} 6 \\ \times 9 \\ \hline \end{array}$
22. $\begin{array}{r} 1 \\ \times 5 \\ \hline \end{array}$	23. $\begin{array}{r} 7 \\ \times 7 \\ \hline \end{array}$	24. $\begin{array}{r} 8 \\ \times 8 \\ \hline \end{array}$	25. $\begin{array}{r} 5 \\ \times 7 \\ \hline \end{array}$	26. $\begin{array}{r} 0 \\ \times 4 \\ \hline \end{array}$	27. $\begin{array}{r} 9 \\ \times 9 \\ \hline \end{array}$	28. $\begin{array}{r} 7 \\ \times 5 \\ \hline \end{array}$
29. $\begin{array}{r} 9 \\ \times 8 \\ \hline \end{array}$	30. $\begin{array}{r} 4 \\ \times 6 \\ \hline \end{array}$	31. $\begin{array}{r} 7 \\ \times 6 \\ \hline \end{array}$	32. $\begin{array}{r} 3 \\ \times 2 \\ \hline \end{array}$	33. $\begin{array}{r} 9 \\ \times 5 \\ \hline \end{array}$	34. $\begin{array}{r} 5 \\ \times 6 \\ \hline \end{array}$	35. $\begin{array}{r} 6 \\ \times 8 \\ \hline \end{array}$

Solve for n.

36. $(5 \times 3) + 6 = n$

$n =$ ___

37. $(8 - 4) \times 5 = n$

$n =$ ___

38. $9 \times (3 + 5) = n$

$n =$ ___

39. $45 + (9 \times 5) = n$

$n =$ ___

40. $36 - (9 \times 4) = n$

$n =$ ___

41. $(8 \times 7) - 38 = n$

$n =$ ___

42. $7 \times n = 49$

$n =$ ___

43. $n \times 3 = 15$

$n =$ ___

44. $n \times 8 = 64$

$n =$ ___

45. $n \times 4 = 36$

$n =$ ___

46. $6 \times n = 42$

$n =$ ___

47. $6 \times n = 0$

$n =$ ___

101

Circle the letter of the correct answer.

1 What is the value of the 9 in 9,058?

a tens
b hundreds
c thousands
d NG

2 3,651 ◯ 3,615

a >
b <

3 Round 850 to the nearest hundred.

a 800
b 900
c NG

4 Round 6,786 to the nearest thousand.

a 8,000
b 7,000
c NG

5 What is the value of the 3 in 632,461?

a tens
b hundreds
c thousands
d NG

6   57
   + 86

a 133
b 143
c 1,313
d NG

7 359 + 283

a 532
b 542
c 552
d NG

8   29,468
   + 36,875

a 66,343
b 66,433
c 67,343
d NG

9 $16.48
   + 37.19

a $43.67
b $53.57
c $53.67
d NG

10 83 − 27

a 56
b 64
c 66
d NG

11 926 − 458

a 432
b 468
c 532
d NG

12   40,276
   − 29,867

a 10,409
b 20,409
c 29,611
d NG

13   9
   × 6

a 54
b 56
c 63
d NG

 score

102

MULTIPLICATION OF WHOLE NUMBERS

Multiples

The 25 students in Miss Lane's class are counting off to form squares for square dancing. Every fifth person will stand in the center of a square. What numbers will the students in the centers have?

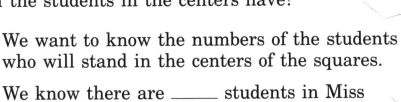

We want to know the numbers of the students who will stand in the centers of the squares.

We know there are _____ students in Miss Lane's class.

We know that every _____ student will stand in the center of a square.

We can count from 1 to 25, marking off every fifth number.

1, 2, 3, 4, ⑤   6, 7, 8, 9, ⑩   11, 12, 13, 14, ⑮

16, 17, 18, 19, ⑳   21, 22, 23, 24, ㉕

We say _____, _____, _____, _____ and _____ are multiples of 5. A **multiple** of a number is a product that has that number for at least one of its factors.

✔ The least multiple of any number is 0 because any number times 0 equals 0. Naming multiples of a number is called **skip-counting.** We skip-count by 5's by saying 0, 5, 10, 15, 20, 25, etc.

Students with the numbers _____, _____, _____, _____ and _____ will stand in the centers of the squares.

Getting Started

Write the first nine multiples of each of these numbers.

6 _____, _____, _____, _____, _____, _____, _____, _____, _____

8 _____, _____, _____, _____, _____, _____, _____, _____, _____

Practice

Write the first nine multiples of each of these numbers.

2 ____, ____, ____, ____, ____, ____, ____, ____, ____

5 ____, ____, ____, ____, ____, ____, ____, ____, ____

7 ____, ____, ____, ____, ____, ____, ____, ____, ____

4 ____, ____, ____, ____, ____, ____, ____, ____, ____

9 ____, ____, ____, ____, ____, ____, ____, ____, ____

Skip-count by 7.

56, ____, ____, ____, ____, ____, ____, ____, 112

Skip-count by 4.

32, ____, ____, ____, ____, ____, ____, ____, 64

Skip-count by 9.

72, ____, ____, ____, ____, ____, ____, ____, 144

Skip-count by 2.

16, ____, ____, ____, ____, ____, ____, ____, 32

Skip-count by 6.

48, ____, ____, ____, ____, ____, ____, ____, 96

Skip-count by 5.

40, ____, ____, ____, ____, ____, ____, ____, 80

Understanding Multiplication Properties

Besides the properties we have already
studied, there are others that help us to
find shortcuts in multiplication.

I can group any way I want in multiplication.

Multiplying by 10 is easy.

The Grouping Property
Factors can be grouped in anyway.

$$(3 \times 2) \times 5 = 3 \times (2 \times 5)$$

$$\underline{\quad} \times 5 = 3 \times \underline{\quad}$$

$$\underline{\quad} = \underline{\quad}$$

The Multiplication-Addition Property
Multiplication can be distributed
over addition.

$$5 \times (4 + 6) = (5 \times 4) + (5 \times 6)$$

$$5 \times \underline{\quad} = \underline{\quad} + \underline{\quad}$$

$$\underline{\quad} = \underline{\quad}$$

Multiplying by 10
If one factor is 10, the product is
the other number followed by a zero.

$$2 \times 10 = \underline{\quad}$$

$$10 \times 7 = \underline{\quad}$$

Getting Started

Solve for n. Use the properties to help you.

1. $4 \times (7 + 3) = n$

$$n = \underline{\quad}$$

2. $8 \times 10 = n$

$$n = \underline{\quad}$$

3. $6 \times (4 \times 10) = n$

$$n = \underline{\quad}$$

4. $9 \times 10 = n$

$$n = \underline{\quad}$$

5. $(2 \times 3) \times 10 = n$

$$n = \underline{\quad}$$

6. $(7 \times 2) + (7 \times 8) = n$

$$n = \underline{\quad}$$

Practice

Solve for *n*. Use the properties to help you.

1. $3 \times (0 \times 5) = n$

    $n =$ ___

2. $5 \times (4 + 3) = n$

    $n =$ ___

3. $(6 \times 3) + (6 \times 7) = n$

    $n =$ ___

4. $7 \times 10 = n$

    $n =$ ___

5. $2 \times (5 \times 8) = n$

    $n =$ ___

6. $9 \times (0 \times 3) = n$

    $n =$ ___

7. $4 \times 10 = n$

    $n =$ ___

8. $8 \times (3 \times 1) = n$

    $n =$ ___

9. $(8 \times 5) \times 0 = n$

    $n =$ ___

10. $(1 \times 1) \times 1 = n$

    $n =$ ___

11. $10 \times 9 = n$

    $n =$ ___

12. $(3 \times 4) + (3 \times 6) = n$

    $n =$ ___

13. $7 \times (9 + 1) = n$

    $n =$ ___

14. $0 \times (8 \times 10) = n$

    $n =$ ___

15. $(4 \times 0) + (4 \times 0) = n$

    $n =$ ___

Add, subtract or multiply.

16. $\begin{array}{r} 6 \\ + 9 \\ \hline \end{array}$

17. $\begin{array}{r} 8 \\ \times 7 \\ \hline \end{array}$

18. $\begin{array}{r} 15 \\ - 9 \\ \hline \end{array}$

19. $\begin{array}{r} 3 \\ + 7 \\ \hline \end{array}$

20. $\begin{array}{r} 5 \\ \times 8 \\ \hline \end{array}$

21. $\begin{array}{r} 6 \\ - 6 \\ \hline \end{array}$

22. $\begin{array}{r} 4 \\ \times 7 \\ \hline \end{array}$

23. $\begin{array}{r} 9 \\ \times 6 \\ \hline \end{array}$

24. $\begin{array}{r} 17 \\ - 8 \\ \hline \end{array}$

25. $\begin{array}{r} 7 \\ + 6 \\ \hline \end{array}$

26. $\begin{array}{r} 0 \\ \times 8 \\ \hline \end{array}$

27. $\begin{array}{r} 5 \\ + 8 \\ \hline \end{array}$

28. $\begin{array}{r} 13 \\ - 6 \\ \hline \end{array}$

29. $\begin{array}{r} 9 \\ - 0 \\ \hline \end{array}$

30. $\begin{array}{r} 7 \\ \times 1 \\ \hline \end{array}$

31. $\begin{array}{r} 6 \\ \times 6 \\ \hline \end{array}$

32. $\begin{array}{r} 4 \\ \times 3 \\ \hline \end{array}$

33. $\begin{array}{r} 8 \\ + 1 \\ \hline \end{array}$

34. $\begin{array}{r} 5 \\ + 5 \\ \hline \end{array}$

35. $\begin{array}{r} 5 \\ \times 5 \\ \hline \end{array}$

36. $\begin{array}{r} 5 \\ - 5 \\ \hline \end{array}$

37. $\begin{array}{r} 14 \\ - 9 \\ \hline \end{array}$

38. $\begin{array}{r} 8 \\ \times 6 \\ \hline \end{array}$

39. $\begin{array}{r} 8 \\ - 3 \\ \hline \end{array}$

40. $\begin{array}{r} 8 \\ \times 8 \\ \hline \end{array}$

41. $\begin{array}{r} 8 \\ - 8 \\ \hline \end{array}$

42. $\begin{array}{r} 8 \\ + 8 \\ \hline \end{array}$

43. $\begin{array}{r} 16 \\ - 7 \\ \hline \end{array}$

44. $\begin{array}{r} 3 \\ + 9 \\ \hline \end{array}$

45. $\begin{array}{r} 9 \\ - 6 \\ \hline \end{array}$

Multiplying Tens and Ones

River Road Foods processes and packs fresh fruits. How many cans of tomatoes will River Road pack in 4 minutes?

Packing Rates	
Food	**Number of cans per minute**
Tomatoes	21
Apples	24
Pumpkin	19

We want to know the number of cans

of tomatoes packed in _____ minutes.

We know that _____ cans of tomatoes are packed in one minute.
To find the number of cans packed in

4 minutes, we multiply _____ by _____.

$$21 \times 4 = ?$$

Multiply the ones.
$4 \times 1 = 4$

Multiply the tens.
$4 \times 2 = 8$

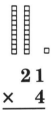

$$\begin{array}{r} 2\,1 \\ \times\ \ 4 \\ \hline \end{array}$$

$$\begin{array}{r} 2\,1 \\ \times\ \ 4 \\ \hline 4 \end{array}$$

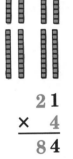

$$\begin{array}{r} 2\,1 \\ \times\ \ 4 \\ \hline 8\,4 \end{array}$$

River Road Foods will pack _____ cans in 4 minutes.

Getting Started

Multiply.

1. $\begin{array}{r} 24 \\ \times\ 2 \\ \hline \end{array}$

2. $\begin{array}{r} 40 \\ \times\ 2 \\ \hline \end{array}$

3. $\begin{array}{r} 31 \\ \times\ 3 \\ \hline \end{array}$

Copy and multiply.

4. 2×13

5. 4×11

6. 4×22

107

Practice

Multiply.

1. $\begin{array}{r} 13 \\ \times\ 2 \\ \hline \end{array}$
2. $\begin{array}{r} 30 \\ \times\ 2 \\ \hline \end{array}$
3. $\begin{array}{r} 58 \\ \times\ 1 \\ \hline \end{array}$
4. $\begin{array}{r} 40 \\ \times\ 2 \\ \hline \end{array}$
5. $\begin{array}{r} 21 \\ \times\ 3 \\ \hline \end{array}$

6. $\begin{array}{r} 42 \\ \times\ 2 \\ \hline \end{array}$
7. $\begin{array}{r} 34 \\ \times\ 2 \\ \hline \end{array}$
8. $\begin{array}{r} 11 \\ \times\ 7 \\ \hline \end{array}$
9. $\begin{array}{r} 24 \\ \times\ 2 \\ \hline \end{array}$
10. $\begin{array}{r} 33 \\ \times\ 3 \\ \hline \end{array}$

11. $\begin{array}{r} 12 \\ \times\ 4 \\ \hline \end{array}$
12. $\begin{array}{r} 11 \\ \times\ 5 \\ \hline \end{array}$
13. $\begin{array}{r} 44 \\ \times\ 2 \\ \hline \end{array}$
14. $\begin{array}{r} 31 \\ \times\ 3 \\ \hline \end{array}$
15. $\begin{array}{r} 32 \\ \times\ 3 \\ \hline \end{array}$

Copy and Do

16. 10×5
17. 36×1
18. 23×3
19. 4×12

20. 3×13
21. 43×2
22. 2×22
23. 9×11

24. 41×2
25. 3×12
26. 2×33
27. 2×31

Apply

Solve these problems.

28. Manuel bought 4 dozen eggs to put into the cakes he was making for the church bake sale. How many eggs did Manuel buy?

29. Beth bought 4 stamps. Each stamp cost 22¢. How much did Beth pay for the stamps?

EXCURSION

Fill in the blanks so that both sides of the sentences are equal.

1. $145 - 12 = 143 - \underline{\hspace{1cm}}$
2. $197 - 78 = \underline{\hspace{1cm}} - 80$

3. $41 - 13 = 48 - \underline{\hspace{1cm}}$
4. $73 - 29 = \underline{\hspace{1cm}} - 30$

5. $187 - 65 = 182 - \underline{\hspace{1cm}}$
6. $395 - 264 = \underline{\hspace{1cm}} - 204$

7. $359 - 126 = 363 - \underline{\hspace{1cm}}$
8. $254 - 181 = \underline{\hspace{1cm}} - 201$

Multiplying, Trading Ones

The fourth grade science lab has
16 stations. Mr. Owens needs to
make a battery and bulb hook-up for
each station. How many batteries
will Mr. Owens need?

We want to find the number of batteries
Mr. Owens needs.

There are _____ stations in the science lab.

Each station requires _____ batteries.

To find the number of batteries needed,

we multiply _____ by _____.

| 2×16 | $\begin{array}{l} 2 \times 6 = 12 \\ 12 = 1 \text{ ten } 2 \text{ ones} \end{array}$ | $\begin{array}{l} 2 \times 1 = 2 \\ 2 \text{ tens } + 1 \text{ ten } = 3 \text{ tens} \end{array}$ |

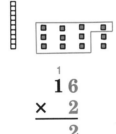 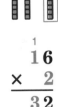

$$\begin{array}{r} 16 \\ \times\ 2 \\ \hline ? \end{array} \qquad \begin{array}{r} {\scriptstyle 1} \\ 16 \\ \times\ 2 \\ \hline 2 \end{array} \qquad \begin{array}{r} {\scriptstyle 1} \\ 16 \\ \times\ 2 \\ \hline 32 \end{array}$$

Mr. Owens needs _____ batteries.

Getting Started

Multiply.

1. $\begin{array}{r} 27 \\ \times\ 3 \\ \hline \end{array}$
2. $\begin{array}{r} 45 \\ \times\ 2 \\ \hline \end{array}$
3. $\begin{array}{r} 34 \\ \times\ 2 \\ \hline \end{array}$
4. $\begin{array}{r} 25 \\ \times\ 3 \\ \hline \end{array}$

Copy and multiply.

5. 48×2 6. 5×19 7. 38×2

Practice

Multiply.

1. 25
   × 3

2. 16
   × 5

3. 34
   × 2

4. 19
   × 3

5. 27
   × 3

6. 24
   × 4

7. 17
   × 5

8. 23
   × 3

9. 23
   × 4

10. 46
    × 2

11. 12
    × 4

12. 29
    × 3

13. 17
    × 4

14. 12
    × 8

15. 13
    × 7

Copy and Do

16. 2 × 36

17. 18 × 4

18. 26 × 3

19. 15 × 4

20. 28 × 2

21. 12 × 7

22. 2 × 43

23. 38 × 2

24. 24 × 3

25. 16 × 3

26. 2 × 19

27. 5 × 12

28. 18 × 3

29. 3 × 29

30. 4 × 19

Apply

Solve these problems.

31. A tablet of colored paper costs 29¢. How much will 3 tablets cost?

32. One pair of jeans costs $23.45. A shirt costs $16.79. The jeans cost how much more than a shirt?

33. A tape costs $5. How much will 16 tapes cost?

34. Mark has 47 cents. Jan has twice as much as Mark. How much does Jan have?

Multiplying 2-Digit Numbers

Paul is stocking the produce bins of his grocery store. He wants to make 6 equal columns of tomatoes. How many tomatoes can Paul display?

We need to find how many tomatoes Paul will display.

There will be _____ tomatoes in each column.

Paul will pack _____ columns of tomatoes.

To find the number of tomatoes Paul can pack, we multiply _____ by _____.

Multiply the ones.
Trade if needed.

$$\overset{2}{2}4 \\ \times\ 6 \\ \hline 4$$

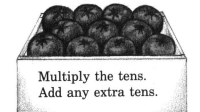

Multiply the tens.
Add any extra tens.

$$\overset{2}{2}4 \\ \times\ 6 \\ \hline 144$$

Paul can pack _____ tomatoes.

Getting Started

Multiply.

1. $\begin{array}{r} 25 \\ \times\ 7 \\ \hline \end{array}$

2. $\begin{array}{r} 32 \\ \times\ 9 \\ \hline \end{array}$

3. $\begin{array}{r} 50 \\ \times\ 6 \\ \hline \end{array}$

4. $\begin{array}{r} 49 \\ \times\ 8 \\ \hline \end{array}$

Copy and multiply.

5. 62×8

6. 27×4

7. 8×36

Practice

Multiply.

1.   26
   × 5
	2. 64
	   × 6
		3. 39
		   × 3
			4. 29
			   × 2
				5. 48
				   × 4

6.   53
   × 8
	7. 96
	   × 2
		8. 88
		   × 3
			9. 21
			   × 9
				10. 32
				   × 7

11.   73
   × 4
	12. 80
	   × 9
		13. 98
		   × 2
			14. 81
			   × 8
				15. 42
				   × 5

Copy and Do

16. 2 × 56   17. 3 × 97   18. 7 × 23   19. 4 × 59   20. 6 × 19

21. 5 × 73   22. 7 × 24   23. 6 × 28   24. 2 × 78   25. 9 × 19

26. 8 × 88   27. 5 × 68   28. 6 × 37   29. 3 × 46   30. 7 × 35

Apply

Solve these problems.

31. The Petersons drove 317 miles the first day of their vacation. They drove 287 miles the second day. How far did the Petersons drive in two days?

32. A washing machine uses 18 gallons of water for each load. How many gallons of water are used for 6 loads of wash?

33. Each tablet contains 32 pieces of paper. How many tablets do you need to buy to get at least 100 pieces of paper?

34. Each glass holds 6 ounces of juice. How many ounces of juice is needed to fill 48 glasses?

Multiplying Money

Eric is buying 7 folders at the school store. How much does this cost him?

SCHOOL SUPPLIES

PENCILS 8¢	ERASERS 15¢
PENS 59¢	TABLETS 39¢
PENNANTS 79¢	FOLDERS 34¢

We want to know the cost of Eric's purchases.

He bought ____ folders.

Each folder cost _____.

We find the total cost by multiplying

_____ by ____.

✔ Remember that $0.34 is another way of writing 34¢.

Multiply the pennies. Trade if needed.

Multiply the dimes. Add any extra dimes. Place the dollar sign and decimal point.

$$\begin{array}{r} \overset{2}{\$0.3}4 \\ \times \quad 7 \\ \hline 8 \end{array}$$

$$\begin{array}{r} \overset{2}{\$0.3}4 \\ \times \quad 7 \\ \hline \$2.38 \end{array}$$

Eric must pay _____ to the school store.

Getting Started

Multiply.

1. $\begin{array}{r} \$0.42 \\ \times \quad 6 \\ \hline \end{array}$

2. $\begin{array}{r} \$0.87 \\ \times \quad 3 \\ \hline \end{array}$

3. $\begin{array}{r} \$0.38 \\ \times \quad 9 \\ \hline \end{array}$

4. $\begin{array}{r} \$0.45 \\ \times \quad 5 \\ \hline \end{array}$

Solve these problems using the information above.

5. Robin buys 5 pencils and 3 erasers. How much does Robin spend?

6. How much more are 3 pennants than 4 tablets?

Practice

Multiply.

1.	$0.63 × 3	2.	$0.72 × 8	3.	$0.16 × 4	4.	$0.49 × 2
5.	$0.84 × 3	6.	$0.67 × 7	7.	$0.89 × 9	8.	$0.85 × 6
9.	$0.53 × 6	10.	$0.09 × 8	11.	$0.75 × 7	12.	$0.67 × 9

Apply

Solve these problems.

13. Adam buys a folder and a pen. He gives the storekeeper a dollar bill. How much change should Adam receive?

14. Nancy has $4.25. She wants to buy 7 pennants and 3 tablets. How much more money does Nancy need?

15. Todd buys 4 pencils and 5 folders. He gives the clerk a five dollar bill. How much change should Todd receive?

16. Mrs. Lopez decides to use the rapid train to go to and from work for 4 days. How much will she save if she usually takes the bus?

114

Make a Table

Our class timed some students walking down the hallway. They walked 6 meters in 9 seconds. At this rate how far would they walk in 81 seconds?

★ SEE

We want to find out how far the students will walk in 81 seconds.

They walk ___ meters in ___ seconds.

★ PLAN

We can make a table comparing the number of seconds to the distance the students walk.

★ DO

Seconds	9	18	27	36	___	54	63	___	81
Distance (in meters)	6	12	18	___	30	___	___	48	___

The students will walk _____ meters in 81 seconds.

★ CHECK

We know the students walk 6 meters in 9 seconds.

We know that in 81 seconds there are 9 groups of 9 seconds each.

If we multiply 6 meters by the number of

groups, we will get _____ meters.

115

Apply

Make a table to help you solve these problems.

1. Laura swims 7 laps on the first day of swim practice. She increases her distance by 2 laps each day. On the last day of practice she swims 25 laps. How many days does practice last?

2. It costs $0.29 to mail a letter and $0.19 to mail a postcard. Betty wrote to 11 friends and spent $2.89 on postage. How many letters and postcards did she write?

3. While looking out the window, I saw some boys and some dogs walk by the house. I counted 22 heads and 68 legs. How many boys and how many dogs passed by?

4. Make a table of at least 4 other length and width measures for a 36-square unit rectangle.

5. The fourth graders are collecting aluminum cans to be recycled. They receive $0.15 a pound for the cans. It takes 25 cans to make a pound. How many empty cans will they need to collect to earn $1.35?

6. To produce a special shade of paint, we use 4 drops of dark green to 1 drop of white to 5 drops of light green. If we use 20 drops of light green, how many drops of dark green and how many drops of white must we use?

7. Read Exercise 3 again. What if I saw 23 heads and 70 legs? Now how many boys and how many dogs passed by?

8. Peppy the puppy looked in the pond and saw 3 times as many gold fish as blue fish and 2 times as many silver fish as blue fish. Does Peppy see more gold fish or more silver fish? Explain how you know.

Calculators, the Multiplication Key

Mary is making a table to show how many eggs there are in any number of cartons. How many eggs are there in 6 cartons?

DOZENS	1	2	3	4	5	6
EGGS	12	24	36	48	60	

Mary found three ways to find the number of eggs in 6 cartons. Complete the codes to see what Mary found.

The addition code

12 ⊞ 12 ⊞ 12 ⊞ 12 ⊞ 12 ⊞ 12 ⊟ ⬭

The equals code

12 ⊞ 12 ⊟ ⊟ ⊟ ⊟ ⊟ ⬭

The multiplication code

12 ⊗ 6 ⊟ ⬭

There are _____ eggs in 6 cartons.

Complete these calculator codes.

45 ⊞ 45 ⊞ 45 ⊞ 45 ⊟ ⬭

45 ⊞ 45 ⊟ ⊟ ⊟ ⬭

45 ⊗ 4 ⊟ ⬭

117

Practice

Enter these codes. Show the results on the screens.

1. 25 [+] 25 [+] 25 [=] ⬭

2. 3 [×] 25 [=] ⬭

3. 49 [+] 49 [=][=][=] ⬭

4. 49 [×] 4 [=] ⬭

5. 3 [×] 5 [×] 6 [=] ⬭

6. 115 [−] 37 [×] 9 [=] ⬭

Use your calculator to find each product.

7. 37 × 9

8. 28 × 7

9. 34 × 8

10. 79 × 6

11. 84 × 7

12. 52 × 4

13. $0.85 × 8

14. $0.96 × 5

EXCURSION

Complete these calculator codes.
What conclusion can you make from the answers?

1 [+] 3 [=] ⬭

2 [×] 2 [=] ⬭

1 [+] 3 [+] 5 [=] ⬭

3 [×] 3 [=] ⬭

1 [+] 3 [+] 5 [+] 7 [=] ⬭

4 [×] 4 [=] ⬭

1 [+] 3 [+] 5 [+] 7 [+] 9 [=] ⬭

5 [×] 5 [=] ⬭

1 [+] 3 [+] 5 [+] 7 [+] 9 [+] 11 [=] ⬭

__ [×] __ [=] ⬭

1 [+] 3 [+] 5 [+] 7 [+] 9 [+] 11 [+] 13 [=] ⬭

__ [×] __ [=] ⬭

1 [+] 3 [+] 5 [+] 7 [+] 9 [+] 11 [+] 13 [+] 15 [=] ⬭

__ [×] __ [=] ⬭

Conclusion: _____

_____

118

Write the first nine multiples of each of these numbers.

1. 3 _____, _____, _____, _____, _____, _____, _____, _____, _____

2. 7 _____, _____, _____, _____, _____, _____, _____, _____, _____

3. 9 _____, _____, _____, _____, _____, _____, _____, _____, _____

Skip-count by 8.

4. 64, _____, _____, _____, _____, _____, _____, _____, 128

Skip-count by 4.

5. 12, _____, _____, _____, _____, _____, _____, _____, 44

Solve for n.

6. $6 \times (0 \times 3) = n$ 7. $8 \times 10 = n$ 8. $(7 \times 2) + (7 \times 3) = n$

$n =$ ___ $n =$ ___ $n =$ ___

9. $9 \times (4 \times 2) = n$ 10. $(5 \times 0) + (5 \times 0) = n$ 11. $10 \times 9 = n$

$n =$ ___ $n =$ ___ $n =$ ___

Multiply.

12. $\begin{array}{r} 21 \\ \times\ 3 \\ \hline \end{array}$ 13. $\begin{array}{r} 11 \\ \times\ 7 \\ \hline \end{array}$ 14. $\begin{array}{r} 42 \\ \times\ 2 \\ \hline \end{array}$ 15. $\begin{array}{r} 12 \\ \times\ 4 \\ \hline \end{array}$

16. $\begin{array}{r} 36 \\ \times\ 2 \\ \hline \end{array}$ 17. $\begin{array}{r} 29 \\ \times\ 3 \\ \hline \end{array}$ 18. $\begin{array}{r} 16 \\ \times\ 4 \\ \hline \end{array}$ 19. $\begin{array}{r} 47 \\ \times\ 2 \\ \hline \end{array}$

20. $\begin{array}{r} \$0.37 \\ \times\ \ \ \ 6 \\ \hline \end{array}$ 21. $\begin{array}{r} \$0.49 \\ \times\ \ \ \ 4 \\ \hline \end{array}$ 22. $\begin{array}{r} \$0.73 \\ \times\ \ \ \ 9 \\ \hline \end{array}$ 23. $\begin{array}{r} \$0.87 \\ \times\ \ \ \ 8 \\ \hline \end{array}$

Circle the letter of the correct answer.

1 What is the value of the 5 in 4,576?
a thousands
b hundreds
c tens
d NG

2 5,219 ◯ 5,129
a <
b >

3 Round 735 to the nearest hundred.
a 700
b 800
c NG

4 Round 7,295 to the nearest thousand.
a 8,000
b 7,000
c NG

5 What is the value of the 0 in 302,926.
a tens
b hundreds
c thousands
d NG

6 49 + 73
a 23
b 112
c 1,112
d NG

7   659
  + 268
a 817
b 917
c 927
d NG

8   3,629
  + 4,381
a 7,000
b 8,000
c 8,010
d NG

9   54,275
  + 27,196
a 71,371
b 81,461
c 81,471
d NG

10 51 − 26
a 25
b 36
c 45
d NG

11   817
   − 298
a 519
b 619
c 681
d NG

12   61,083
   − 28,596
a 32,487
b 32,587
c 47,513
d NG

13 24 × 4
a 86
b 96
c 816
d NG

 score

DIVIDING BY A 1-DIGIT NUMBER

Dividing by 2 or 3

Lori is fixing lunches and is putting 2 cookies in each lunch box. How many lunch boxes can she supply with cookies?

We want to know how many lunch boxes Lori can supply with 2 cookies each.

We know she has _____ cookies to share.

There are _____ cookies for each lunch.
To find how many lunches can be supplied with cookies, we

divide _____ by _____.

In all	In each	Boxes

$$12 \div 2 = 6 \quad \text{or} \quad 2\overline{)12}$$

12 — dividend 2 — divisor 6 — quotient 6 — quotient 2)12 — divisor, dividend

Lori can supply 2 cookies each to _____ lunches.

Getting Started

Divide.

1. $6 \div 3 =$ _____

2. $14 \div 2 =$ _____

3. $8 \div 2 =$ _____

4. $24 \div 3 =$ _____

5. $15 \div 3 =$ _____

6. $6 \div 2 =$ _____

7. $2\overline{)16}$

8. $3\overline{)27}$

9. $3\overline{)18}$

Practice

Divide.

1. $10 \div 2 =$ _____
2. $12 \div 3 =$ _____
3. $24 \div 3 =$ _____
4. $18 \div 2 =$ _____

5. $21 \div 3 =$ _____
6. $18 \div 3 =$ _____
7. $27 \div 3 =$ _____
8. $15 \div 3 =$ _____

9. $3\overline{)12}$
10. $3\overline{)6}$
11. $2\overline{)14}$
12. $3\overline{)27}$

13. $2\overline{)16}$
14. $2\overline{)10}$
15. $3\overline{)9}$
16. $2\overline{)6}$

Apply

Solve these problems.

17. Joan and Angie each have 12 sweaters to store in boxes. Joan will store 3 sweaters in each box. Angie can only put 2 of her sweaters in a box. How many boxes will Joan and Angie both need for all their sweaters?

18. Pat is putting marbles into bags. He has 24 marbles and wants to put 3 marbles into each bag. How many bags will Pat need?

EXCURSION

Complete these tables of Hindu-Arabic numbers and Roman Numerals.

Hundreds	
100	C
200	
	CCC
400	CD
500	D
	DC
700	DCC
	DCCC
	CM

Tens	
10	X
	XX
30	
40	XL
50	L
60	
	LXX
80	
	XC

Ones	
1	I
	II
3	
4	IV
5	V
	VI
7	
8	
	IX

122

Dividing by 4 or 5

Roy is packing apples for 4 gift boxes. How many apples should he pack into each box?

We want to know how many apples should go in each box.

There are _____ apples.

Roy is packing _____ boxes.

To find the number of apples for each box,

we divide _____ by _____.

In all	Boxes	In each		
24	÷ 4	= _____	or	4)‾2‾4‾
↑	↑	↑		↑
dividend	divisor	quotient		divisor

quotient

4)‾2‾4‾ dividend

↑

divisor

Roy should put _____ apples into each box.

Getting Started

Divide.

1. 36 ÷ 4 = _____   2. 45 ÷ 5 = _____   3. 16 ÷ 4 = _____   4. 20 ÷ 5 = _____

5. 5)‾3‾0‾   6. 4)‾1‾2‾   7. 4)‾3‾6‾   8. 5)‾1‾0‾

Practice

Divide.

1. $25 \div 5 =$ _____   2. $10 \div 5 =$ _____   3. $8 \div 4 =$ _____   4. $28 \div 4 =$ _____

5. $24 \div 4 =$ _____   6. $18 \div 3 =$ _____   7. $20 \div 5 =$ _____   8. $15 \div 5 =$ _____

9. $16 \div 4 =$ _____   10. $32 \div 4 =$ _____   11. $24 \div 3 =$ _____   12. $30 \div 5 =$ _____

13. $35 \div 5 =$ _____   14. $12 \div 4 =$ _____   15. $20 \div 4 =$ _____   16. $36 \div 4 =$ _____

17. $4\overline{)12}$ 18. $5\overline{)25}$ 19. $5\overline{)30}$ 20. $2\overline{)18}$

21. $4\overline{)20}$ 22. $4\overline{)16}$ 23. $3\overline{)27}$ 24. $4\overline{)28}$

25. $5\overline{)10}$ 26. $5\overline{)20}$ 27. $5\overline{)35}$ 28. $4\overline{)8}$

29. $2\overline{)12}$ 30. $4\overline{)24}$ 31. $5\overline{)45}$ 32. $5\overline{)40}$

Apply

Solve these problems.

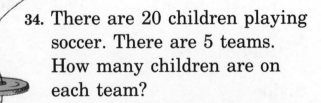

33. There are 24 children in Miss Chen's class. The children sit at 4 tables. How many children are at each table?

34. There are 20 children playing soccer. There are 5 teams. How many children are on each team?

35. There are 28 children in Mr. Orr's class. 4 children were absent on Tuesday. How many children were present in Mr. Orr's class?

36. Kay is sewing 5 buttons on each blouse. On Friday, Kay sewed on 30 buttons. How many blouses did Kay put buttons on?

Dividing by 6 or 7

Mr. Lopez spent $24 on concert tickets for his family. How many tickets did he buy?

We want to know the number of tickets Mr. Lopez bought.

He spent _____ on all the tickets.

Each ticket cost _____.
To find the number of tickets,

we divide _____ by _____.

_____ × 6 = 24?   6 × _____ = 24?

24 ÷ 6 = _____   or   6)‾24

Mr. Lopez bought _____ tickets.

Getting Started

Divide.

1. 54 ÷ 6 = ___   2. 28 ÷ 7 = ___   3. 42 ÷ 6 = ___   4. 14 ÷ 7 = ___

5. 56 ÷ 7 = ___   6. 18 ÷ 6 = ___   7. 30 ÷ 6 = ___   8. 42 ÷ 7 = ___

9. 6)‾12   10. 6)‾24   11. 7)‾21   12. 7)‾35

13. 7)‾49   14. 6)‾36   15. 7)‾63   16. 6)‾48

125

Practice

Divide.

1. $24 \div 3 =$ ___   2. $28 \div 4 =$ ___   3. $35 \div 7 =$ ___   4. $30 \div 6 =$ ___

5. $12 \div 6 =$ ___   6. $16 \div 2 =$ ___   7. $14 \div 7 =$ ___   8. $56 \div 7 =$ ___

9. $54 \div 6 =$ ___   10. $63 \div 7 =$ ___   11. $24 \div 6 =$ ___   12. $28 \div 7 =$ ___

13. $18 \div 6 =$ ___   14. $28 \div 4 =$ ___   15. $42 \div 7 =$ ___   16. $36 \div 6 =$ ___

17. $6\overline{)30}$ 18. $6\overline{)36}$ 19. $7\overline{)21}$ 20. $7\overline{)49}$

21. $6\overline{)24}$ 22. $7\overline{)42}$ 23. $6\overline{)18}$ 24. $7\overline{)28}$

25. $7\overline{)63}$ 26. $5\overline{)40}$ 27. $6\overline{)54}$ 28. $6\overline{)48}$

29. $7\overline{)35}$ 30. $4\overline{)32}$ 31. $6\overline{)42}$ 32. $7\overline{)56}$

Apply

Solve these problems.

33. Tickets for the school carnival and dinner were $7 each. The Johnson family paid $35 for tickets. How many Johnsons went to the carnival?

34. Ruth bought 6 albums for $8 each. Randy bought 7 albums for $7 each. How much more did Randy spend for his albums?

35. Danny bought 3 concert tickets for $5 each. Marta bought 2 tickets at $6 each. How much did they pay for all the tickets?

36. All children's books were on sale for $6 each. Rene bought books worth $30. How many books did Rene buy?

Dividing by 8 or 9

Mrs. Ferris is buying one place setting of dinnerware at a time to complete her set. How much will she pay for one place setting?

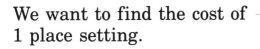

We want to find the cost of 1 place setting.

The sale price on the place setting is _____

for _____ of them.

To find the cost of one place setting, we divide

_____ by _____.

$$\$48 \div 8 = \rule{1cm}{0.4pt} \quad \text{or} \quad 8)\overline{\$48}$$

Mrs. Ferris will pay _____ for one place setting.

Getting Started

Divide.

1. $64 \div 8 = \rule{0.8cm}{0.4pt}$ 2. $36 \div 9 = \rule{0.8cm}{0.4pt}$ 3. $18 \div 9 = \rule{0.8cm}{0.4pt}$ 4. $45 \div 9 = \rule{0.8cm}{0.4pt}$

5. $56 \div 8 = \rule{0.8cm}{0.4pt}$ 6. $72 \div 8 = \rule{0.8cm}{0.4pt}$ 7. $48 \div 8 = \rule{0.8cm}{0.4pt}$ 8. $27 \div 9 = \rule{0.8cm}{0.4pt}$

9. $3)\overline{15}$ 10. $8)\overline{32}$ 11. $9)\overline{72}$ 12. $9)\overline{54}$

13. $8)\overline{72}$ 14. $9)\overline{63}$ 15. $8)\overline{24}$ 16. $8)\overline{40}$

Practice

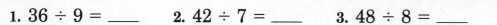

Divide.

1. $36 \div 9 =$ _____   2. $42 \div 7 =$ _____   3. $48 \div 8 =$ _____   4. $64 \div 8 =$ _____

5. $27 \div 9 =$ _____   6. $81 \div 9 =$ _____   7. $56 \div 8 =$ _____   8. $16 \div 8 =$ _____

9. $18 \div 9 =$ _____   10. $45 \div 9 =$ _____   11. $25 \div 5 =$ _____   12. $63 \div 9 =$ _____

13. $48 \div 6 =$ _____   14. $24 \div 8 =$ _____   15. $72 \div 8 =$ _____   16. $32 \div 8 =$ _____

17. $8\overline{)32}$ 18. $8\overline{)16}$ 19. $6\overline{)36}$ 20. $9\overline{)45}$

21. $9\overline{)63}$ 22. $9\overline{)27}$ 23. $8\overline{)72}$ 24. $8\overline{)24}$

25. $9\overline{)36}$ 26. $8\overline{)48}$ 27. $4\overline{)16}$ 28. $8\overline{)56}$

29. $3\overline{)9}$ 30. $9\overline{)54}$ 31. $9\overline{)18}$ 32. $9\overline{)81}$

Apply

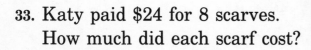
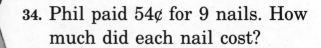

Solve these problems.

33. Katy paid $24 for 8 scarves. How much did each scarf cost?

34. Phil paid 54¢ for 9 nails. How much did each nail cost?

35. Leigh paid $40 for 8 baseballs. Later, she sold the baseballs for $7 each. How much profit did Leigh make on each baseball?

36. There are 9 players on a softball team. All 45 people who came to practice were put on teams. Each team paid a fee of $8 to use the field. How much was collected from the teams?

Understanding 1 and 0 in Division

One and zero are special numbers in division. Understanding these rules will help you be a better mathematician.

When I divide by 1, I get the same number.

When I divide a number by itself, I get 1.

If the divisor is 1, the quotient is equal to the dividend.

$$6 \div 1 = \underline{\quad} \qquad 1\overline{)6}$$

If the divisor and the dividend are the same number, the quotient is 1.

$$8 \div 8 = \underline{\quad} \qquad 8\overline{)8}$$

If the dividend is 0, the quotient is 0.

$$0 \div 4 = \underline{\quad} \qquad 4\overline{)0}$$

NEVER divide by zero. The divisor can never be zero.

Getting Started

Divide.

1. $9\overline{)9}$ 2. $1\overline{)7}$ 3. $5\overline{)0}$ 4. $6\overline{)0}$

5. $8\overline{)8}$ 6. $1\overline{)1}$ 7. $7\overline{)0}$ 8. $1\overline{)3}$

9. $4 \div 4 = \underline{\quad}$ 10. $8 \div 1 = \underline{\quad}$ 11. $0 \div 1 = \underline{\quad}$ 12. $2 \div 2 = \underline{\quad}$

Practice

Divide.

$3\overline{)\overset{?}{3}}$

$1\overline{)\overset{?}{3}}$

1. $2\overline{)2}$ 2. $5\overline{)10}$ 3. $4\overline{)4}$ 4. $7\overline{)14}$ 5. $1\overline{)1}$

6. $2\overline{)0}$ 7. $1\overline{)4}$ 8. $2\overline{)6}$ 9. $9\overline{)9}$ 10. $3\overline{)18}$

11. $1\overline{)7}$ 12. $1\overline{)8}$ 13. $2\overline{)12}$ 14. $4\overline{)12}$ 15. $2\overline{)4}$

16. $5\overline{)5}$ 17. $9\overline{)27}$ 18. $1\overline{)9}$ 19. $7\overline{)49}$ 20. $9\overline{)0}$

21. $7\overline{)35}$ 22. $3\overline{)27}$ 23. $8\overline{)8}$ 24. $7\overline{)63}$ 25. $3\overline{)0}$

26. $7\overline{)56}$ 27. $5\overline{)35}$ 28. $9\overline{)72}$ 29. $3\overline{)3}$ 30. $2\overline{)8}$

31. $1\overline{)2}$ 32. $8\overline{)40}$ 33. $1\overline{)0}$ 34. $6\overline{)6}$ 35. $4\overline{)0}$

36. $18 \div 9 =$ ____   37. $6 \div 1 =$ ____   38. $6 \div 3 =$ ____   39. $28 \div 7 =$ ____

40. $3 \div 1 =$ ____   41. $18 \div 6 =$ ____   42. $5 \div 1 =$ ____   43. $7 \div 7 =$ ____

44. $48 \div 6 =$ ____   45. $54 \div 6 =$ ____   46. $0 \div 9 =$ ____   47. $20 \div 5 =$ ____

48. $40 \div 5 =$ ____   49. $1 \div 1 =$ ____   50. $0 \div 6 =$ ____   51. $45 \div 9 =$ ____

Working with Remainders

Keith wants to buy as many pretzels as he can for 43¢. How many can he buy? How much money will he have left?

We want to know the number of pretzels Keith will buy and the amount he will have left.

We know Keith has _____ to spend.

Each pretzel costs _____.

To find the number of pretzels that can be bought,

and the left-over money, we divide _____ by _____.

Guess the closest fact that is not too big.	Multiply.	Subtract.	The remainder must be less than the divisor.
$\begin{array}{r} 8 \\ 5¢\overline{)43¢} \end{array}$	$\begin{array}{r} 8 \\ 5¢\overline{)43¢} \\ 40 \quad (8 \times 5) \end{array}$	$\begin{array}{r} 8 \text{ pretzels} \\ 5¢\overline{)43¢} \\ -40 \\ \hline 3 \text{ remainder} \end{array}$	$\begin{array}{r} 8 \text{ R3} \\ 5¢\overline{)43¢} \\ -40 \\ \hline 3 \\ (3¢ < 5¢) \end{array}$

Keith can buy _____ pretzels. He will have _____ left.

Getting Started

Divide. Show your work.

1. $6\overline{)13}$ 2. $4\overline{)23}$ 3. $2\overline{)19}$ 4. $7\overline{)32}$ 5. $8\overline{)23}$

6. $9\overline{)30}$ 7. $5\overline{)37}$ 8. $3\overline{)25}$ 9. $8\overline{)58}$ 10. $6\overline{)39}$

Practice

Divide. Show your work.

1. 8)43   2. 5)39   3. 4)34   4. 9)86   5. 7)45

6. 2)13   7. 6)27   8. 3)28   9. 6)34   10. 4)30

11. 5)39   12. 9)51   13. 8)31   14. 7)29   15. 3)16

EXCURSION

Complete the tables.

Multiply	Add	Find Missing Factor	Find Missing Addend
1 × 9 = ____	0 + 9 = ____	9 × ____ = 9	0 + ____ = 9
2 × 9 = ____	1 + 8 = ____	9 × ____ = 18	1 + ____ = 9
3 × 9 = ____	2 + 7 = ____	9 × ____ = 27	2 + ____ = 9
4 × 9 = ____	3 + 6 = ____	9 × ____ = 36	3 + ____ = 9
5 × 9 = ____	4 + 5 = ____	9 × ____ = 45	4 + ____ = 9
6 × 9 = ____	5 + 4 = ____	9 × ____ = 54	5 + ____ = 9
7 × 9 = ____	6 + 3 = ____	9 × ____ = 63	6 + ____ = 9
8 × 9 = ____	7 + 2 = ____	9 × ____ = 72	7 + ____ = 9
9 × 9 = ____	8 + 1 = ____	9 × ____ = 81	8 + ____ = 9

Dividing, 2-digit Quotients

The Girl Scouts have to carry 52 pieces of kindling to their campsite. How many pieces of wood will each scout have to carry?

We are looking for the number of pieces of wood each scout will carry. Altogether, there are

_____ pieces of kindling wood to be carried.

There are _____ scouts.

To find the number of pieces of wood each

scout will carry, we divide _____ by _____.

Divide the 5 tens by 4. Each scout will carry ten pieces with 1 ten left over.	$4\overline{)52}$ with quotient 1, $\frac{4}{1}$	Divide. $4\overline{)5}$ quotient 1 Multiply. $4 \times 1 = 4$ Subtract. $5 - 4 = 1$ Compare. $1 < 4$
Trade the 1 ten for ten ones.	$4\overline{)52}$ quotient 1, $4\downarrow$, 12	Bring down the ones digit. There are now 12 ones.
Divide the 12 ones by 4. Each scout will carry 3 more pieces for a total of 13 each.	$4\overline{)52}$ quotient 13, $\frac{4}{12}$, $\frac{12}{0}$	Divide. $4\overline{)12}$ quotient 3 Multiply. $4 \times 3 = 12$ Subtract. $12 - 12 = 0$

Each scout must carry _____ pieces of wood.

Getting Started

Divide. Show your work.

1. $3\overline{)42}$

2. $4\overline{)92}$

Copy and divide.

3. $50 \div 5$

4. $96 \div 8$

Practice

Divide. Show your work.

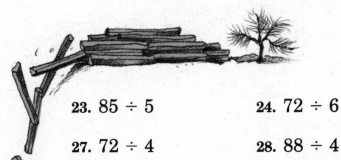

1. 5)75 2. 3)63 3. 4)80 4. 4)96 5. 2)56

6. 3)72 7. 7)84 8. 5)80 9. 6)96 10. 9)90

11. 8)88 12. 3)81 13. 4)56 14. 7)91 15. 6)84

16. 2)94 17. 3)75 18. 7)98 19. 3)90 20. 4)76

Copy and Do

21. 78 ÷ 6 22. 90 ÷ 2 23. 85 ÷ 5 24. 72 ÷ 6

25. 60 ÷ 5 26. 60 ÷ 2 27. 72 ÷ 4 28. 88 ÷ 4

29. 66 ÷ 3 30. 76 ÷ 2 31. 87 ÷ 3 32. 96 ÷ 8

Apply

Solve these problems.

33. Gene bought 3 thank you notes for 75¢. How much did each card cost?

34. Lemons cost 8¢ each. Sally has 96¢. How many lemons can Sally buy?

35. Rhoda fed her horse 3 apples a day for lunch. How many apples did the horse eat in 27 days?

36. The tennis club used 45 tennis balls in a tournament. Tennis balls are sold 3 in a can. How many cans did the club use?

Dividing, 2-digit Quotients with Remainders

Scott, Sam and Tom were quizzing
each other with 52 multiplication
fact cards. Scott dealt all the
cards so that each boy received
the same number. He put the extra
cards in the center. How many
cards will each boy receive?
How many will be put in the center?

We want to know the number of cards dealt to each
boy and the number left over for the center.

There are _____ cards all together.

The cards are dealt out to _____ boys.
To find the number of cards each boy will get and

the number in the center, we divide _____ by _____.

Divide the tens.	Bring down the ones.	Subtract. 22 − 21 = 1
Guess the closest fact	Divide the ones.	Compare. 1 < 3
that is not too big.	Guess the closest fact	Write the remainder.
Multiply. 3 × 1 = 3	that is not too big.	
Subtract. 5 − 3 = 2	Multiply. 3 × 7 = 21	
Compare. 2 < 3		

$$\begin{array}{r} 1 \\ 3\overline{)52} \\ \underline{3} \\ 2 \end{array}$$

$$\begin{array}{r} 17 \\ 3\overline{)52} \\ \underline{3} \\ 22 \\ \underline{21} \end{array}$$

$$\begin{array}{r} 17\ \text{R1} \\ 3\overline{)52} \\ \underline{3} \\ 22 \\ \underline{21} \\ 1 \end{array}$$

Each boy will get _____ cards. There will be _____ card left over.

Getting Started

Divide. Show your work.

Copy and divide.

3. 76 ÷ 2

4. 90 ÷ 4

1. 3)19

2. 6)65

Practice

Divide. Show your work.

1. 4)37
2. 7)85
3. 2)57
4. 6)91
5. 5)72

6. 9)93
7. 8)67
8. 3)76
9. 4)71
10. 2)19

11. 3)97
12. 9)98
13. 8)89
14. 6)85
15. 7)96

Copy and Do

16. 47 ÷ 3
17. 54 ÷ 5
18. 86 ÷ 4
19. 62 ÷ 6

20. 92 ÷ 7
21. 91 ÷ 2
22. 98 ÷ 8
23. 59 ÷ 3

24. 71 ÷ 4
25. 87 ÷ 5
26. 76 ÷ 7
27. 80 ÷ 6

Apply

Solve these problems.

28. Margaret has 76¢ to buy stickers. Stickers cost 5¢ each. How many stickers can Margaret buy? How much will she have left over?

29. Yoko has divided her 51 books equally on 4 shelves. How many books go on each shelf? How many are left over?

30. John has 65 flowers that he wants to plant in 6 rows. How many flowers will go into each row. How many will be left over?

31. Thomas is putting 5 flowers into each vase. He is filling 16 vases. How many flowers does Thomas need to put into the vases?

Drawing a Picture or Diagram

Five girls are running a race. Elaine is 50 yards behind Diane. Cassie is 10 yards behind Elaine. Barb is 50 yards ahead of Cassie. Ann is 20 yards behind Barb. Ann is 30 yards behind Diane.
What is the order of the girls at this time?

★ **SEE**

We want to know the order of the five girls in the race.

We know Elaine is _____ yards behind Diane.

_____ is 10 yards behind _____. Cassie

is _____ yards behind Barb. Ann is _____ yards

behind Barb. Ann is _____ yards behind Diane.

★ **PLAN**

We draw a diagram of the race, showing positions 10 yards apart. Using the facts, we place the initial of each girl to show her position.

★ **DO**

The order of the girls from first to last is

_____, _____, _____, _____ and _____.

★ **CHECK**

We compare the results of the race with the facts in the original problem to see if each girl is in position.

Apply

Draw a picture to help you solve each problem.
Remember to use the four-step plan.

1. Sal is waiting to buy tickets for a movie. There are 5 people waiting ahead of him and 7 people waiting behind him. How many people are in line for tickets?

2. If it takes 3 minutes to make a cut, how long will it take to cut a log that is 20 feet long into 10 equal lengths?

3. If you count the number of pickets and spaces along a fence, you will find that the number of spaces is always one less than the number of pickets. How many spaces will a bicycle wheel with 15 spokes contain?

4. Valleyview is south of Columbus but north of Lexington. Trenton is south of Valleyview but north of Lexington. Mintown is north of Valleyview but south of Columbus. Which town is the second most southerly town of the five?

5. One dozen eggs and 2 half gallons of milk cost $3.35. Two dozen eggs and 2 half gallons of milk cost $4.30. How can you use subtraction to find which costs more, 1 dozen eggs or 1 half gallon of milk?

6. Five dogs are chasing a cat. The dogs are 3 yards behind the cat and running hard. The cat is 12 feet from a tree. The cat and the dogs are running at the same rate. Will the cat reach the tree and safety before the dogs catch the cat?

7. A brown, a gray, and a white horse were in a race on a rainy day. Draw a picture to show how many different ways the horses can finish if the gray never wins on rainy days.

Calculators, the Division Key

Natalie is packing lunches for a picnic. She needs to buy 5 apples. How much will Natalie pay for the 5 apples?

We want to know the price for 5 apples.

We know that _____ apples cost _____.

To find the cost of 5 apples, we first find

the cost of 1 by dividing _____ by _____. Then,

we multiply the cost of 1 apple by _____.

This can be done on the calculator in one code.

$\boxed{\cdot}$ 51 $\boxed{\div}$ 3 $\boxed{\times}$ 5 $\boxed{=}$ $\bigcirc$

Natalie will pay _____ for 5 apples.

Complete these calculator codes.

1. 42 $\boxed{\div}$ 7 $\boxed{=}$ $\bigcirc$

2. 76 $\boxed{\div}$ 2 $\boxed{=}$ $\bigcirc$

3. 96 $\boxed{\div}$ 4 $\boxed{=}$ $\bigcirc$

4. 52 $\boxed{\div}$ 4 $\boxed{=}$ $\bigcirc$

5. 36 $\boxed{\div}$ 9 $\boxed{\times}$ 7 $\boxed{=}$ $\bigcirc$

6. 84 $\boxed{\div}$ 4 $\boxed{\times}$ 3 $\boxed{=}$ $\bigcirc$

7. 72 $\boxed{\div}$ 6 $\boxed{\times}$ 9 $\boxed{=}$ $\bigcirc$

8. 75 $\boxed{\div}$ 5 $\boxed{\times}$ 9 $\boxed{=}$ $\bigcirc$

Practice

Complete these calculator codes.

1. 85 ÷ 5 = ⬭
2. 57 ÷ 3 = ⬭
3. 91 ÷ 7 = ⬭
4. 96 ÷ 6 = ⬭
5. 88 ÷ 2 = ⬭
6. 90 ÷ 9 = ⬭
7. 48 ÷ 4 × 9 = ⬭
8. 63 ÷ 7 × 8 = ⬭
9. 63 ÷ 9 × 7 = ⬭
10. 75 ÷ 5 × 6 = ⬭
11. 62 + 26 ÷ 4 = ⬭
12. 216 − 158 ÷ 2 = ⬭

Apply

Solve these problems.

13. Jeff can clean 4 rugs every 76 minutes. How long will it take Jeff to clean 9 rugs?

14. Nathan can jog 5 miles in 65 minutes. How long will it take Nathan to jog 8 miles?

15. Sandi earns $32 every 4 days selling flowers. How much will Sandi earn in 7 days?

16. Bananas are on sale at 6 for 96¢. How much do 8 bananas cost?

EXCURSION

Find the missing numbers.

1. The product of 2 numbers is 45.
   Their sum is 14.
   What are the numbers?

2. The sum of 2 numbers is 60.
   Their difference is 12.
   What are the numbers?

3. The quotient of two numbers is 15.
   Their sum is 144.
   What are the numbers?

4. Five times one number is three more than six times another number. The difference between the numbers is 1. What are the numbers?

7
CHAPTER TEST

Divide.

1. $5\overline{)30}$ 2. $7\overline{)49}$ 3. $1\overline{)6}$ 4. $8\overline{)56}$ 5. $4\overline{)4}$

6. $3\overline{)9}$ 7. $6\overline{)42}$ 8. $9\overline{)0}$ 9. $2\overline{)18}$ 10. $6\overline{)36}$

11. $45 \div 5 = $ _____   12. $21 \div 7 = $ _____   13. $36 \div 4 = $ _____   14. $18 \div 9 = $ _____

15. $24 \div 8 = $ _____   16. $24 \div 6 = $ _____   17. $49 \div 7 = $ _____   18. $25 \div 5 = $ _____

Divide. Show your work.

19. $4\overline{)17}$ 20. $7\overline{)50}$ 21. $3\overline{)26}$ 22. $9\overline{)46}$

23. $3\overline{)36}$ 24. $5\overline{)50}$ 25. $2\overline{)84}$ 26. $4\overline{)76}$

27. $6\overline{)73}$ 28. $8\overline{)94}$ 29. $2\overline{)93}$ 30. $7\overline{)70}$

31. $4\overline{)82}$ 32. $5\overline{)79}$ 33. $9\overline{)97}$ 34. $3\overline{)88}$

CUMULATIVE REVIEW

Circle the letter of the correct answer.

1 Round 809 to the nearest hundred.

a 700
b 800
c NG

2 Round 8,575 to the nearest thousand.

a 7,000
b 8,000
c NG

3 What is the value of the 3 in 423,916?

a tens
b hundreds
c thousands
d NG

4
```
  587
+ 274
```

a 751
b 761
c 861
d NG

5
```
  4,297
+ 3,486
```

a 7,683
b 7,783
c 8,783
d NG

6
```
  57,198
+ 23,488
```

a 70,686
b 80,686
c 81,686
d NG

7
```
  73
- 29
```

a 52
b 56
c 102
d NG

8
```
  603
- 256
```

a 347
b 357
c 453
d NG

9
```
  42,823
- 29,647
```

a 13,176
b 13,276
c 27,224
d NG

10 8×3

a 24
b 25
c 32
d NG

11
```
  37
×  2
```

a 64
b 74
c 614
d NG

12
```
  59
×  6
```

a 304
b 354
c 356
d NG

13 $4\overline{)93}$

a 2 R1
b 23
c 23 R1
d NG

 score

142

MEASUREMENT

Telling Time

Mr. Jameson can drive home from work in 25 minutes. Draw both a standard clock and a digital clock to show the time when Mr. Jameson will arrive.

We want to know what time Mr. Jameson will get home.
The time now is _____.
His trip home will take _____ minutes.

Arrival Time

Arrival Time

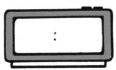

Mr. Jameson will get home at _____ or _____

minutes to _____.

Getting Started

Show the times.

1. five after twelve

2. quarter to four

3. 7:35

Write the times as you would say them.

4.

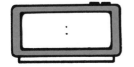

_____

5.

_____

6.

_____

Practice

Show the times.

1. 8:20

2. 3:50

3. noon

4. quarter to eleven

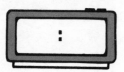

5. ten minutes after six

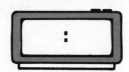

6. three twenty-five

Write the times as you would say them.

7.

_____

8.

_____

9.

_____

10.

_____

11.

_____

12.

_____

Apply

Solve these problems.

13. The donut shop opens at 8:30 AM. The baker needs 2 hours and 25 minutes to prepare bakery for his first customers. At what time should he start baking?

14. At 11:50 AM, Mrs. Miller dismisses her morning kindergarten class. She has 1 hour and 50 minutes until the afternoon class arrives. What time will she greet her afternoon students?

Telling Time, AM and PM

It takes 20 minutes to load the
buses after school. What time
did school end?

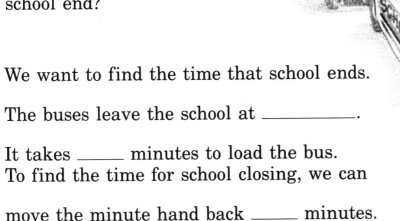

We want to find the time that school ends.

The buses leave the school at _____.

It takes _____ minutes to load the bus.
To find the time for school closing, we can

move the minute hand back _____ minutes.

AM is from
midnight to noon.

12	1	2	3	4	5	6	7	8	9	10	11
midnight						AM					

PM is from
noon to midnight.

12	1	2	3	4	5	6	7	8	9	10	11
noon						PM					

It is 12:10 PM

Move the minute hand
back 20 minutes.

School Closing Time

School ends at _____.

Getting Started

Write the times.

1. 45 minutes later
   than 9:15 AM _____

2. 15 minutes earlier
   than 3:04 PM _____

3. 3 hours after
   10:00 AM _____

4. 4 hours before
   12:00 midnight _____

5. 1 hour and 20 minutes
   before 6:45 AM _____

6. 25 minutes after
   12:15 AM _____

145

Practice

Write the times.

1. 30 minutes later
   than 4:15 AM   _____

2. 20 minutes earlier
   than 12:45 PM   _____

3. 25 minutes before
   2:15 PM   _____

4. 40 minutes after
   6:22 AM   _____

5. 2 hours after
   noon   _____

6. 1 hour and 15 minutes
   before 5:00 PM   _____

Apply

Solve these problems.

7. What time is 2 hours and 25
   minutes before 8:30 AM?

8. What time is 1 hour and 52
   minutes after 11:50 AM?

9. School begins at 8:30 AM. Gina
   wakes up at 7:15 AM. How
   much time does Gina have
   before school?

10. Ralph ran a marathon in 3
    hours and 56 minutes. He
    began the race at 9:25 AM.
    When did Ralph finish the
    race?

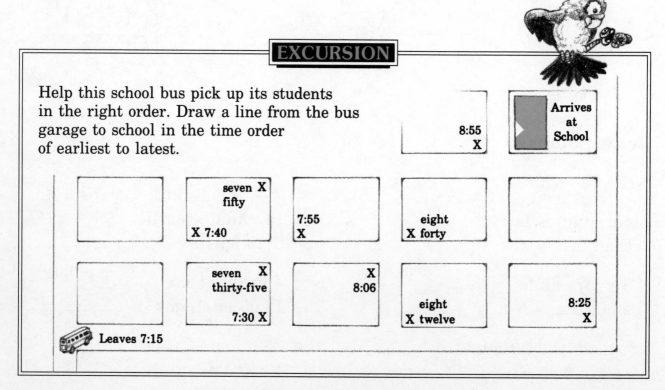

EXCURSION

Help this school bus pick up its students
in the right order. Draw a line from the bus
garage to school in the time order
of earliest to latest.

8:55 X

Arrives at School

seven X fifty
X 7:40

7:55 X

eight X forty

seven X thirty-five
7:30 X

X 8:06

eight X twelve

8:25 X

Leaves 7:15

Using Customary Units of Length

Some customary units of length
are **inch, foot, yard** and **mile.**
Is the height of the Chrysler
Building in New York City about
1,000 inches or 1,000 feet?

We know:
This is an inch unit.

├──────────────┤

1 foot = 12 inches	1 yard = 3 feet	1 mile = 5,280 feet
_____ ft = _____ in.	_____ yd = _____ ft	_____ mi = _____ ft
	_____ yd = _____ in.	_____ mi = _____ yd

The Chrysler Building is about 1,000 _____ tall.

Getting Started

Choose inches, feet, yards or miles to complete
these sentences.

1. A jet flies about 6 _____
high.

2. A soccer field is 110

_____ long.

3. A hand is about 5 _____
wide.

4. The United States is about

3,000 _____ wide.

Complete the table.

5.

yards	1	2	3	4	5	6	7	8	9
inches	36	72							

Practice

Choose inches, feet, yards or miles to complete these sentences.

1. The front door is 3 _____ wide.

2. A tree is 10 _____ tall.

3. Your nose is about

   3 _____ long.

4. Your classroom is about

   10 _____ wide.

5. A homerun is about

   300 _____ long.

6. A pencil is about

   7 _____ long.

7. A football field is 100 _____ long.

8. Your waist is about 25 _____ around.

9. The Mississippi River is about 2,000 _____ long.

10. The Empire State Building is about 1,000 _____ high.

Complete the table.

11.

yards	1	2	3	4	5	6	7	8	9	10
feet	3									

Apply

Solve these problems.

12. It is 27 miles from Ken's house to his grandparents' house and back. Last summer, Ken made 6 trips to see his grandparents. How many miles did Ken travel on all these trips?

13. Liz began her vacation with an airplane ride that took her 796 miles from home. Her aunt then picked her up at the airport and they drove another 378 miles. How many miles did Liz travel to get to her vacation spot?

Using Customary Units of Capacity

Some customary units of capacity are **cup, pint, quart** and **gallon.** Does the tub hold about 12 quarts or 12 gallons of water?

We know:
    1 pint = 2 cups   1 quart = 2 pints   1 gallon = 4 quarts

_____ pt = _____ c   _____ qt = _____ pt   _____ gal = _____ qt

                              _____ qt = _____ c   _____ gal = _____ pt

The bathtub probably holds about   _____ gal = _____ c

12 _____ of water.

Getting Started

Circle the better estimate of capacity.

1.

2 cups   2 quarts

2.

6 pints   6 gallons

3.

2 quarts   2 gallons

4.

1 pint   1 quart

Complete the table.

5.

gallons	1	2	3	4	5	6	7	8	9	10
quarts	4									

149

Practice

Circle the better estimate of capacity.

1.

   1 pint   1 gallon

2.

   1 quart   1 gallon

3.

   8 cups   8 quarts

4.

   1 cup   1 gallon

Complete each table.

5.

pints	1	2	3	4	5	6	7	8	9
cups	2								

6.

quarts	1	2	3	4	5	6	7	8	9
pints	2								

Apply

Solve these problems.

7. Ronnie bought 9 quarts of milk. Each quart cost 67¢. How much did Ronnie pay for milk?

8. The dairy company produced 3,249 gallons of milk on Monday and 2,976 gallons on Tuesday. How many gallons of milk did the dairy produce in two days?

9. On Monday, a gas station had 16,075 gallons of gas delivered. By Wednesday 11,887 gallons were sold. How many gallons of gas were left?

10. Takashi drives a milk collection truck. After three stops, he has picked up 3,246 gallons. How many more gallons are needed to fill Takashi's milk truck if it's capacity is 6,000 gallons?

Using Customary Units of Weight

Some customary units of weight are **ounces, pounds** and **tons**. Would the weight of a stick of butter more likely be 4 ounces or 4 pounds?

We know:

1 pound = 16 ounces

___ lb = ___ oz

1 ton = 2,000 pounds

___ T = _____ lb

Study these comparisons.

About 1 ounce

About 1 pound

About 1 ton

The stick of butter probably weighs about 4 _____.

Getting Started

Would these objects be weighed in ounces, pounds or tons?

1.

_____

2.

_____

3.

_____

Use the table to help complete these measurements.

Pounds	1	2	3	4	5	6
Ounces	16	32	48	64	80	96

4. 50 oz = 3 lb ___ oz

5. 2 lb 5 oz = ___ oz

6. 4 lb 7 oz = ___ oz

7. 72 oz = ___ lb ___ oz

Practice

Would these objects be weighed in ounces, pounds or tons?

1.

_____

2.

_____

3.

_____

4.

_____

5.

_____

6.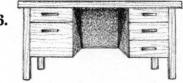

_____

Use the table on page 151 to help complete these measurements.

7. 53 oz = 3 lb _____ oz

8. 18 oz = _____ lb _____ oz

9. 4 lb 6 oz = _____ oz

10. 3 lb 4 oz = _____ oz

11. 85 oz = _____ lb _____ oz

12. 100 oz = _____ lb _____ oz

EXCURSION

Arrange these weights in order from least to greatest. Then place each letter or number in that order, from left to right, on the blanks below.

C = 32 ounces
2 = 1 ton
U = 3 pounds

I = 1 pound, 8 ounces
R = 1,500 pounds
4 = 3,000 pounds

____ ____ ____ ____ SMART ____ ME.

152

Measuring Length in Centimeters

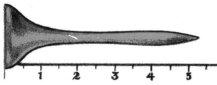

My little finger is about a centimeter wide.

The **metric system** is another measurement system that we frequently use. The **centimeter** is a unit of length in this system. Measure this golf tee to the nearest centimeter.

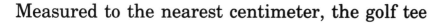

✔ This metric rule is divided into centimeters. A **cm** is the symbol for centimeter. The small line between centimeter markings helps you to know to which centimeter your measurement is closer.

Measured to the nearest centimeter, the golf tee

is _____ centimeters long.

Getting Started

Measure each bar to the nearest centimeter.

1. _____ cm   2. _____ cm

3. _____ cm

4. _____ cm

Measure each object to the nearest centimeter.

5.  _____ cm   6.  _____ cm

7. Estimate the length of your arm in centimeters. _____ cm

8. Measure your arm to the nearest centimeter. _____ cm

153

Practice

Measure each object to the nearest centimeter.

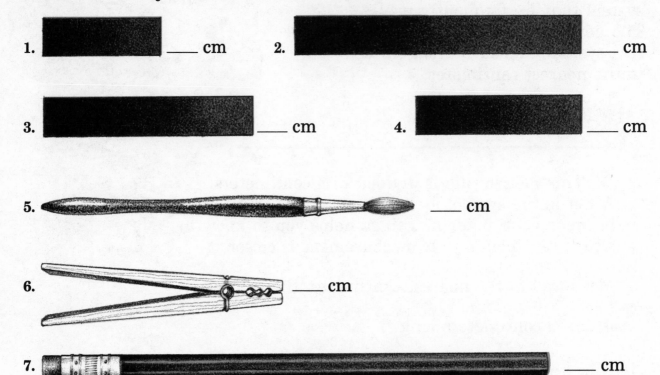

1. _____ cm   2. _____ cm

3. _____ cm   4. _____ cm

5. _____ cm

6. _____ cm

7. _____ cm

8. _____ cm

Estimate these lengths in centimeters.
Then measure these to the nearest centimeter.

9. The width of your hand

   estimated width _____ cm

   actual width _____ cm

10. The length of your foot

    estimated length _____ cm

    actual length _____ cm

11. The width of one of your thumbnails

    estimated width _____ cm

    actual width _____ cm

12. Your height

    estimated height _____ cm

    actual height _____ cm

13. Find the length of this path.

_____ cm

Understanding Decimeters, Meters and Kilometers

Some other units in length in the metric system are **decimeters, meters** and **kilometers.** How do these compare with centimeters?

We know:

$$1 \text{ decimeter} = 10 \text{ centimeters}$$

_____ dm = _____ cm

1 meter = 10 decimeters

_____ m = _____ dm

_____ m = _____ cm

1 kilometer = 1,000 meters

_____ km = _____ m

Study these comparisons.

 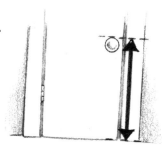 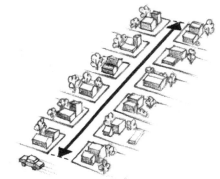

About 1 decimeter   About 1 meter   About 1 kilometer

It takes _____ centimeters to make a decimeter, _____ centimeters

to make a meter and _____ meters to make a kilometer.

Getting Started

Circle the best estimate of measurement.

1. the width of this page

   21 cm   21 m   21 km

2. the distance from Chicago to Miami

   2,000 dm   2,000 m   2,000 km

3. Complete this table.

meters	1	2	3	4	5	6	7	8
decimeters	10							

155

Practice

Circle the best estimate of measurement.

1. the length of 6 city blocks

   1 dm   1 km   1 m

2. the height of your classroom

   4 cm   4 m   4 km

3. the length of a paper clip

   3 cm   3 dm   3 m

4. the length of a school playground

   75 m   75 dm   75 km

5. the distance a car travels in 1 hour

   80 cm   80 m   80 km

6. the height of a box of cereal

   3 cm   3 dm   3 m

7. Complete this table.

meters	1	2	3	4	5	6	7	8
centimeters	100							

8. Complete the table and use it for problems 9 and 10.

Average Athlete's Pace

minutes	10	20	30	40	50	60
kilometers	3	6				

9. Approximately how far can an athlete run in one hour?

10. What would be the approximate time for a 15-kilometer run?

Apply

Solve these problems.

11. A fence is constructed of 25 sections. Each section is 6 meters long. How long is the fence?

12. The puppy is 38 centimeters long. The kitten is 3 decimeters long. Which pet is longer? How much longer is it?

Understanding Metric Units of Capacity

Two of the most often used metric units of capacity are the **liter** and the **milliliter.** Would you probably drink 250 liters or 250 milliliters of milk at one meal?

We know:
1 liter = 1,000 milliliters

_____ L = _____ mL

Study these comparisons.

About 1 liter   About 250 milliliters   About 10 milliliters

A glass might hold about 250 _____ of milk.

Getting Started

Circle the better estimate of capacity.

1.

15 mL   15 L

2.

1 mL   1 L

3.

150 mL   150 L

4.

1 mL   1 L

Practice

Circle the better estimate of capacity.

1.
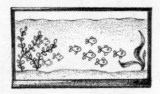

25 mL   25 L

2.

1 mL   1 L

3.

5 mL   5 L

4.

200 mL   200 L

Apply

Solve these problems.

5. A pitcher holds 3 liters of juice. The fourth grade fills the pitcher 16 times at the class picnic. How many liters of juice does the fourth grade use?

6. Marcie takes 8 milliliters of vitamin C, 6 milliliters of vitamin B and 9 milliliters of vitamin A everyday. How many milliliters of vitamins does Marcie take daily?

EXCURSION

Circle the smaller containers that can be filled by the larger container in each exercise.

Understanding Metric Units of Weight

Two of the most commonly used metric units of weight are **grams** and **kilograms.** Would a penny weigh about 3 grams or 3 kilograms?

We know:
1 kilogram = 1,000 grams

_____ kg = _____ g

Study these comparisons.

About 1,000 kg   About 1 kg   About 1 g

A penny weighs about 3 _____.

Getting Started

Circle the better estimate of weight.

1.

1,000 g   1,000 kg

2.

5 g   5 kg

3.

30 g   30 kg

4.

350 g   350 kg

Practice

Circle the better estimate of weight.

1.

   120 g   120 kg

2.

   1 g   1 kg

3.

   1 g   1 kg

4.

   6 g   6 kg

5.

   6 g   6 kg

6.

   1 g   1 kg

7.

   25 g   25 kg

8.

   88 g   88 kg

Apply

Solve these problems.

9. A large paper clip weighs 3 grams. Sean has a box of paper clips that has a net weight of 87 grams. How many paper clips are in the box?

10. Oranges cost 68¢ a kilogram. Mary bought 6 kilograms of oranges. How much did Mary pay for the oranges?

Making a Model

How many ways can you tear off 4 attached stamps from a sheet of postage stamps?

★ **SEE**

We want to know how many patterns of 4 attached stamps we can make.

★ **PLAN**

We can use a sheet of graph paper to represent the stamps and cut out different patterns of four squares.

★ **DO**

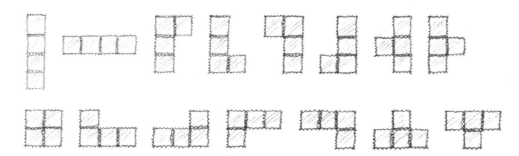

There are _____ different ways to tear off 4 attached stamps.

★ **CHECK**

$4 + 0 = 4$ There are _____ ways we can tear off stamps with 4 in a row or column.

$3 + 1 = 4$ There are _____ ways we can tear off stamps with 3 in one row or column and one in another row or column.

$2 + 2 = 4$ There is _____ way we can tear off stamps with 2 stamps in one row or column and 2 stamps in another row or column.

161

Apply

Make a model to help you solve each problem.

1. Move one block to another stack so the sums of all stacks are equal.

2. It takes 27 sugar cubes to fill a cubical box. How many of the cubes will be touching the sides, top or bottom of the box?

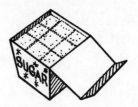

3. Change the arrangement of the discs on the left to the arrangement on the right by moving only 3 of the discs.

 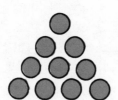

4. Form 5 equilateral triangles using 9 sticks of equal length.

5. Kevin makes a triangle with cubic blocks. He puts 1 block in the first row, 2 blocks in the second row, 3 blocks in the third row, and so on. Predict whether he will need more or fewer than 100 blocks to make 10 rows. Then prove that your prediction was correct.

6. A lady bug walks around the edges of the top of a box of crackers. The top is shaped like a rectangle. When the bug gets back to where she started, she had walked 48 cm. If the top of the box is 6 cm wide, explain how you could find the length of the top of the box.

7. Read Exercise 2 again. What if it took 64 cubes to fill the box? Now how many of the cubes would be touching the sides, top, and bottom of the box?

8. There are 12 cubic blocks on the bottom layer of a box. The box is completely filled with blocks. Why could there not be 10 layers if there are fewer than 100 blocks in the box?

Write the times. Include AM or PM.

1. 45 minutes before midnight

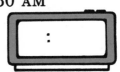

2. 3 hours and 15 minutes after 10:30 AM

Circle the best estimate for each measurement.

3.

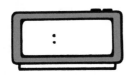

6 in.   6 ft   6 mi

4.

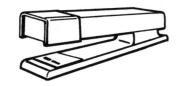

7 in.   7 ft   7 yd

5.

1 pt   1 qt   1 gal

6.

2 c   2 pt   2 qt

7.

1 oz   1 lb

8.

15 oz   15 lb

9.

3 cm   3 dm   3 m

10.

100 dm   100 m   100 km

11.

2 mL   2 L

12.

150 g   150 kg

CUMULATIVE REVIEW

Circle the letter of the correct answer.

1 Round 650 to the nearest hundred.
   a 60
   b 700
   c NG

2 Round 4,296 to the nearest thousand.
   a 4,000
   b 5,000
   c NG

3 What is the value of the 0 in 625,309?
   a ten thousands
   b thousands
   c hundreds
   d NG

4   3,475
  + 2,686
   a 5,061
   b 5,161
   c 6,161
   d NG

5   36,439
  + 17,806
   a 43,235
   b 54,215
   c 54,245
   d NG

6   822
  − 387
   a 435
   b 535
   c 662
   d NG

7   86,042
  − 41,385
   a 44,357
   b 45,343
   c 54,357
   d NG

8 6×8
   a 48
   b 54
   c 63
   d NG

9   26
  × 3
   a 68
   b 78
   c 618
   d NG

10 65×7
   a 425
   b 435
   c 635
   d NG

11 $42 \div 7$
   a 5
   b 7
   c 9
   d NG

12 $4\overline{)48}$
   a 1
   b 2
   c 12
   d NG

13 $86 \div 6$
   a 14 R2
   b 14 R24
   c 14
   d NG

score

MULTIPLYING WHOLE NUMBERS

Multiplying by Powers of 10

Ricky's job is shoveling snow from his front walk. The walk is 9 meters long. Find the length of Ricky's shoveling job in centimeters.

We want to know how many meters of walk Ricky has to shovel.

The walk is _____ meters long.

Each meter contains _____ centimeters.
To find the length of the walk in centimeters,

we multiply _____ by _____.

Study these multiplications.

3 × 1 = 3	4 × 1 = 4	6 × 2 = 12	9 × 6 = 54
3 × 10 = 30	4 × 10 = 40	6 × 20 = 120	9 × 60 = 540
3 × 100 = 300	4 × 100 = 400	6 × 200 = 1,200	9 × 600 = 5,400
3 × 1,000 = 3,000	4 × 1,000 = 4,000	6 × 2,000 = 12,000	9 × 6,000 = 54,000

> Multiply the digits that are not zeros.
> The product has the same number of zeros
> as there are zeros in the factors.

$$9 \times 100 = \underline{}$$

Ricky's front walk is _____ centimeters long.

Getting Started

Multiply.

1. 6 × 100 = _____   2. 100 × 5 = _____   3. 7 × 1,000 = _____

4. 10 × 9 = _____   5. 6,000 × 7 = _____   6. 6 × 9,000 = _____

Practice

Multiply.

1. $5 \times 100 =$ _____
2. $6 \times 3{,}000 =$ _____
3. $20 \times 9 =$ _____

4. $10 \times 7 =$ _____
5. $1{,}000 \times 7 =$ _____
6. $80 \times 3 =$ _____

7. $400 \times 5 =$ _____
8. $2 \times 9{,}000 =$ _____
9. $9 \times 700 =$ _____

10. $800 \times 8 =$ _____
11. $3 \times 5{,}000 =$ _____
12. $7{,}000 \times 8 =$ _____

13. $4 \times 40 =$ _____
14. $300 \times 7 =$ _____
15. $6{,}000 \times 2 =$ _____

16. $6 \times 70 =$ _____
17. $5 \times 2{,}000 =$ _____
18. $80 \times 9 =$ _____

19. $600 \times 5 =$ _____
20. $4{,}000 \times 8 =$ _____
21. $30 \times 9 =$ _____

22. $7 \times 700 =$ _____
23. $5{,}000 \times 6 =$ _____
24. $300 \times 4 =$ _____

25. $80 \times 7 =$ _____
26. $6{,}000 \times 7 =$ _____
27. $4 \times 9{,}000 =$ _____

28. $5 \times 800 =$ _____
29. $3 \times 700 =$ _____
30. $8 \times 5{,}000 =$ _____

31. $2 \times 8{,}000 =$ _____
32. $9 \times 9{,}000 =$ _____
33. $6 \times 40 =$ _____

34. $7{,}000 \times 2 =$ _____
35. $500 \times 4 =$ _____
36. $9 \times 60 =$ _____

37. $6{,}000 \times 6 =$ _____
38. $4 \times 8{,}000 =$ _____
39. $400 \times 9 =$ _____

Apply

Solve these problems.

40. How many centimeters long is a table that is 9 decimeters in length?

41. A carton of drinking straws contains 800 straws. How many straws are in 7 cartons?

42. Computers cost $2,000 each. How much will the school pay for 7 computers?

43. A small car weighs 3,000 pounds. How much do 8 small cars weigh?

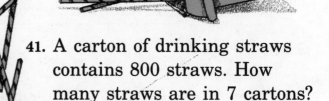

Multiplying 3-digit Numbers

Mach 1 is the unit used to measure the speed of sound. Major Joseph Rogers was the first person to fly a plane faster than Mach 2. How fast was Major Rogers flying when he reached Mach 2?

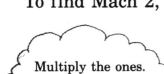
Mach 1 = 742 miles per hour

We want to know the miles per hour speed for Mach 2.

We know Mach 1 is _____ miles per hour.

Mach 2 is _____ times as fast.

To find Mach 2, we multiply _____ by _____.

Multiply the ones.	Multiply the tens.	Multiply the hundreds.
7 4 **2** × _____ **2** ——— **4**	7 **4** 2 × _____ **2** ——— **8 4**	**7** 4 2 × _____ **2** ——— **1,4 8 4**

Major Rogers was flying _____ miles per hour when he reached Mach 2.

Getting Started

Multiply.

1. 223
    ×   4

2. 112
    ×   5

3. 730
    ×   3

4. 411
    ×   5

Copy and multiply.

5. 304 × 2

6. 131 × 5

7. 612 × 4

8. 243 × 3

167

Practice

Multiply.

1. 823
   × 3

2. 510
   × 5

3. 132
   × 4

4. 721
   × 4

5. 634
   × 2

6. 124
   × 3

7. 704
   × 2

8. 911
   × 5

Copy and Do

9. 2×734

10. 3×204

11. 620×4

12. 814×2

13. 433×3

14. 311×5

15. 4×323

16. 5×921

Apply

Solve these problems.

17. There are 212 rubber bands in each box. How many rubber bands are in 4 boxes?

18. Marty ran 425 meters in 2 minutes. Todd ran 512 meters in the same time. How much farther did Todd run?

EXCURSION

What is a Roman emperor's favorite food? Find the correct letters by matching the numerals under each blank with the Roman Numeral in the chart.

S XXII	L XXXVII	A XI
E IV	C I	S LXVII
D LVI	A XLVI	A XXIX
A II	R XVI	S VII

__ __ __ __ __ __
1   2   4   7 11 16

__ __ __ __ __ __
22 29 37 46 56 67

Multiplying Money

Mrs. Juarez is planning to cook dinner on the grill. She needs 4 pounds of steak. How much will it cost if she buys porterhouse steaks?

Sirloin
$3.29/lb
T-bone
$4.09/lb
Porterhouse
$3.19/lb

Steak Sale!

We want to know how much money Mrs. Juarez will spend on steaks.

She needs _____ pounds of steak.

She wants to buy _____ steak

which sells for _____ a pound.

To find the total cost of the steak,

we multiply _____ by _____.

Multiply the pennies. Trade if needed.	Multiply the dimes. Add the extra dimes. Place the decimal point.	Multiply the dollars and add the dollar sign.

$$\begin{array}{r} \overset{3}{\$3.1}9 \\ \times4 \\ \hline 6 \end{array}$$

$$\begin{array}{r} \overset{3}{\$3.1}9 \\ \times4 \\ \hline .76 \end{array}$$

$$\begin{array}{r} \$3.19 \\ \times4 \\ \hline \$12.76 \end{array}$$

Mrs. Juarez will spend _____ on steak.

Getting Started

Multiply.

1. $6.13
    ×   5

2. $8.26
    ×   3

3. $7.18
    ×   5

4. $4.37
    ×   2

Copy and multiply.

5. 6 × $4.09

6. $3.29 × 2

7. 5 × $3.19

8. 2 × $6.01

169

Practice

Multiply.

1. $6.23
    × 4

2. $7.17
    × 5

3. $5.38
    × 2

4. $9.15
    × 6

5. $4.08
    × 7

6. $8.14
    × 6

7. $3.49
    × 2

8. $6.26
    × 3

9. $2.25
    × 3

10. $9.09
    × 8

11. $7.29
    × 3

12. $3.17
    × 4

Copy and Do

13. 3 × $7.26

14. $4.12 × 8

15. $7.19 × 5

16. 2 × $8.37

17. $6.09 × 7

18. $8.13 × 6

19. 4 × $9.23

20. 3 × $4.29

Apply

Solve these problems.

21. Hal bought 5 gallons of paint. Each gallon costs $7.15. How much did Hal pay for the paint?

22. A fishing rod costs $8.97. A spinning reel costs $7.97. What is the total cost of the rod and reel?

23. Radial tires are $49.35 each. Regular tires are $34.89 each. How much more are the radial tires?

24. Oil filters are packed 6 to a box. One oil filter costs $1.09. How much does one box cost?

Use the data on page 169 to solve these problems.

25. How much more will 3 pounds of T-bone steaks cost than 3 pounds of sirloin steaks?

26. Mr. Kelly bought 2 pounds of T-bone and 2 pounds of porterhouse steaks. How much change did he receive from a $20 bill?

More Multiplying 3-digit Numbers

The distance from Denver to Seattle is approximately 3 times farther than the distance from Chicago to Pittsburgh. About how far is it from Seattle to Denver?

We want to know the approximate distance between Seattle and Denver.

The distance from Chicago to Pittsburgh

is _____ miles.

The distance from Seattle to Denver

is approximately _____ times that number.

To find the distance between Seattle and Denver,

we multiply _____ by _____.

Multiply the ones. Trade if needed.	Multiply the tens. Add any extra tens. Trade if needed.	Multiply the hundreds. Add any extra hundreds.

$$\begin{array}{r} \overset{2}{4}5\,7 \\ \times\quad 3 \\ \hline 1 \end{array}$$

$$\begin{array}{r} \overset{1\,2}{4}5\,7 \\ \times\quad 3 \\ \hline 7\,1 \end{array}$$

$$\begin{array}{r} \overset{1}{4}5\,7 \\ \times\quad 3 \\ \hline 1{,}3\,7\,1 \end{array}$$

It is about _____ miles from Seattle to Denver.

Getting Started

Multiply.

1. $\begin{array}{r} 5\,2\,5 \\ \times\quad 7 \\ \hline \end{array}$

2. $\begin{array}{r} 2\,8\,9 \\ \times\quad 4 \\ \hline \end{array}$

3. $\begin{array}{r} 3\,2\,8 \\ \times\quad 8 \\ \hline \end{array}$

4. $\begin{array}{r} \$2.48 \\ \times\quad 6 \\ \hline \end{array}$

Copy and multiply.

5. $\$5.96 \times 9$

6. 709×5

7. 492×3

8. 587×2

Practice

Multiply.

1. $\begin{array}{r} 357 \\ \times\ \ \ 4 \\ \hline \end{array}$

2. $\begin{array}{r} 292 \\ \times\ \ \ 8 \\ \hline \end{array}$

3. $\begin{array}{r} 537 \\ \times\ \ \ 5 \\ \hline \end{array}$

4. $\begin{array}{r} 673 \\ \times\ \ \ 2 \\ \hline \end{array}$

5. $\begin{array}{r} 896 \\ \times\ \ \ 6 \\ \hline \end{array}$

6. $\begin{array}{r} 383 \\ \times\ \ \ 7 \\ \hline \end{array}$

7. $\begin{array}{r} \$4.77 \\ \times\ \ \ 3 \\ \hline \end{array}$

8. $\begin{array}{r} 709 \\ \times\ \ \ 9 \\ \hline \end{array}$

9. $\begin{array}{r} 372 \\ \times\ \ \ 8 \\ \hline \end{array}$

10. $\begin{array}{r} 628 \\ \times\ \ \ 3 \\ \hline \end{array}$

11. $\begin{array}{r} 548 \\ \times\ \ \ 6 \\ \hline \end{array}$

12. $\begin{array}{r} 419 \\ \times\ \ \ 5 \\ \hline \end{array}$

Copy and Do

13. 5×386

14. 457×9

15. $\$6.75 \times 2$

16. 3×628

17. 727×8

18. $\$2.94 \times 5$

19. 7×929

20. 6×848

Apply

Solve these problems.

21. The Cammero family drove 346 miles on their vacation. The Johnsons drove 4 times as far as the Cammeros. How far did the Johnsons drive?

22. The distance from San Francisco to Los Angeles is 403 miles. Mr. Harris left San Francisco at 10:00 AM and drove 115 miles. How far does Mr. Harris still have to drive?

23. A jet airliner can hold 186 people. How many people can 7 jet airliners carry?

24. A china platter costs $6.75 and cereal bowls cost $3.95 each. How much would Sharon pay for a platter and set of 4 bowls?

172

Multiplying 4-digit Numbers

The course of the North Coast Cross Country Ski Race is 8 miles long. How many yards long is the race course?

We want to know how many yards long the ski race is.

The race is ____ miles long.

There are _____ yards in 1 mile.

To find the total number of yards in the race,

we multiply _____ by _____.

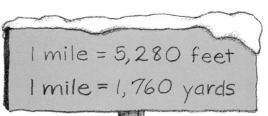

I mile = 5,280 feet
I mile = 1,760 yards

Multiply the ones. Trade if needed.	Multiply the tens. Add any extra tens. Trade if needed.	Multiply the hundreds. Add any extra hundreds. Trade if needed.	Multiply the thousands. Add any extra thousands.

$$
\begin{array}{r} 1,760 \\ \times \quad 8 \\ \hline 0 \end{array}
\qquad
\begin{array}{r} {}^{4} \\ 1,760 \\ \times \quad 8 \\ \hline 80 \end{array}
\qquad
\begin{array}{r} {}^{6\ 4} \\ 1,760 \\ \times \quad 8 \\ \hline 080 \end{array}
\qquad
\begin{array}{r} {}^{6} \\ 1,760 \\ \times \quad 8 \\ \hline 14,080 \end{array}
$$

There are _____ yards in the North Coast Ski Race.

Getting Started

Multiply.

1. $\begin{array}{r} 6,243 \\ \times \quad 3 \\ \hline \end{array}$
2. $\begin{array}{r} 4,086 \\ \times \quad 3 \\ \hline \end{array}$
3. $\begin{array}{r} 5,248 \\ \times \quad 7 \\ \hline \end{array}$
4. $\begin{array}{r} \$75.76 \\ \times \quad 5 \\ \hline \end{array}$

Copy and multiply.

5. $4,273 \times 2$
6. $\$16.59 \times 9$
7. $\$90.06 \times 8$
8. $3,876 \times 6$

Practice

Multiply.

1. $\begin{array}{r}3{,}216\\\times\quad5\end{array}$	2. $\begin{array}{r}7{,}926\\\times\quad8\end{array}$	3. $\begin{array}{r}2{,}079\\\times\quad6\end{array}$	4. $\begin{array}{r}8{,}273\\\times\quad2\end{array}$
5. $\begin{array}{r}\$37.86\\\times\quad7\end{array}$	6. $\begin{array}{r}9{,}376\\\times\quad3\end{array}$	7. $\begin{array}{r}5{,}163\\\times\quad4\end{array}$	8. $\begin{array}{r}\$48.06\\\times\quad9\end{array}$
9. $\begin{array}{r}1{,}673\\\times\quad8\end{array}$	10. $\begin{array}{r}\$32.85\\\times\quad5\end{array}$	11. $\begin{array}{r}8{,}269\\\times\quad2\end{array}$	12. $\begin{array}{r}4{,}675\\\times\quad4\end{array}$

Copy and Do

13. $8 \times 4{,}271$ 14. $3 \times 6{,}129$ 15. $\$63.38 \times 9$ 16. $4{,}350 \times 2$

17. $4{,}925 \times 9$ 18. $4 \times \$57.83$ 19. $5 \times 6{,}256$ 20. $9{,}816 \times 6$

Apply

Solve these problems.

21. The highest mountain in Russia is 18,510 feet tall. The highest mountain in the United States is 1,810 feet higher than that. How tall is the highest mountain in the U.S.?

22. A computer with 1K memory can store 1,024 bits of information. How many bits of information can an 8K computer store?

23. The race cars drove a total of 4 miles in 9 laps. How many feet did they travel?

24. A dump truck can hold 1,426 pounds of dirt. How many pounds can the dump truck haul in 7 trips?

25. Rebecca ran 450 yards less than 6 miles. How many yards did Rebecca run?

26. It costs $23.43 for a pair of jeans and $14.26 for a shirt. Pablo bought 2 pairs of jeans and 3 shirts. How much did Pablo spend?

Multiplying by Multiples of 10

Ronald is learning health skills in his CPR class. He is taking his pulse to find his heart rate for one minute. How many times will Ronald's heart beat in one hour?

... 70, 71, 72

We want to know how often Ronald's heart beats hourly.

His heart beats _____ times in one minute,

and there are _____ minutes in one hour.

To find Ronald's hourly heart rate,

we multiply _____ by _____.

Multiply by the digit in the ones place.	Multiply by the digit in the tens place.

$$\begin{array}{r} 72 \\ \times 60 \\ \hline 0 \end{array}$$

$$\begin{array}{r} {\scriptstyle 1} \\ 72 \\ \times 60 \\ \hline 4{,}320 \end{array}$$

Ronald's heart beats _____ times in one hour.

Getting Started

Multiply.

1. $\begin{array}{r} 36 \\ \times 20 \\ \hline \end{array}$

2. $\begin{array}{r} 35 \\ \times 40 \\ \hline \end{array}$

3. $\begin{array}{r} 50 \\ \times 60 \\ \hline \end{array}$

4. $\begin{array}{r} 125 \\ \times 30 \\ \hline \end{array}$

Copy and multiply.

5. 625×70

6. 820×80

7. 635×50

8. 708×90

Practice

Multiply.

1. $\begin{array}{r} 52 \\ \times\,30 \\ \hline \end{array}$

2. $\begin{array}{r} 76 \\ \times\,40 \\ \hline \end{array}$

3. $\begin{array}{r} 27 \\ \times\,70 \\ \hline \end{array}$

4. $\begin{array}{r} 80 \\ \times\,90 \\ \hline \end{array}$

5. $\begin{array}{r} 48 \\ \times\,20 \\ \hline \end{array}$

6. $\begin{array}{r} 63 \\ \times\,60 \\ \hline \end{array}$

7. $\begin{array}{r} 400 \\ \times\,\ 50 \\ \hline \end{array}$

8. $\begin{array}{r} 88 \\ \times\,80 \\ \hline \end{array}$

9. $\begin{array}{r} 153 \\ \times\,\ 30 \\ \hline \end{array}$

10. $\begin{array}{r} 400 \\ \times\,\ 70 \\ \hline \end{array}$

11. $\begin{array}{r} 94 \\ \times\,50 \\ \hline \end{array}$

12. $\begin{array}{r} 785 \\ \times\,\ 20 \\ \hline \end{array}$

Copy and Do

13. 40×253

14. 70×36

15. 90×573

16. 426×30

17. 651×60

18. 20×879

19. 89×50

20. 80×600

Apply

Solve these problems.

21. How many minutes are there in 36 hours?

22. How many seconds are there in 15 minutes?

23. Charlotte can walk 1 kilometer in 9 minutes. One day, Charlotte walked for 90 minutes. How many kilometers did she walk?

24. A container holds 245 milliliters of juice. The cafeteria used 80 containers. How many milliliters of juice did the cafeteria use?

25. The school photographer took 875 pictures. Each picture takes 40 seconds to develop. How many seconds will it take to develop the pictures?

26. Bobby read 16 chapters of a book. Each chapter was 30 pages long. Bobby took 50 minutes to read each chapter. How long did it take him to read the book?

176

Multiplying by 2-digit Numbers

January, usually the coldest month of the year, is named for the Roman god, Janus. How many hours are there in the month of January?

We want to know the total number of hours in January.

January has _____ days.

There are _____ hours in one day.

To find the total number of hours, we multiply _____ by _____.

Multiply by the ones.	Multiply by the tens.	Add the products.

$$
\begin{array}{r}
3\,1 \\
\times\,2\,4 \\
\hline
1\,2\,4
\end{array} \leftarrow 4 \times 31
$$

$$
\begin{array}{r}
3\,1 \\
\times\,2\,4 \\
\hline
1\,2\,4 \\
6\,2\,0
\end{array} \leftarrow 20 \times 31
$$

$$
\begin{array}{r}
3\,1 \\
\times\,2\,4 \\
\hline
1\,2\,4 \\
6\,2\,0 \\
\hline
7\,4\,4
\end{array} \leftarrow 24 \times 31
$$

There are _____ hours in January.

Getting Started

Multiply.

1. $\begin{array}{r} 23 \\ \times\,32 \\ \hline \end{array}$

2. $\begin{array}{r} 42 \\ \times\,24 \\ \hline \end{array}$

3. $\begin{array}{r} 50 \\ \times\,35 \\ \hline \end{array}$

4. $\begin{array}{r} 64 \\ \times\,22 \\ \hline \end{array}$

Copy and multiply.

5. 12×14

6. 21×28

7. 53×23

8. 96×11

Practice

Multiply.

1. $\begin{array}{r} 32 \\ \times\,43 \\ \hline \end{array}$
2. $\begin{array}{r} 71 \\ \times\,56 \\ \hline \end{array}$
3. $\begin{array}{r} 23 \\ \times\,23 \\ \hline \end{array}$
4. $\begin{array}{r} 75 \\ \times\,11 \\ \hline \end{array}$

5. $\begin{array}{r} 32 \\ \times\,32 \\ \hline \end{array}$
6. $\begin{array}{r} 22 \\ \times\,43 \\ \hline \end{array}$
7. $\begin{array}{r} 61 \\ \times\,38 \\ \hline \end{array}$
8. $\begin{array}{r} 80 \\ \times\,49 \\ \hline \end{array}$

9. $\begin{array}{r} 54 \\ \times\,12 \\ \hline \end{array}$
10. $\begin{array}{r} 62 \\ \times\,33 \\ \hline \end{array}$
11. $\begin{array}{r} 84 \\ \times\,21 \\ \hline \end{array}$
12. $\begin{array}{r} 32 \\ \times\,42 \\ \hline \end{array}$

Copy and Do

13. 41×38
14. 24×62
15. 63×33
16. 60×57

17. 76×81
18. 79×51
19. 96×11
20. 23×52

Apply

Solve these problems.

21. How many hours are there in 2 weeks and 5 days?

22. How many inches are there in 25 feet and 11 inches?

23. How many ounces are there in 3 pounds 9 ounces?

24. How many feet are there in 15 yards 2 feet?

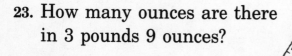

More 2-digit Multiplying

Elmer's boss told him to pack as many bags of sugar as he could fit on the shelf. How many pounds of sugar does the store have on display?

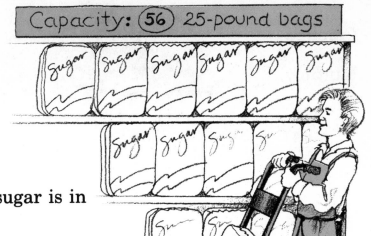

Capacity: (56) 25-pound bags

We want to find how much sugar is in the store's inventory.

Each sugar bag weighs _____ pounds.

There are _____ bags of sugar in stock.

To find the total number of pounds of sugar,

we multiply _____ by _____.

Multiply by the ones.	Multiply by the tens.	Add the products.

$$\begin{array}{r} \overset{3}{5}6 \\ \times 25 \\ \hline 280 \end{array} \leftarrow 5 \times 56$$

$$\begin{array}{r} \overset{1}{5}6 \\ \times 25 \\ \hline 280 \\ 1120 \end{array} \leftarrow 20 \times 56$$

$$\begin{array}{r} 56 \\ \times 25 \\ \hline 280 \\ 1120 \\ \hline 1,400 \end{array} \leftarrow 25 \times 56$$

There are _____ pounds of sugar in the store's inventory.

Getting Started

Multiply.

1. $\begin{array}{r} 36 \\ \times 24 \\ \hline \end{array}$
2. $\begin{array}{r} 23 \\ \times 42 \\ \hline \end{array}$
3. $\begin{array}{r} 39 \\ \times 56 \\ \hline \end{array}$
4. $\begin{array}{r} 74 \\ \times 38 \\ \hline \end{array}$

Copy and multiply.

5. 86×58
6. 73×66
7. 48×93
8. 47×47

Practice

Multiply.

1. 26
× 34

2. 42
× 29

3. 85
× 37

4. 67
× 26

5. 73
× 48

6. 96
× 53

7. 59
× 74

8. 77
× 23

9. 89
× 76

10. 45
× 67

11. 28
× 98

12. 56
× 39

13. 35
× 35

14. 82
× 64

15. 19
× 56

16. 97
× 48

Copy and Do

17. 29 × 46

18. 85 × 37

19. 52 × 74

20. 65 × 98

21. 57 × 58

22. 26 × 76

23. 87 × 38

24. 79 × 89

Apply

Solve these problems.

25. Each package of trivia cards contains 75 questions. There are 25 packages in the game. How many trivia questions are there in the game?

26. There are 28 chairs in each classroom in Ryan School. The school has 15 classrooms. How many classroom chairs are in the school?

27. Eric rode his bicycle 26 miles, and still has 17 miles to go. How far will Eric ride his bike?

28. There are 96 oranges in each crate. Casey put 38 crates in inventory. How many oranges are in inventory?

180

Multiplying Larger Numbers

Marcia is the summer hostess at the Village Lunch Shop. Her regular work week is 35 hours long. How much does Marcia earn each week?

Village Lunch Shop Wages	
Host/Hostess	$4.85
Cook	$4.16
Busperson	$3.78
Dishwasher	$3.52

We want to know Marcia's weekly wage.

We know Marcia works _____ hours each week,

and earns _____ each hour.

To find her total weekly wages,

we multiply _____ by _____.

Please wait for Hostess

Multiply by the ones.

$$\begin{array}{r} \overset{42}{\$4.85} \\ \times35 \\ \hline 2425 \end{array} \leftarrow 5 \times 485$$

Multiply by the tens.

$$\begin{array}{r} \overset{21}{\$4.85} \\ \times35 \\ \hline 2425 \\ 14550 \end{array} \leftarrow 30 \times 485$$

Add the products. Place the dollar sign and decimal point.

$$\begin{array}{r} \$4.85 \\ \times35 \\ \hline 2425 \\ 14550 \\ \hline \$169.75 \end{array}$$

Marcia earns _____ each week.

Getting Started

Multiply.

1. $\begin{array}{r} \$3.65 \\ \times28 \\ \hline \end{array}$

2. $\begin{array}{r} 575 \\ \times47 \\ \hline \end{array}$

3. $\begin{array}{r} \$8.09 \\ \times53 \\ \hline \end{array}$

4. $\begin{array}{r} 639 \\ \times82 \\ \hline \end{array}$

Copy and multiply.

5. $\$0.85 \times 39$

6. $\$7.00 \times 56$

7. 825×78

8. 960×62

Practice

Multiply.

1. 216×27

2. $\$9.45 \times 46$

3. $\$8.73 \times 39$

4. $\$0.46 \times 78$

5. 915×67

6. 707×54

7. $\$6.38 \times 85$

8. 784×96

9. $\$3.90 \times 59$

10. 458×66

11. 823×92

12. $\$5.85 \times 78$

13. 867×84

14. $\$6.81 \times 49$

15. $\$9.06 \times 37$

16. 738×29

Copy and Do

17. 47×368

18. $\$5.47 \times 34$

19. 296×88

20. $56 \times \$8.28$

21. $\$9.25 \times 67$

22. 96×428

23. $72 \times \$7.93$

24. 408×27

Apply

Solve these problems. Use the chart on page 181.

25. Winston cooked for the Village Lunch Shop for 4 weeks. He worked 8 hours a day for 5 days each week. What did he earn during that time?

26. Richard worked as a busperson for 40 hours. How much more did he earn than the dishwasher who worked 40 hours?

27. Penny washed dishes at the Village Lunch Shop for 35 hours. How much did she earn?

28. Lisa works 32 hours each week as a cook and 10 hours as a hostess. How much will Lisa earn in 3 weeks?

Using Estimation

Estimation is used to see if an answer seems reasonable. How many days are in the 9 years shown here? The years 1984 and 1988 each have an extra day because they are leap years.

We want to find the number of days in the years 1981 through 1989.

There are _____ years, and each year

has _____ days.

1988 and 1984 have _____ extra days in them

because they are _____.

To find the total number of days in these years,

we multiply _____ by _____ and add _____.

$$\begin{array}{r} 365 \\ \times \quad 9 \\ \hline \end{array}$$ _____ + _____ = _____

There are _____ days in 1981 through 1989.

Use estimation to check if your answer seems reasonable.

365 is about 370.

$$\begin{array}{r} 370 \\ \times \quad 9 \\ \hline \end{array}$$

The answer seems reasonable.

Getting Started

Multiply. Use estimation to check your answers.

1. $\begin{array}{r} 68 \\ \times 39 \\ \hline \end{array}$

2. $\begin{array}{r} 94 \\ \times \quad 8 \\ \hline \end{array}$

3. $\begin{array}{r} 27 \\ \times 58 \\ \hline \end{array}$

Copy and multiply. Use estimation to check your answers.

4. 186×7

5. $\$4.37 \times 55$

6. 749×89

183

Practice

Multiply. Use estimation to check your answers.

1. 77
   × 32

2. 57
   × 89

3. 92
   × 8

4. 476
   × 67

5. $5.09
   ×   62

6. 895
   × 82

Copy and Do

7. 83 × 7

8. 6 × 247

9. 39 × 81

10. 73 × 24

11. 75 × 87

12. 13 × 98

13. 9 × 576

14. 37 × $6.58

Apply

Solve these problems. Use estimation to check your answers.

15. Brenda runs up the stadium steps each day. There are 89 steps in the stadium. How many steps does Brenda run in 38 days?

16. It takes 4 cups of whole wheat flour to make 1 loaf of bread. The City Bakery bakes 673 loaves of bread each day. How many cups of flour are used each day?

17. Juan has saved $136.46 to buy a color T.V. set. The T.V. set sells for $249.19. How much more does Juan need to save?

18. Paint sells for $7.79 a gallon. Mr. Jameson used 18 gallons of paint to paint his farm buildings. How much did the paint cost Mr. Jameson?

19. Annette gets 3¢ for each can she saves. One week Annette received 87¢. How many cans did she save?

20. Pete and his sister have the same birth date. When Pete is 12, his sister is 23. How many days older is Pete's sister?

Making a Tally

How many times does each digit, 0 through 9, appear in the counting numbers 1 through 50?

★ **SEE**

We want to know how many times each digit appears in the counting numbers 1 through 50.

We know the digits are 0, 1, ___, ___, ___, ___, ___, ___, ___ and ___.

★ **PLAN**

We will make a list of the digits from 0 through 9. Then we will count from 1 through 50 and make a tally mark next to each of the digits in the numbers.

✔ Don't forget to cross the fifth tally mark, to make them easier to count.

★ **DO**

0 ‖   5 ‖
1 卌 卌 ‖   6 ‖
2 ‖‖‖   7 ‖
3 ‖   8 ‖
4 ‖   9 ‖

(The numbers 1 through 20 have been tallied. Complete the tally for the numbers from 21 through 50.)

Digits	0	1	2	3	4	5	6	7	8	9
Times Used										

★ **CHECK**

There are _____ one-digit numbers and _____ two-digit numbers from 1 through 50. 9 + (41 × 2) = 91 There

are _____ tallies.

Apply

Tally the data found in each situation.

1. Look in the White Pages of a phone book and pick ten random phone numbers. Tally the digits used in each phone number. How does this set of tallies compare to the one gathered in problem 3?

2. Consider the vowels a, e, i, o and u. Count the number of times each vowel is used in the sentence:

   Now is the time for all good men to come to the aid of their country.

3. Look in the Yellow Pages of a phone book and pick ten random phone numbers. Tally the digits used in these numbers.

4. Survey the students in your room and tally the number of pennies, nickels, dimes and quarters they have.

5. Conduct a class survey and determine the most frequent date on all the coins in the room.

6. Measure the distance around one wrist of each person in your classroom, to the nearest inch. Tally the findings.

7. Suppose in Exercise 3 you had chosen 20 phone numbers at random from the same page. How do you think this would change your tally?

8. Suppose you toss a penny 50 times. Predict the number of times it would land heads. Then toss a penny to check your prediction.

9. Douglas Dog ordered some cartons of canned dog food. The number of cartons he ordered is a two-digit number. The number of cans in each carton is a two-digit number. If you round to estimate the greatest number of cans that he could have ordered, what would be your estimate?

Calculators, Working with Money

Mrs. Wallace bought 2 blouses and 4 ties at the Daisy Sale. She used her calculator to find the total cost of her purchases. Then she used estimation to see if that total made sense. How much did Mrs. Wallace pay for her purchases?

Daisy Sale
Belts ~ $8.25
Ties ~ $9.50
Blouses ~ $21.75

We want to know how much money Mrs. Wallace spent at the Daisy Sale.

She bought _____ blouses for _____ each.

She also bought _____ ties for _____ each. To find the total cost of each item, we multiply the cost of one by the number of items purchased. We use the $\boxed{\cdot}$ key to enter money amounts like $21.75. Complete these codes.

Blouses   21 $\boxed{\cdot}$ 75 $\boxed{\times}$ ___ $\boxed{=}$ $\bigcirc$

Ties   9 $\boxed{\cdot}$ 5 $\boxed{\times}$ ___ $\boxed{=}$ $\bigcirc$

✔ The cost of the blouses appears as 43.5. We have to write the dollar sign and zero for the answer to read $43.50. The cost of the ties is $38.00. When we enter the numbers on the calculator, we also can omit the zeros to the far right of the decimal point.
To find the total cost, complete this code.

43 $\boxed{\cdot}$ 5 $\boxed{+}$ 38 $\boxed{=}$ $\bigcirc$

The total cost of the purchases is _____.

Estimate to see if the answer seems reasonable.

Blouses $21.75 → $22 × 2 =
Ties $ 9.50 → $10 × 4 = + ____
          Total Cost
          Estimate

Practice

Use your calculator to find each answer.

1. $26.75
   × 3

2. $18.79
   × 9

3. $37.35
   × 12

4. $57.38
   × 25

5. $9.75
   × 36

6. $11.75
   × 45

7. $65.48
   × 82

8. $49.75
   × 26

Apply

Use the ad to help solve these problems.
Use estimation to check your answers.

☆ Cassettes...$8.96
☆ Records...$3.49
☆ Albums...$12.69
☆ SALE! ☆

9. What is the cost of 2 cassettes and 3 records?

10. How much are 2 albums and 3 cassettes?

11. How much more are 2 cassettes than 5 records?

12. In another store, cassettes are on sale at 2 for $15. How much will you save if you buy 6 cassettes on sale?

EXCURSION

Play this game with a friend. Pick 2 numbers from the apple and multiply them. If your product is a number on the board, put your initial on it. The winner is the first to have 3 numbers in a row.

9   18
16   8
15   4   12
19

228	224	216
270	144	240
171	120	108

Multiply. Use estimation to check your answers.

1. 224
    × 3

2. $3.43
    × 4

3. 679
    × 7

4. 425
    × 9

5. 3,208
    × 5

6. 5,728
    × 2

7. $38.51
    × 6

8. 7,286
    × 8

9. 21
    × 32

10. 43
    × 23

11. 57
    × 11

12. 72
    × 43

13. 76
    × 29

14. 59
    × 75

15. 83
    × 46

16. 67
    × 96

17. 245
    × 36

18. $7.93
    × 18

19. 425
    × 86

20. 729
    × 79

21. $6.37
    × 45

22. 4,759
    × 8

23. 6,904
    × 9

24. $5.94
    × 63

25. 748
    × 59

26. 286
    × 43

27. $8.99
    × 74

28. 987
    × 39

CUMULATIVE REVIEW

Circle the letter of the correct answer.

1 Round 723 to the nearest hundred.
- **a** 700
- **b** 800
- **c** NG

2 Round 5,329 to the nearest thousand.
- **a** 5,000
- **b** 6,000
- **c** NG

3 What is the value of the 5 in 315,603?
- **a** tens
- **b** hundreds
- **c** thousands
- **d** NG

4
$$\begin{array}{r} 4{,}279 \\ +\ 3{,}651 \end{array}$$
- **a** 7,820
- **b** 7,930
- **c** 8,930
- **d** NG

5
$$\begin{array}{r} 20{,}926 \\ +\ 50{,}285 \end{array}$$
- **a** 70,211
- **b** 71,101
- **c** 71,211
- **d** NG

6
$$\begin{array}{r} 703 \\ -\ 246 \end{array}$$
- **a** 447
- **b** 543
- **c** 557
- **d** NG

7
$$\begin{array}{r} 52{,}186 \\ -\ 19{,}429 \end{array}$$
- **a** 32,657
- **b** 32,757
- **c** 47,363
- **d** NG

8 $63 \div 9$
- **a** 7
- **b** 8
- **c** 9
- **d** NG

9 $72 \div 3$
- **a** 20
- **b** 22
- **c** 24
- **d** NG

10 $4\overline{)93}$
- **a** 2 R1
- **b** 23
- **c** 23 R1
- **d** NG

11 Choose the best estimate of length.

(((·chalk·)))
- **a** 7 cm
- **b** 7 dm
- **c** 7 m

12 Choose the best estimate of weight.
- **a** 2 oz
- **b** 2 lb

13
$$\begin{array}{r} 4{,}032 \\ \times\qquad 3 \end{array}$$
- **a** 1,296
- **b** 12,096
- **c** 12,396
- **d** NG

14 27×46
- **a** 1,222
- **b** 1,322
- **c** 1,442
- **d** NG

☐ score

190

10
DIVISION OF WHOLE NUMBERS

Dividing, 3-digit Quotients

Sidney and Alicia have 254 invitations to address for a PTA social. How many invitations will each girl have to do?

We want to know the number of invitations each girl will write.

All together, there are _____ invitations.

There are _____ girls doing the addressing. To find the number of invitations each girl

will write, we divide _____ by _____.

Divide the hundreds.	Divide the tens.	Trade the extra ten for 10 ones. Divide the ones.

$$\begin{array}{r} 1 \\ 2\overline{)254} \\ \underline{2} \\ 0 \end{array}$$

$$\begin{array}{r} 12 \\ 2\overline{)254} \\ \underline{2}\downarrow \\ 5 \\ \underline{4} \\ 1 \end{array}$$

$$\begin{array}{r} 127 \\ 2\overline{)254} \\ \underline{2}\downarrow \\ 5 \\ \underline{4}\downarrow \\ 14 \\ \underline{14} \\ 0 \end{array}$$

Each girl will write at least 100 invitations

Each girl will write at least 120 invitations

Each girl will write 127 invitations

Sidney and Alicia will each have to write _____ invitations.

Getting Started

Divide. Show your work.   Copy and divide.

1. $3\overline{)636}$ 2. $4\overline{)456}$ 3. $392 \div 2$ 4. $714 \div 6$

Practice

Divide. Show your work.

1. 3)366   2. 2)648   3. 5)555   4. 4)844

5. 3)651   6. 4)856   7. 2)658   8. 6)672

9. 4)968   10. 7)791   11. 3)759   12. 2)938

Copy and Do

13. 575 ÷ 5   14. 736 ÷ 4   15. 832 ÷ 2   16. 864 ÷ 3

17. 996 ÷ 2   18. 579 ÷ 3   19. 912 ÷ 4   20. 597 ÷ 3

Apply

Solve these problems.

21. A computer printer printed 924 lines in 4 minutes. How many lines were printed each minute?

22. Ivan helped his grandfather box up his collection of 462 books that he will donate to 3 school libraries. How many books will each library receive?

23. There are 3 feet in 1 yard. Change 486 feet to yards.

24. The pond is 165 yards wide. How wide is the pond in feet?

Dividing, Remainders

The Quick Computer Company manufactures computer disks. In one day, the company made 748 disks. How many packages did the company produce? How many disks were left over?

We want to find the number of packages of disks produced and the number of disks left over.

Quick Computer made _____ disks in one day.

There are _____ disks in a package.
To find the number of packages, we divide

_____ by _____. The remainder is the number of disks left over.

Divide the hundreds.	Divide the tens.	Divide the ones.

$$\begin{array}{r} 1 \\ 6\overline{)748} \\ 6\downarrow \\ \hline 14 \end{array}$$

$$\begin{array}{r} 12 \\ 6\overline{)748} \\ 6 \\ \hline 14 \\ 12\downarrow \\ \hline 28 \end{array}$$

$$\begin{array}{r} 124 \text{ R4} \\ 6\overline{)748} \\ 6 \\ \hline 14 \\ 12 \\ \hline 28 \\ 24 \\ \hline 4 \end{array}$$

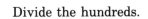

Divide. $6\overline{)7}^{\,1}$
Multiply. $6 \times 1 = 6$
Subtract. $7 - 6 = 1$
Compare. $1 < 6$
Bring down the tens.

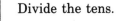

Divide. $6\overline{)14}^{\,2}$
Multiply. $6 \times 2 = 12$
Subtract. $14 - 12 = 2$
Compare. $2 < 6$
Bring down the ones.

Divide. $6\overline{)28}^{\,4}$
Multiply. $6 \times 4 = 24$
Subtract. $28 - 24 = 4$
Compare. $4 < 6$
Write the remainder.

The company made _____ packages.

There were _____ disks left over.

Getting Started

Divide. Show your work.

1. $4\overline{)849}$

2. $5\overline{)673}$

Copy and divide.

3. $793 \div 2$

4. $796 \div 6$

Practice

Divide. Show your work.

1. 4)449 2. 6)682 3. 3)635 4. 2)869

5. 5)594 6. 4)925 7. 7)784 8. 6)826

9. 8)916 10. 5)727 11. 2)916 12. 7)919

13. 4)857 14. 6)885 15. 3)558 16. 5)962

Copy and Do

17. $437 \div 2$ 18. $789 \div 4$ 19. $896 \div 8$ 20. $416 \div 3$

21. $775 \div 6$ 22. $815 \div 5$ 23. $593 \div 2$ 24. $779 \div 7$

25. $956 \div 7$ 26. $651 \div 3$ 27. $912 \div 5$ 28. $852 \div 4$

Apply

Solve these problems.

29. Li is packing tomato plants into boxes that hold 5 plants each. Li has 598 plants. How many boxes will she need?

30. Mr. Hawthorne is putting 4 chairs at each table in his cafe. If Mr. Hawthorne has 462 chairs, how many tables can he supply?

Dividing, Zeros in Quotients

How long will it take for
424 quarts of blood to be
pumped through the human heart?

4 QUARTS
EACH
MINUTE

We want to know the number of minutes it will

take for the heart to pump _____ quarts of blood.

We know that _____ quarts are pumped

each _____.
To find the length of time it takes to pump

the blood, we divide _____ by _____.

Divide the hundreds.	Divide the tens. $2 < 4$ therefore we write a 0 in tens.	Bring down the ones. Divide the ones.

$$\begin{array}{r} 1 \\ 4\overline{)424} \\ \underline{4} \\ 02 \end{array}$$

$$\begin{array}{r} 10 \\ 4\overline{)424} \\ \underline{4\downarrow} \\ 2 \end{array}$$

$$\begin{array}{r} 106 \\ 4\overline{)424} \\ \underline{4\downarrow} \\ 24 \\ \underline{24} \\ 0 \end{array}$$

It will take _____ minutes to pump 424 quarts
of blood through the heart.

Getting Started

Divide. Show your work.

1. $7\overline{)735}$ 2. $5\overline{)534}$ 3. $3\overline{)309}$ 4. $2\overline{)803}$

Copy and divide.

5. $826 \div 8$ 6. $816 \div 4$ 7. $600 \div 6$ 8. $948 \div 9$

195

Practice

Divide. Show your work.

1. 6)618

2. 4)832

3. 7)749

4. 2)816

5. 9)927

6. 5)545

7. 8)854

8. 9)906

Copy and Do

9. 436 ÷ 4

10. 200 ÷ 2

11. 709 ÷ 7

12. 651 ÷ 6

13. 837 ÷ 8

14. 320 ÷ 3

15. 529 ÷ 5

16. 973 ÷ 9

Apply

Solve these problems.

17. How many gallons of water are there in 408 quarts?

18. Change 318 feet to yards.

19. Change 36 feet to inches.

20. How many pints are there in 216 quarts?

EXCURSION

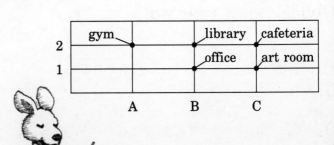

Study the grid. Complete these statements.

The gym is at (_2_ , _A_).

The office is at (___ , _B_).

The cafeteria is at (___ , ___).

The _____ is at (_2_ , _B_).

The _____ is at (_1_ , _C_).

	A	B	C
2	gym	library	cafeteria
1		office	art room

Dividing Larger Dividends

It took the Johnson family 6 hours to drive from Argus to Chester, through Lincoln. What was their rate of speed in miles per hour?

Argus

136 Miles

Lincoln

188 Miles

Chester

We are looking for the Johnson's rate of speed in miles per hour.

We need to add _____ and _____ to get the total distance traveled.

The Johnsons traveled _____ miles from Argus to Chester.

It took them _____ hours to make this trip.

To find the rate of speed, we divide the total miles

by the number of hours. We divide _____ by _____.

| Divide the hundreds.
3 < 6
Trade the 3 hundreds for 30 tens. | Divide the tens.
Write the quotient digit above the tens. | Trade the 2 tens for 20 ones.
Divide the ones. |

$$6\overline{)324}$$

$$\begin{array}{r} 5 \\ 6\overline{)324} \\ 30 \\ \hline 2 \end{array}$$

$$\begin{array}{r} 54 \\ 6\overline{)324} \\ 30\downarrow \\ \hline 24 \\ 24 \\ \hline 0 \end{array}$$

The Johnson family drove at a rate of speed

of _____ miles per hour.

Getting Started

Divide. Show your work.   Copy and divide.

1. $4\overline{)276}$ 2. $8\overline{)433}$ 3. $850 \div 9$ 4. $249 \div 3$

Practice

Divide. Show your work.

1. 7)511

2. 4)268

3. 2)108

4. 6)354

5. 9)468

6. 3)159

7. 5)262

8. 8)290

9. 5)476

10. 2)137

11. 9)755

12. 4)317

13. 8)363

14. 3)209

15. 7)539

16. 6)540

Copy and Do

17. $627 \div 8$

18. $248 \div 5$

19. $615 \div 9$

20. $137 \div 2$

21. $316 \div 6$

22. $209 \div 7$

23. $312 \div 4$

24. $115 \div 3$

25. $423 \div 7$

26. $196 \div 5$

27. $120 \div 3$

28. $517 \div 6$

Apply

Solve these problems.

29. It is 385 miles from Al's house to his grandparents. It takes Al's family 7 hours to drive there. What is their rate of speed in miles per hour?

30. The cafeteria serves 6-ounce glasses of milk. How many full glasses of milk can be poured from 225 ounces of milk?

31. How many pints are there in 10 gallons?

32. How much farther is it from Lincoln to Chester than from Lincoln to Argus? Use the map on page 197.

Dividing Money

At the print shop, Fred had 5 copies made of his science report. What was the cost of each copy?

We want to know the cost of making one copy of Fred's report.

Fred paid _____ to get _____ copies made. To find the cost of one copy, we divide the cost of all the copies by the number of copies made.

We divide _____ by _____.

Divide the dollars. 2 < 5 Place a zero above the 2. Place the decimal point above the one in the dividend.	Trade the 2 dollars for 20 dimes. Divide the dimes.	Trade the 4 left-over dimes for pennies. Divide the pennies. Place the dollar sign.

$$\begin{array}{r} 0. \\ 5\overline{)\$2\,45} \end{array}$$

$$\begin{array}{r} 0.4 \\ 5\overline{)\$2.45} \\ \underline{2\,0} \\ 4 \end{array}$$

$$\begin{array}{r} \$0.49 \\ 5\overline{)\$2.45} \\ \underline{2\,0} \\ 45 \\ \underline{45} \\ 0 \end{array}$$

One copy cost Fred _____.

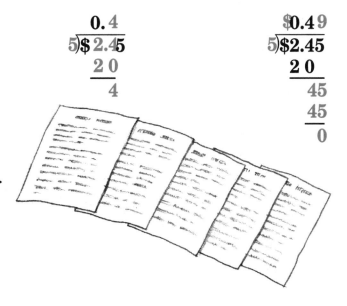

Getting Started

Divide. Show your work.

1. $7\overline{)\$3.36}$

2. $3\overline{)\$6.81}$

3. $4\overline{)\$1.80}$

Copy and divide.

4. $\$7.45 \div 5$

5. $\$4.74 \div 6$

6. $\$9.09 \div 9$

Practice

Divide. Show your work.

1. 4)$5.16

2. 8)$3.36

3. 7)$8.26

4. 3)$3.09

5. 9)$5.76

6. 2)$7.58

7. 5)$9.35

8. 6)$2.88

9. 7)$7.14

10. 6)$4.62

11. 8)$9.44

12. 3)$9.18

Copy and Do

13. $6.25 ÷ 5

14. $4.24 ÷ 8

15. $1.38 ÷ 2

16. $8.13 ÷ 3

17. $9.52 ÷ 7

18. $1.56 ÷ 6

19. $9.20 ÷ 4

20. $7.65 ÷ 9

Apply

Solve these problems.

21. Rob bought 5 paperback books for $7.95. What was the cost of each book?

22. Two hundred eight quarts of milk are poured into gallon jugs. How many jugs will be needed?

23. Vince and Don bought 3 birthday cards, each costing $1.20. They decided to split the cost evenly. How much did each boy pay?

24. A 6-pound package of hamburger costs $8.34. How much would a 4-pound package cost?

Dividing by Multiples of 10

Madalana is making bows that use
20 centimeters of ribbon each.
How many bows can Madalana make
with one spool of ribbon?

We want to find the number of bows Madalana
can make from one spool of ribbon.

Madalana uses _____ centimeters of ribbon in
one bow.

A spool contains _____ centimeters of ribbon.

To find the number of bows, we divide _____

by _____.

We know that:
$12 \div 2 = 6.$

**We use this fact
to find
$120 \div 20$.**

$$\begin{array}{r} 6 \\ 20{\overline{)120}} \\ 120 \\ \hline 0 \end{array}$$

Madalana can make _____ bows from one spool
of ribbon.

Getting Started

Divide. Show your work.

1. $30{\overline{)60}}$ 2. $20{\overline{)80}}$ 3. $80{\overline{)640}}$ 4. $40{\overline{)240}}$

Copy and divide.

5. $60 \div 20$ 6. $90 \div 30$ 7. $320 \div 40$ 8. $360 \div 60$

Practice

Divide. Show your work.

1. $20\overline{)60}$
2. $30\overline{)60}$
3. $40\overline{)80}$
4. $30\overline{)90}$
5. $60\overline{)60}$

6. $50\overline{)150}$
7. $70\overline{)490}$
8. $60\overline{)300}$
9. $80\overline{)240}$
10. $90\overline{)270}$

11. $40\overline{)360}$
12. $20\overline{)160}$
13. $70\overline{)490}$
14. $90\overline{)270}$
15. $80\overline{)400}$

16. $30\overline{)150}$
17. $60\overline{)480}$
18. $50\overline{)200}$
19. $60\overline{)240}$
20. $90\overline{)540}$

21. $20\overline{)100}$
22. $40\overline{)320}$
23. $30\overline{)210}$
24. $70\overline{)140}$
25. $80\overline{)240}$

Copy and Do

26. $270 \div 30$
27. $450 \div 50$
28. $420 \div 60$
29. $560 \div 80$
30. $200 \div 40$
31. $810 \div 90$

Apply

Solve these problems.

32. There are 30 pounds of potatoes in each sack. How many sacks of potatoes will be needed to fill an order of 180 pounds?

33. There are 20 small glasses of juice in each quart. How many glasses can be made from 80 quarts?

Dividing by Multiples of 10, Remainders

Pam counted 625 pennies in her savings.
How many penny wrappers will she use
to package them for the bank?
How many pennies will she have left over?

We want to find the number of penny
wrappers that Pam needs.

She has _____ pennies in her savings.

A penny wrapper will hold _____ pennies.
To find the number of penny wrappers needed,
we divide the total number of pennies by the
number of pennies in one wrapper.

We divide _____ by _____.

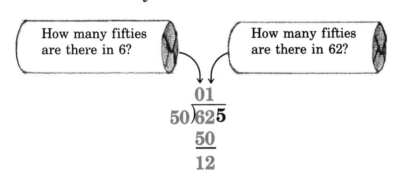

Pam needs _____ wrappers. She will have

_____ pennies left over.

Getting Started

Divide. Show your work.

1. 10)‾38   2. 40)‾725   3. 70)‾90   4. 20)‾738

Copy and divide.

5. 87 ÷ 40   6. 906 ÷ 70   7. 67 ÷ 50   8. 959 ÷ 90

Practice

Divide. Show your work.

1. 30)68   2. 40)75   3. 10)83   4. 20)96

5. 50)600   6. 80)960   7. 70)824   8. 60)730

9. 80)325   10. 40)765   11. 20)708   12. 50)436

13. 70)842   14. 90)425   15. 60)375   16. 30)852

Copy and Do

17. 800 ÷ 40   18. 735 ÷ 60   19. 867 ÷ 30

20. 428 ÷ 70   21. 650 ÷ 50   22. 329 ÷ 80

Apply

Solve these problems.

23. There are 40 paper clips to a box. How many boxes will you buy if you need 360 paper clips for your project?

24. A container holds 80 milliliters of juice. How many containers are needed to hold 480 milliliters of juice?

25. Robbie worked 40 hours a week on his summer job. His paycheck for one week amounted to $240. How much did Robbie make per hour?

26. There are 50 clothespins to a box. Each box costs $3.75. How much will 350 clothespins cost?

Dividing, 2-digit Divisors

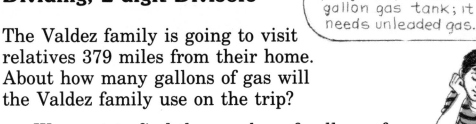

The Valdez family is going to visit relatives 379 miles from their home. About how many gallons of gas will the Valdez family use on the trip?

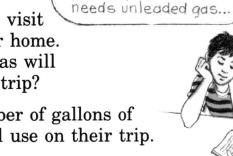

We want to find the number of gallons of gas the Valdez family will use on their trip.

The Valdez family is driving _____ miles.

Their car gets _____ miles on each gallon of gas. To find the number of gallons needed we divide the distance by the number of miles per gallon. We divide _____ by _____.

Round the divisor to its nearest 10. Estimate how many 40's are in 379.

$$42\overline{)379}$$

Since 379 ÷ 40 is about 9, use 9 as the digit in the quotient.

$$\begin{array}{r} 9\,\text{R1} \\ 42\overline{)379} \\ \underline{378} \longleftarrow 9 \times 42 \\ 1 \end{array}$$

✔ We check a division problem by using multiplication, and addition if there is a remainder.

$$\begin{array}{rl} 42 & \textbf{divisor} \\ \times\ 9 & \times\ \textbf{quotient} \\ \hline 378 & \\ +\quad 1 & +\ \textbf{remainder} \\ \hline 379 & \textbf{dividend} \end{array}$$

The Valdez family will use about _____ gallons of gas on their trip.

Getting Started

Divide. Check your work.   Copy and divide.

1. $22\overline{)176}$ 2. $49\overline{)325}$ 3. $225 \div 31$ 4. $142 \div 18$

Practice

Divide. Check your work.

1. $31\overline{)162}$ 2. $38\overline{)250}$ 3. $42\overline{)298}$

4. $72\overline{)598}$ 5. $37\overline{)285}$ 6. $28\overline{)186}$

7. $51\overline{)268}$ 8. $19\overline{)165}$ 9. $89\overline{)812}$

Copy and Do

10. $268 \div 43$ 11. $208 \div 45$ 12. $846 \div 92$

13. $198 \div 32$ 14. $658 \div 73$ 15. $575 \div 67$

16. $322 \div 46$ 17. $585 \div 68$ 18. $148 \div 21$

19. $561 \div 58$ 20. $389 \div 53$ 21. $233 \div 32$

22. $248 \div 28$ 23. $616 \div 83$ 24. $321 \div 47$

Apply

Solve these problems.

25. Miss Douglas worked 71 hours during one pay period. She made $568. How much does Miss Douglas earn in one hour?

26. Mr. Kowalski put 14 gallons of gas into his car. His car averages 37 miles to a gallon. About how far can Mr. Kowalski drive his car on this tank of gas?

Trial Quotients

Raoul is keeping a diary
on the development of the
puppy his parents gave him.
Help him convert the puppy's
weight to pounds and left-over
ounces.

We want to know the puppy's weight
in pounds and ounces.

The scale reads that the puppy

weighs _____ ounces.

There are _____ ounces in a pound.

To convert from ounces to pounds,
we divide the total number of ounces
by the number of ounces in one pound.

We divide _____ by _____.

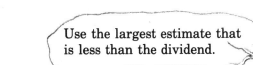

Estimate the quotient.
Multiply to check.

Use the largest estimate that
is less than the dividend.

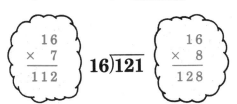

$$\begin{array}{r} 7 \text{ R9} \\ 16\overline{)121} \\ 112 \\ \hline 9 \end{array}$$

The puppy weighs _____ pounds _____ ounces.

Getting Started

Divide.

1. $12\overline{)108}$ 2. $53\overline{)348}$ 3. $31\overline{)248}$

Copy and divide.

4. $268 \div 27$ 5. $144 \div 24$ 6. $340 \div 84$

Practice

Divide.

1. $43\overline{)344}$

2. $56\overline{)180}$

3. $72\overline{)608}$

4. $37\overline{)163}$

5. $94\overline{)715}$

6. $86\overline{)816}$

7. $16\overline{)100}$

8. $48\overline{)312}$

9. $55\overline{)476}$

Copy and Do

10. $250 \div 39$

11. $512 \div 62$

12. $273 \div 57$

13. $288 \div 48$

14. $743 \div 85$

15. $214 \div 96$

16. $536 \div 75$

17. $160 \div 23$

18. $308 \div 68$

Apply

Solve these problems.

19. How many feet and inches are there in 105 inches?

20. How many days are there in 168 hours?

EXCURSION

These nine numbers have one thing in common. Can you find what it is?

222	315	2,124
405	999	6,111
210	1,905	1,158

Partial Dividends

Quan's job at the dairy is to run the machine that attaches the labels to the bottles. Quan figures that 330 bottles pass through the machine in one hour. How many cases of milk are labeled in one hour? How many bottles are left over?

We want to know the number of cases of milk Quan labels in one hour.

Quan's machine labels _____ bottles in an hour.

There are _____ bottles in a case.
To find the number of cases, we divide the total number of bottles by the number in one

case. We divide _____ by _____.

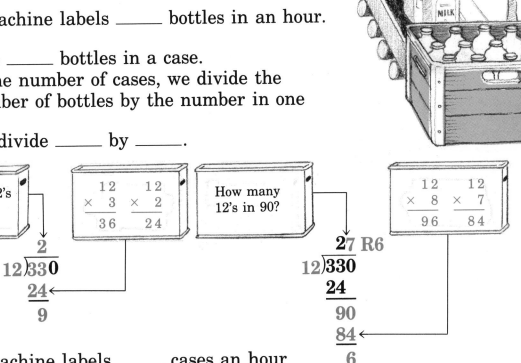

Quan's machine labels _____ cases an hour

with _____ bottles labeled for the next case.

Getting Started

Divide.

1. $26\overline{)475}$
2. $36\overline{)829}$
3. $63\overline{)245}$

Copy and divide.

4. $930 \div 24$
5. $856 \div 35$
6. $758 \div 48$

Practice

Divide.

1. $24\overline{)536}$

2. $18\overline{)627}$

3. $39\overline{)846}$

4. $21\overline{)756}$

5. $58\overline{)427}$

6. $63\overline{)915}$

7. $37\overline{)854}$

8. $16\overline{)898}$

9. $84\overline{)963}$

Copy and Do

10. $945 \div 45$

11. $763 \div 17$

12. $812 \div 26$

13. $518 \div 63$

14. $838 \div 28$

15. $946 \div 37$

16. $683 \div 12$

17. $915 \div 48$

18. $709 \div 29$

Apply

Solve these problems.

19. Mr. Wallace drove 385 miles at 55 miles per hour. How many hours did Mr. Wallace drive?

20. How many pounds are there in 950 ounces?

21. Sandy ran 720 meters running wind sprints. She ran 45 meters each time. How many sprints did Sandy run?

22. Richard used 864 grams of batter to make cookies for the bake sale. Each cookie weighed 24 grams and was sold for 15¢. How much did the bake sale make from Richard's cookies?

Finding Averages

Andy, Bart and Larry are the top collectors of autographs in their class. Andy has 14 autographs. Bart has 9 and Larry has 13. What is the average number of autographs each boy has?

We want to find the average number of autographs each of the boys has.

Andy has _____ autographs, Bart has _____ and

Larry has _____ .

To find the average, we add all the individual numbers of autographs, and divide that sum by

the number of boys. We add _____ , _____ and

_____ and divide by _____ .

```
  14    3)‾‾‾
   9
+ 13
```

The three boys have an average of _____ autographs each.

Getting Started

Find the average of each set of numbers.

1. 16, 54

2. 34, 27, 48, 51, 35

3. 158, 196, 243, 203

_____

_____

_____

Practice

Find the average of each set of numbers.

1. 17, 28, 36 _____
2. 146, 254 _____
3. 86, 58, 37, 49, 45 _____

4. 624, 534, 810, 712
5. 1,496, 4,868
6. 3,467, 2,948, 4,511

_____ _____ _____

Apply

Solve these problems.

7. Maria bowled games of 125, 136, and 138. What was Maria's average score?

8. Mrs. Jordan drove 243 miles on Monday and 485 miles on Tuesday. What was her average driving distance for one day?

9. Art earned $243 in May, $316 in June, $375 in July and $286 in August. What was Art's average monthly earnings?

10. Arnold took part in a free-throw contest. His scores were 13, 19, 17, 18 and 18. Find his average score and how many times he scored below it.

Use this graph of Martina's free throws to solve problems 11 through 16.

11. In which round did Martina get her highest score? _____

12. What was her highest score?

_____

13. In which round did Martina get her lowest score? _____

14. What was her lowest score?

_____

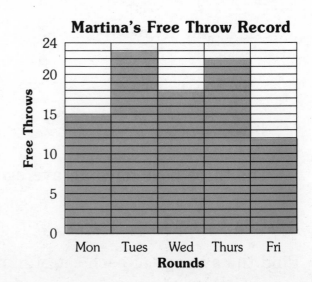

Martina's Free Throw Record

15. What was Martina's average?

_____

Making a Graph

On each bounce, Amy's playground ball bounces exactly half the height from which it is dropped. She drops the ball from a height of 48 inches. How high will it bounce on the fourth bounce?

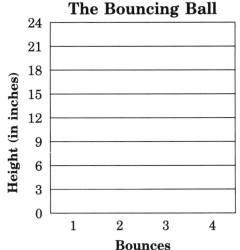

★ **SEE**

We want to know how high Amy's ball will bounce on the fourth bounce.

We know that the ball bounces ____ of the height of the previous bounce. Amy starts by dropping the ball from a height of _____ inches.

★ **PLAN**

We can make a bar graph of the ball's height after each bounce. Each bar will be one half the height of the one before it.

★ **DO**

The Bouncing Ball

The ball will bounce _____ inches on the fourth bounce.

★ **CHECK**

48 ÷ 2 = _____

_____ ÷ _____ = _____   _____ ÷ _____ = _____   _____ ÷ _____ = _____

Apply

Make a graph to help solve each problem.

1. The length of blue whales reaches up to 30 meters, gray whales up to 15 meters, humpback whales up to 15 meters, killer whales up to 9 meters and bowhead whales up to 18 meters. Create a graph to illustrate and compare the lengths of these whales.

2. A plain pizza costs $5.00. Each additional item, such as mushrooms, onions and peppers, costs $0.50 each. Provide a graph to show the costs and the number of extra items on pizzas less than $8.00.

3. It costs 25 cents to mail a package that weighs one ounce or less, and 20 cents for each additional ounce or fraction thereof. Construct a graph to illustrate the weight and cost of packages that can be mailed for under one dollar.

4. Gwen babysits for $2.00 per hour before midnight, and $3.00 per hour after midnight. Make a graph to show Gwen's total earnings if she babysits from 9 PM one evening until 3 AM the next morning.

5. The Fighting Flamingos, a football team, played 10 games during their regular season. A graph kept by their coach showed that their average score per game was 15 points. How many points in all did they score during their season?

6. A graph shows that, in their first game, the six players on the Beastly Bulls Basketball Team made these scores: 18, 14, 12, 20, 16, and 10. If they want to have no less than the same total score in their next game, what average number of points must each player score?

7. When computing to find data for a graph, how do you know that you can find 350 ÷ 70 by finding 35 ÷ 7?

8. When dividing to find data, how can you use a calculator to check a quotient with a remainder?

Calculators, Comparison Shopping

Mrs. Anderson is shopping for the best buy in cereal. Should Mrs. Anderson buy the 8-ounce or the 14-ounce box of cereal?

We are looking for the best buy in cereal.

The 8-ounce box is sold for _____.

The 14-ounce box costs _____.

To decide which is the better buy, we must find the **unit cost** of each container. To find the unit cost, we divide the total cost of the package by the number of units in it. We divide

$2.40 by 8 and _____ by _____.

Complete these codes.

2 [·] 4 [÷] 8 [=] (_____)

0.3 means $0.30 or 30¢.

3 [·] 92 [÷] 14 [=] (_____)

0.28 means $_____ or _____¢.

30¢ > 28¢

The _____-ounce box is the better buy.

Find the cost per ounce. Circle the best buy.

1. 8 ounces $4.48 _____ per oz

   16 ounces $8.32 _____ per oz

2. 6 ounces $1.74 _____ per oz

   8 ounces $2.24 _____ per oz

   12 ounces $3.72 _____ per oz

215

Practice

Use your calculator to find each answer.

1. 7)$8.61

2. 6)$9.24

3. 15)$3.00

4. 26)$6.76

5. 34)$8.16

6. 59)$3.54

Find the cost per unit. Circle the best buy.

7. 6 ounces $1.38 _____ per oz

   8 ounces $1.92 _____ per oz

8. 24 ounces $7.68 _____ per oz

   36 ounces $8.28 _____ per oz

9. 7 pounds $3.01 _____ per lb

   9 pounds $3.96 _____ per lb

   15 pounds $6.75 _____ per lb

10. 6 pounds $2.40 _____ per lb

    15 pounds $6.00 _____ per lb

    25 pounds $9.75 _____ per lb

Apply

Solve these problems.

11. A store sells one brand of hot chocolate at 3 pounds for $2.43. They sell another brand at 5 pounds for $3.95. Which is the better buy? How much do you save?

12. The school store sells binders for $1.35 each. If you buy 6 binders of the same color, the cost is $7.74. How much is saved if you buy 6 red binders?

EXCURSION

Find the missing digits.

```
        5
1. 26)6 5
      52
      1 5
     130
```

```
        22
2.  1)9 9
     82
      9
     __
```

216

Divide. Show your work.

1. 3)696   2. 5)555   3. 2)843   4. 4)725

5. 2)408   6. 3)900   7. 4)813   8. 3)625

9. 6)276   10. 7)399   11. 8)623   12. 9)738

13. 4)$8.24   14. 8)$5.76   15. 2)$9.38   16. 7)$4.97

17. 27)162   18. 39)247   19. 53)325   20. 44)428

21. 18)468   22. 25)$9.00   23. 39)756   24. 57)912

Find the average of each set of numbers.

25. 6, 9, 4, 5, 1   26. 92, 46, 75, 55

_____   _____

27. 47, 69, 101, 45, 48   28. 155, 245, 125

_____   _____

CUMULATIVE REVIEW

Circle the letter of the correct answer.

1 Round 639 to the nearest hundred.

    a 600
    b 700
    c NG

2 Round 7,350 to the nearest thousand.

    a 7,000
    b 8,000
    c NG

3 What is the value of the 1 in 517,296?

    a thousands
    b ten thousands
    c hundred thousands
    d NG

4
$$3,249 + 1,816$$

    a 4,055
    b 4,065
    c 5,065
    d NG

5
$$26,795 + 27,586$$

    a 43,271
    b 44,381
    c 54,381
    d NG

6
$$829 - 136$$

    a 693
    b 713
    c 793
    d NG

7
$$13,053 - 12,875$$

    a 178
    b 1,178
    c 1,822
    d NG

8 Choose the better estimate of weight.

    a 1.5 g
    b 1.5 kg

9 Choose the better estimate of volume.

    a 350 mL
    b 350 L

10
$$\$2.79 \times 6$$

    a $12.24
    b $16.74
    c $16.76
    d NG

11 39×23

    a 117
    b 897
    c 7,107
    d NG

12
$$607 \times 58$$

    a 34,204
    b 35,786
    c 36,206
    d NG

13 $624 \div 3$

    a 28
    b 208
    c 280
    d NG

14 $42\overline{)226}$

    a 5
    b 5 R26
    c 526
    d NG

☐ score

11
GEOMETRY

Points, Lines and Segments

"As the crow flies" is an expression which means the shortest distance between two points. Draw a line that shows this distance between Becky's and Allen's homes.

The shortest path from Becky's house to Allen's house is a straight path through the park.

A straight path from point A to point B is called a **line segment.** Points A and B are called **endpoints.**

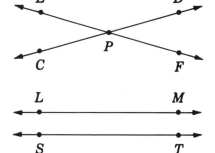

 We say: **segment** AB or **segment** BA.
 We write: $\overline{AB}$ or $\overline{BA}$.

A line segment is part of a **line.** A line extends indefinitely in both directions.

 We say: **line** XY or **line** YX.
 We write: $\overleftrightarrow{XY}$ or $\overleftrightarrow{YX}$.

✔ Notice that a line does not have endpoints.

Some lines **intersect.** Line CD intersects line EF at point P.

Some lines do not intersect. Line LM is **parallel** to line ST.

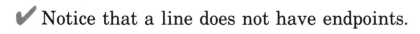

Getting Started

Write the name for this figure.

1. • C

Draw and label this figure.

2. $\overline{TV}$

219

Practice

Write the name for each figure.

1.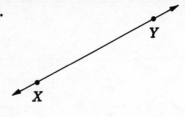

_____

2.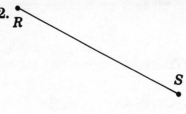

_____

3. • C

_____

4.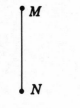

_____

5.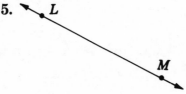

_____

6.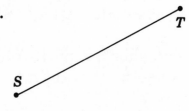

_____

Draw and label each figure.

7. Point _R_

8. Line _XY_

9. $\overline{AB}$

10. Line _MN_ parallel to line _RS_

11. $\overleftrightarrow{CD}$

12. Line _CD_ intersecting line _MN_

Tell whether each pair of lines is intersecting or parallel.

13.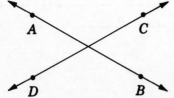

_____

14.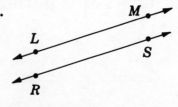

_____

15.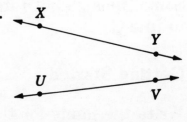

_____

16. Name six different line segments in this line.

____ ____ ____

____ ____ ____

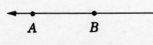

220

Rays and Angles

Turn on a flashlight. The beam of light is like a special kind of line called a ray. How is a beam like a ray?

A **ray** is part of a line. It has one endpoint and extends indefinitely in one direction.
We write: ray AB or $\overrightarrow{AB}$.

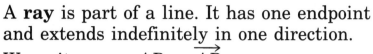

✔ Notice that we name a ray starting with its endpoint.

Two rays which intersect at a common endpoint form an **angle.** The common endpoint is called the **vertex** of the angle. We name an angle using 1 or 3 of its points.
This is angle CDE or $\angle CDE$
        angle EDC or $\angle EDC$
        angle D or $\angle D$.

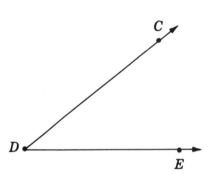

✔ Notice when using three points to name an angle, the vertex is always in the middle.

An angle that forms a square corner is called a **right angle.** $\angle XYZ$ is a right angle. The ⌐ shows the angle is a right angle.
The flashlight beam, like the ray, has _____

endpoint and extends indefinitely in _____ direction.

Getting Started

Write the name of each figure.

1.

2.

3.

_____   _____   _____

Draw and label each figure.

_____

4. $\angle LMN$ 5. $\overrightarrow{ZY}$ 6. Right angle COB

Practice

Write the name of each figure.

1.

2.

3.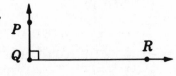

_____

_____

_____

4.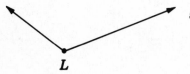

5.

6.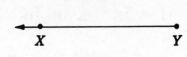

_____

_____

_____

Draw and label each figure.

7. $\overrightarrow{MN}$

8. $\angle MNO$

9. Ray TS

10. Right angle ABC

11. $\overleftrightarrow{KL}$

12. $\angle Q$

EXCURSION

List all of the different line segments in line segment AM.

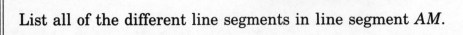

_____   _____

_____

There are _____ different line segments.

Plane Figures

How can the images on a movie screen help you to understand plane figures?

A **plane** figure is a "flat" shape. It has length and width, but no height.
We think of plane figures as being on the surface of things, like the figures drawn on this page, or images we see in a movie. Some plane figures are called **polygons.**

Polygons have only straight sides. **Triangles** have 3 sides; **quadrilaterals** have 4; **pentagons** have 5; **hexagons** have 6 and **octagons** have 8 sides.

Plane figures, like movie images, have _____

and _____, but no height.

Getting Started

Name the kind of polygon. List its line segments and angles.

1. Kind of polygon

_____

2. Line segments

$\overline{AB}$ _____

_____ _____

_____ _____

3. Angles

$\angle A$ _____

_____ _____

_____ _____

Draw and label each polygon.

4. Triangle *XYZ*

5. Quadrilateral *ABCD*

223

Practice

Name each kind of polygon.
List its line segments and angles.

1.

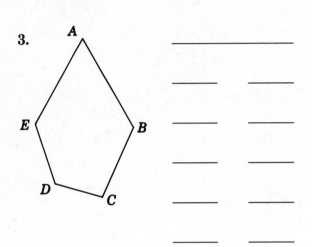

_____

____ ____

____ ____

____

2.

_____

____ ____

____ ____

____ ____

____ ____

3.

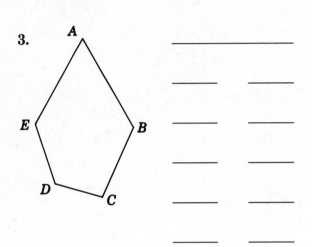

_____

____ ____

____ ____

____ ____

____ ____

4.

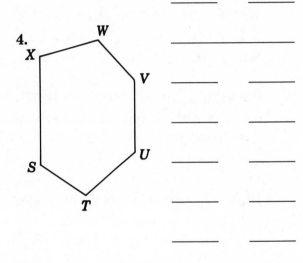

_____

____ ____

____ ____

____ ____

____ ____

____ ____

____ ____

Draw and label each polygon.

5. Pentagon *ABCDE*   6. Quadrilateral *RSTU*   7. Octagon *ABCDEFGH*

Complete the chart.

Polygon	Number of Sides	Number of Angles
8. Triangle		
9. Quadrilateral		
10. Pentagon		
11. Hexagon		
12. Octagon		

224

Congruent and Similar Figures

Plane figures that have the same shape are called **similar** figures. Plane figures that have the same shape and size are called **congruent** figures. Which triangle is similar to triangle *ABC*? Which triangle is congruent to triangle *ABC*?

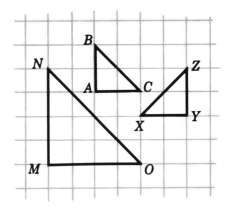

Graph paper can be used to show that two plane figures are similar.

Triangle *ABC* is similar to triangles _____ and _____. Tracing paper can be used to show that two plane figures are congruent.

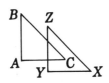

Triangle *ABC* is congruent to triangle _____.

Getting Started

Tell if each pair of figures is similar. Write **yes** or **no.**

1.

   _____

2.

   _____

Tell if each pair of figures is congruent. Write **yes** or **no.**

3.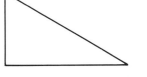

   _____

4.

   _____

Practice

Tell if each pair of figures is similar. Write **yes** or **no.**

1. 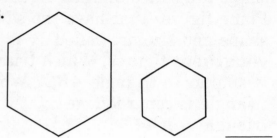 _____

2. 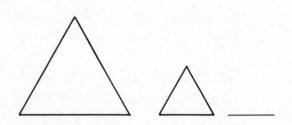 _____

3. 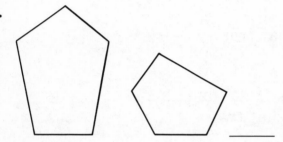 _____

4. 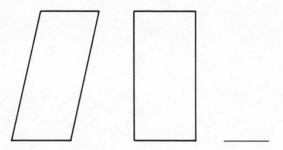 _____

Tell if each pair of figures is congruent. Write **yes** or **no.**

5. 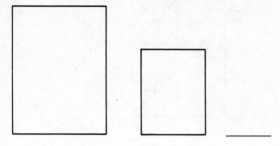 _____

6. 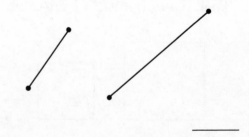 _____

7. 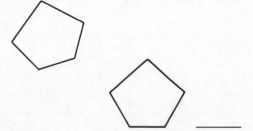 _____

8. 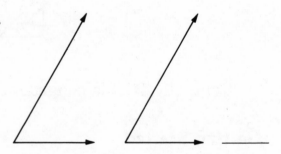 _____

9. 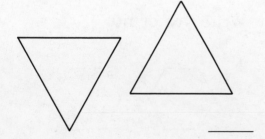 _____

10. 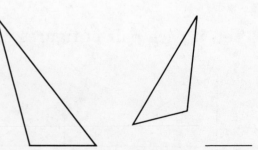 _____

Parallelograms

Which of these plane figures have
sides made of parallel lines?

Figure _____ has no straight lines.

Figure _____ has no sets of parallel lines.

A polygon in which the opposite sides are
parallel and congruent is called a
parallelogram. Congruent sides are line
segments which have the same length.
A **rectangle** is a parallelogram with four right

angles. Figure _____ is a rectangle.
A **square** is a parallelogram with four right
angles and all four sides congruent.

Figure _____ is a square.

✔ A square is a special kind of rectangle.

Figures _____, _____, _____ and _____ have
opposite sides that are parallel.

Getting Started

Write a **P** for a parallelogram, an **R** for a
rectangle and an **S** for a square.

1.

_____

2.

_____

3.

_____

4.

_____

Practice

Write a **P** for a parallelogram, an **R** for a rectangle and an **S** for a square.

1. 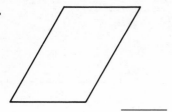 _____

2. 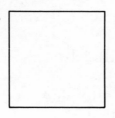 _____

3. 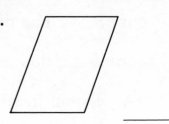 _____

4.  _____

5. 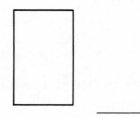 _____

6. 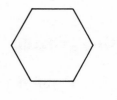 _____

7. 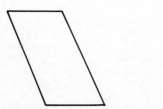 _____

8. 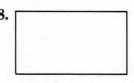 _____

9. 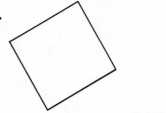 _____

10. _____

11. _____

12. _____

13. _____

14. _____

15. 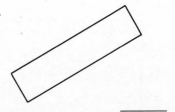 _____

16.  _____

17. 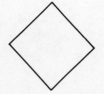 _____

18. _____

228

Finding Perimeter

Dino is fencing in a section of the yard for his dog. How many meters of fencing will Dino need?

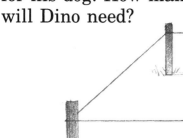

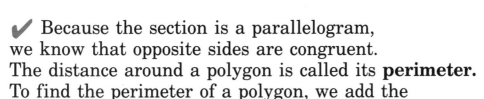

We want to know the distance around the dog's section of the yard. This section is shaped like a parallelogram.

The length of the section is _____ meters.

Its width is _____ meters.

✔ Because the section is a parallelogram, we know that opposite sides are congruent. The distance around a polygon is called its **perimeter.** To find the perimeter of a polygon, we add the

lengths of all the sides. We add _____, _____,

_____ and _____.

$3 + 5 + 3 + 5 =$ _____

Dino will need _____ meters of fencing.

Getting Started

Find the perimeter of each figure.

1.

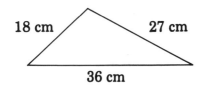

18 cm   27 cm

36 cm

_____

2.

16 m

_____

229

Practice

Find the perimeter of each figure.

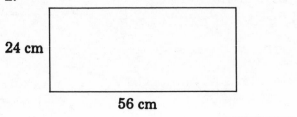

1.

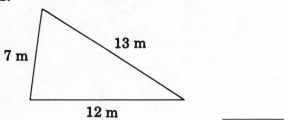

7 m 13 m 12 m

_____

2.

24 cm 56 cm

_____

3.

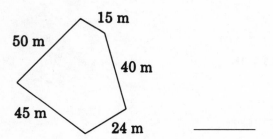

15 m 50 m 40 m 45 m 24 m

_____

4.

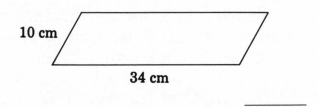

10 cm 34 cm

_____

5.

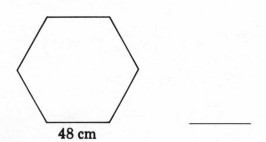

48 cm

_____

6.

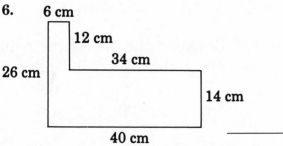

6 cm 12 cm 34 cm 26 cm 14 cm 40 cm

_____

Apply

Solve these problems.

7. Find the perimeter of a rectangular parking lot that is 28 meters wide and 47 meters long.

8. Allison drew a pentagon with all the sides equal in length. One side was 14 centimeters. What was the perimeter of the pentagon?

9. Complete the table.

Squares

Side	1 cm	2 cm	3 cm	4 cm	5 cm
Perimeter	4 cm				

Finding Area

Dino's father told him the dog had to have at least 10 square meters to play in. Will the fenced-in section be big enough?

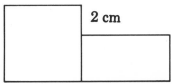

We need to find the number of square meters in the dog's yard.

There are _____ rows of square meters with

_____ square meters in each row.
The number of square units is called the **area.**
To find the area of the section, we multiply the number of rows by the number of square

units in each row. We multiply _____ by _____.

_____ × _____ = _____

There are _____ square meters in the dog's yard.

It _____ big enough for the dog.
We can use a **formula** to find the area of a rectangle or a square.

Rectangle

Width (W)

Length (L)

Square

Side (S)

✔ The area of a rectangle is equal to the length multiplied by the width.
$A = L \times W$

✔ The area of a square is equal to the side multiplied by itself.
$A = S \times S$

Getting Started

Find the area of each figure.

1.

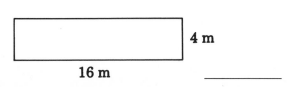

4 m

16 m

_____

2.

2 cm

3 cm

5 cm   6 cm

_____

Practice

Find the area of each figure.

1.

4 m
12 m

_____

2.

9 m

_____

3.

9 mm
3 mm

_____

Find the area of the shaded part of each figure.

4.

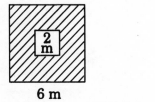

2 m
6 m

_____

5.

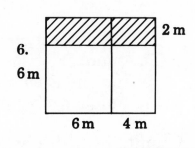

3 cm
4 cm
3 cm
6 cm

_____

6.

2 m
6 m
6 m   4 m

_____

Apply

Solve these problems.

7. Fritz is tiling a floor. The length of the floor is 3 meters. The width is 4 meters. How many square meters of floor does Fritz have to tile?

8. Wayne has a rectangle that is 5 centimeters by 12 centimeters. Rosa has a square that is 8 centimeters on a side. Who has the larger polygon? How much larger is it?

Complete these tables.

9.   Rectangles

Length	6 cm	5 cm	2 cm	5 cm	9 cm
Width	4 cm	4 cm	8 cm	7 cm	2 cm
Area					

10.   Squares

Side	2 cm	10 cm	6 cm	11 cm	7 cm
Area					

Solid Figures

Many of the objects used in our daily lives are
shaped like these solid figures.

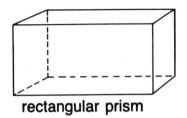

cube rectangular prism pyramid

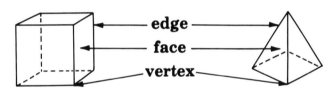

cylinder cone sphere

Solid figures have length and width as well as height.
Some figures such as cubes, prisms and pyramids
have **faces, vertices** and **edges.**

edge
face
vertex

Getting Started

Write the name of the solid figure you see in each object.

1.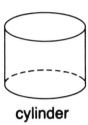

2.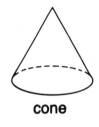

3.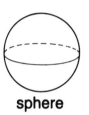

_____ _____ _____

4.

5.

6.

_____ _____ _____

233

Practice

Write the name of the solid figure you see in each object.

1.

_____

2.

_____

3.

_____

4.

_____

5.

_____

6.

_____

Complete the table.

7.

Figure	Number of Faces	Number of Edges	Number of Vertices
(cube)	6	12	8
(rectangular prism)			
(pyramid)			

EXCURSION

These polygons are **symmetrical.** They can be divided into two identical figures by at least one line segment, called an **axis of symmetry.** Draw all axes of symmetry for these polygons. Complete the chart.

Symmetrical Polygons

Sides	4			
Angles	4			
Axes of Symmetry	2			

Finding Volume

One way to measure the volume of a solid figure is in cubic units. How many cubic units are in this prism?

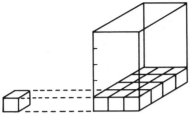

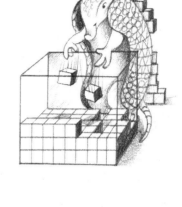

We want to find the volume of the prism in cubic units.

The prism is _____ cubic units long, _____

cubic units wide and _____ cubic units high. To find the volume, we multiply the number of cubic units in a row, by the number of rows, and again by the number of units high. We

multiply _____ by _____ by _____.

There are _____ cubic units in the prism. We can use a formula to find the volume of a prism.

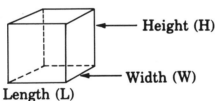

Height (H)

Width (W)

Length (L)

✔ The volume of a prism is equal to the length multiplied by the width multiplied by the height.

V = L × W × H

Getting Started

Find the volume of each prism.

1.
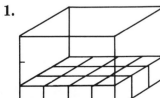

_____

2.

_____

235

Practice

Find the volume of each prism.

1.

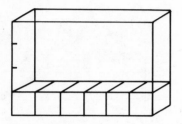

_____

2.

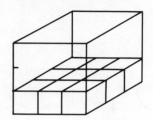

_____

3.

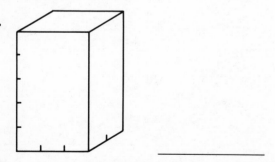

_____

4.

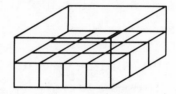

_____

5.

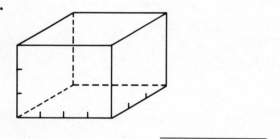

_____

6.

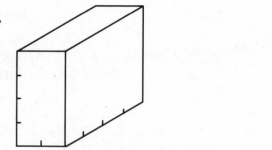

_____

7.

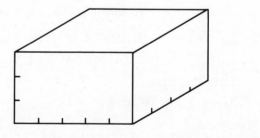

_____

8.

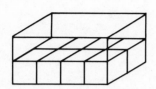

_____

9.

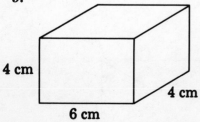

4 cm

4 cm

6 cm

_____

10.

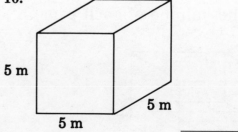

5 m

5 m

5 m

_____

Restating the Problem

Jose has $1.20 in coins. Half of the coins are nickels and half are dimes. What is the value of his nickels?

★ SEE

We want to find the value of Jose's nickels.

We know that the value of all his coins is _____.

Half of the coins are _____ and half are _____.

★ PLAN

We want to express this problem in our own way, so that we really understand it.

★ DO

Any way we reword the problem is good, as long as it helps us to understand it better. We know that the value of any number of nickels is one half the value of the same number of dimes.

Number of Nickels	Number of Dimes	Value of Nickels	Value of Dimes	Total Value of the Coins
6	6	$0.30	$0.60	$0.90
7	_____	_____	_____	_____
_____	_____	_____	_____	_____

The value of Jose's nickels is _____.

★ CHECK

$$\begin{array}{cc} 5¢ & 10¢ \\ \times\,8 & \times\,\ 8 \end{array} \qquad 80¢ + 40¢ = \underline{\hspace{2cm}}$$

Apply

Restate the problem in your own words to help you understand each problem.

1. Suppose there are 20 pinchworms in the bottom of a jar. Pinchworms multiply so fast that they double their number every minute. If it takes forty minutes for the pinchworms to fill the jar, how long will it take them to fill half of the jar?

2. It is 34 miles from Bay City to Hamilton. It is 28 miles from Hamilton to Glenville. Glenville is on the road between Bay City and Hamilton. How far is it from Bay City to Glenville?

3. Kyle bought a bat for $5.00. Then he bought a ball costing $3.00 more than the bat. How much did he spend?

4. If you can buy thirteen stamps for a cent and a quarter, what is the cost of one stamp?

5. If five boys can paint 5 garages in five days, how many boys would it take to paint 25 garages in 25 days?

6. I went to the store and bought several items that were the same price. I bought as many items as the number of total cents in the cost of each item. My bill was $1.44. How many items did I buy?

7. Read Exercise 3 again. What if the ball costs half as much as the bat. Then how much would Kyle spend for both items?

8. Explain how you would find the perimeter of a rectangle if the length were given in feet and the width in yards?

9. Read Exercise 2 again. Write a problem about 3 towns where the distance between the nearest two towns is 5 miles and between the two towns farthest apart is 15 miles.

10. Suppose you know the length, width, and area of a rectangle. How would you affect the area if you double just the length? if you double both the length and width?

Write the name for each figure.

1.

_____

2.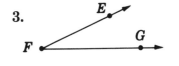

_____

3.

_____

Name each kind of polygon.

4.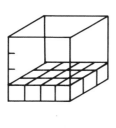

_____

5.

_____

6.

_____

Find the perimeter.

7.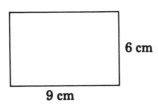

12 m

14 m   16 m

18 m   _____

8.

18 m

14 m   5 m

10 m

9 m

8 m   _____

Find the area.

9.

6 cm

9 cm

_____

10.

5 cm

_____

Find the volume.

11.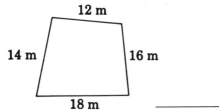

_____

12.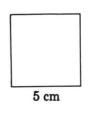

_____

239

CUMULATIVE REVIEW

Circle the letter of the correct answer.

1 Round 4,628 to the nearest thousand.

   a 4,000
   b 5,000
   c NG

2 What is the value of the 9 in 629,206?

   a tens
   b thousands
   c hundred thousands
   d NG

3   4,268
   + 3,659

   a 7,817
   b 7,927
   c 8,927
   d NG

4   39,475
   + 26,628

   a 66,103
   b 56,003
   c 56,093
   d NG

5 707 − 388

   a 389
   b 419
   c 481
   d NG

6   36,239
   − 14,856

   a 22,383
   b 22,623
   c 21,383
   d NG

7 Choose the better estimate of volume.

   a 1 pint
   b 1 quart

8 $3.25 × 7

   a $21.45
   b $21.75
   c $22.75
   d NG

9   16
   × 45

   a 144
   b 490
   c 720
   d NG

10   516
   × 25

   a 3,612
   b 12,700
   c 12,900
   d NG

11 27)‾162

   a 5
   b 6
   c 7
   d NG

12 629 ÷ 34

   a 18
   b 18 R17
   c 180 R17
   d NG

13 Name the figure.

   a square
   b rectangle
   c parallelogram
   d NG

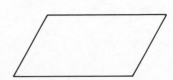

score

Fractional Parts

Fractions can help you talk about a part of a figure, or some of a set of things. What part of this rectangle is red? What part of this set of cars is not red?

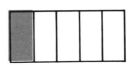

The rectangle is divided into _____ equal parts.

_____ part is red.

We write: $\dfrac{1}{5}$ ← **numerator**   We say: **one-fifth.**
            ← **denominator**

_____ of the rectangle is red.

There are _____ cars.

_____ cars are not red.

We write: $\dfrac{2}{3}$.   We say: **two-thirds.**

_____ of the cars are not red.

Getting Started

Write a fraction to show what part of each figure is red.

1.

2.

3.

Write a fraction to show what part of each set is *not* red.

4.

5.

6.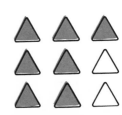

241

Practice

Write a fraction to show what part of each figure is red.

1.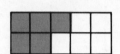

2.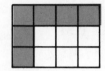

3.

4.

5.

6.

Write a fraction to show what part of each set is *not* red.

7.

8.

9.

10.

Apply

Solve these problems.

11. What part of the triangle is red?

12. What part of the octagon is *not* red?

13. What part of the set of coins are pennies?

14. Write a fraction to show what part of the set of figures are squares.

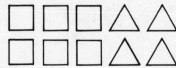

242

Finding a Fraction of a Number, Unit Fractions

Mark and Nadia are trading seashells for a science project. Mark gives Nadia $\frac{1}{5}$ of his seashells. How many seashells does Nadia get from Mark?

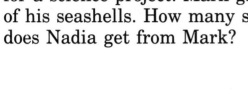

We want to know how many seashells Mark gives Nadia.

Mark has _____ seashells.

He gives Nadia _____ of them.

To find the number of seashells, we need

to multiply _____ by $\frac{1}{5}$.

✔ $\frac{1}{5}$ is called a **unit fraction** because its numerator is one. To multiply by a unit fraction, we simply divide by the denominator.

We divide _____ by _____.

Mark gave Nadia _____ seashells.

Getting Started

Find the part.

1. $\frac{1}{3}$ of 9 = _____

2. $\frac{1}{6}$ of 36 = _____

3. $\frac{1}{2}$ of 32 = _____

4. $\frac{1}{4}$ of 48 = _____

5. $\frac{1}{7}$ of 84 = _____

6. $\frac{1}{12}$ of 180 = _____

Practice

Find the part.

1. $\frac{1}{5}$ of 15 = _____

2. $\frac{1}{8}$ of 64 = _____

3. $\frac{1}{9}$ of 63 = _____

4. $\frac{1}{6}$ of 36 = _____

5. $\frac{1}{3}$ of 36 = _____

6. $\frac{1}{2}$ of 56 = _____

7. $\frac{1}{7}$ of 84 = _____

8. $\frac{1}{4}$ of 96 = _____

9. $\frac{1}{3}$ of 87 = _____

10. $\frac{1}{6}$ of 96 = _____

11. $\frac{1}{12}$ of 72 = _____

12. $\frac{1}{15}$ of 750 = _____

Apply

Solve these problems.

13. Betty bought 36 pencils. She gave $\frac{1}{2}$ to her best friend. How many pencils did Betty give away?

14. Peter's baseball team played 21 games. They won $\frac{1}{3}$ of the games. How many games did the team win?

15. There are 32 children in Mr. Chan's class. One day, $\frac{1}{4}$ of the class was absent. How many children were absent?

16. There are 65 children on the school swimming team. $\frac{1}{5}$ of the team are boys. How many boys are on the team?

17. Mr. James planted 56 trees. $\frac{1}{4}$ of the trees were maples. How many trees were maples?

18. Mrs. Spencer bought 156 apples. $\frac{1}{6}$ of the apples were spoiled. How many apples were not spoiled?

19. Ed lives 924 meters from school. He jogs $\frac{1}{3}$ of the way there and walks the rest. How far does Ed walk?

20. A book has 216 pages. Lucia has read $\frac{1}{12}$ of the book. How many pages does Lucia have left to read?

Finding a Fraction of a Number

Pat looks for sales when she shops for clothes. How much will Pat pay for a blouse?

BLOUSES
2/3 ORIGINAL PRICE
WERE $12

We want to know the sale price of a blouse.

The original price of the blouse was _____.

The sale price is _____ of the original price.

To find the sale price, we need to find $\frac{2}{3}$

of _____.

✔ To multiply a number by a **non-unit fraction,** we divide it by the denominator and multiply it by the numerator.

We divide _____ by _____ and multiply by _____.

$12 ÷ _____ = _____   _____ × _____ = _____

Pat will pay _____ for a blouse.

Getting Started

Find the part.

1. $\frac{3}{4}$ of 16 = _____

2. $\frac{5}{8}$ of $72 = _____

3. $\frac{3}{16}$ of 224 = _____

Find the sale price.

4. $\frac{5}{6}$ of a price of $36

5. $\frac{3}{5}$ of a price of $365

6. $\frac{2}{3}$ of a price of $672

_____

_____

_____

245

Practice

Find the part.

1. $\frac{2}{5}$ of $25 = _____

2. $\frac{3}{4}$ of $36 = _____

3. $\frac{3}{8}$ of 72 = _____

4. $\frac{5}{6}$ of 54 = _____

5. $\frac{7}{9}$ of 90 = _____

6. $\frac{2}{3}$ of $30 = _____

7. $\frac{7}{8}$ of 64 = _____

8. $\frac{3}{4}$ of $84 = _____

9. $\frac{5}{11}$ of $121 = _____

Find the sale price.

10. $\frac{3}{8}$ of a price of $56

11. $\frac{3}{4}$ of a price of $28

12. $\frac{3}{5}$ of a price of $25

_____

_____

_____

13. $\frac{5}{7}$ of a price of $49

14. $\frac{5}{8}$ of a price of $80

15. $\frac{2}{3}$ of a price of $33

_____

_____

_____

16. $\frac{2}{3}$ of a price of $57

17. $\frac{5}{6}$ of a price of $126

18. $\frac{1}{2}$ of a price of $96

_____

_____

_____

Apply

Solve these problems.

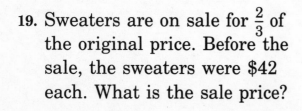

19. Sweaters are on sale for $\frac{2}{3}$ of the original price. Before the sale, the sweaters were $42 each. What is the sale price?

20. The original price of a jogging suit was $80. It is on sale for $\frac{3}{4}$ of the price. How much can be saved if you buy the suit on sale?

Find the sale price.

21.

Sale $\frac{2}{5}$ off			
Original Price	$65	$140	$585
Sale Price			

Understanding Equivalent Fractions

Fractions that name the same amount are called **equivalent fractions**. Name the two fractions that are equivalent to $\frac{2}{3}$.

 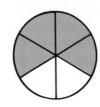 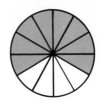

We want to find two fractions

that are equivalent to ____.

Each large rectangle below is the same size. We can shade in the same amount of space in each rectangle to find equivalent **thirds, sixths** and **twelfths.**

$$\frac{1}{3} \qquad \frac{2}{3}$$

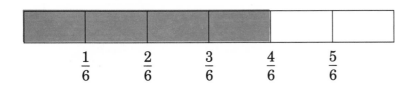

$$\frac{1}{6} \qquad \frac{2}{6} \qquad \frac{3}{6} \qquad \frac{4}{6} \qquad \frac{5}{6}$$

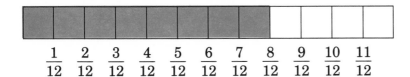

$$\frac{1}{12} \quad \frac{2}{12} \quad \frac{3}{12} \quad \frac{4}{12} \quad \frac{5}{12} \quad \frac{6}{12} \quad \frac{7}{12} \quad \frac{8}{12} \quad \frac{9}{12} \quad \frac{10}{12} \quad \frac{11}{12}$$

$\frac{2}{3}$, ____ and ____ are equivalent fractions.

Getting Started

Write the missing numerators.

1.
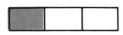

$$\frac{1}{3} = \frac{}{6}$$

2.

$$\frac{3}{5} = \frac{}{10}$$

3.

$$\frac{}{4} = \frac{6}{8}$$

247

Practice

Write the missing numerators.

1.

$$\frac{1}{2} = \frac{}{4}$$

2.

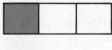

$$\frac{}{8} = \frac{1}{4}$$

3.

$$\frac{1}{3} = \frac{}{6}$$

4.

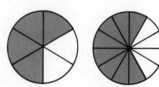

$$\frac{8}{10} = \frac{}{5}$$

5.

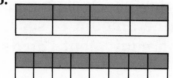

$$\frac{4}{8} = \frac{}{16}$$

6.

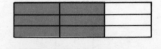

$$\frac{}{6} = \frac{8}{12}$$

7.

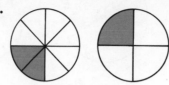

$$\frac{3}{4} = \frac{}{16}$$

8.

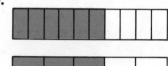

$$\frac{6}{12} = \frac{}{6}$$

9.

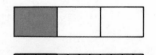

$$\frac{}{10} = \frac{3}{5}$$

10.

$$\frac{}{5} = \frac{6}{10}$$

11.

$$\frac{5}{7} = \frac{}{14}$$

12.

$$\frac{}{3} = \frac{4}{12}$$

13.

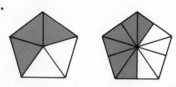

$$\frac{4}{8} = \frac{}{16}$$

14.

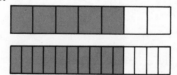

$$\frac{}{8} = \frac{2}{4}$$

15.

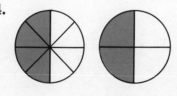 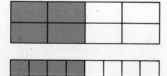 

$$\frac{6}{9} = \frac{}{18}$$

Finding Equivalent Fractions

Bobbi discovered a shortcut for finding equivalent fractions. Use her shortcut to find the missing numbers.

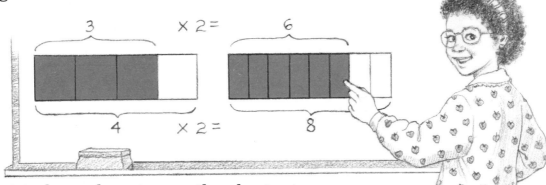

We want to know how to use the shortcut for finding equivalent fractions.
We can compare the shaded areas of the rectangles, to see what has happened to the numerator and denominator in equivalent fractions.

$$\frac{3}{4} = \frac{6}{8}$$

What number times 4 equals 8? What number times 3 equals 6?

$$\frac{3}{4} \times \underline{\quad} = \frac{6}{8}$$

The numerator and the denominator are multiplied by the same number.

Usually, we know the denominator of an equivalent fraction.

What number times 3 equals 12?

$$\frac{2}{3} = \frac{\underline{\quad}}{12}$$

Multiply the numerator by the same number.

Getting Started

Write the missing numerators.

1. $\frac{1}{4} = \frac{}{8}$

2. $\frac{1}{3} = \frac{}{9}$

3. $\frac{1}{6} = \frac{}{24}$

4. $\frac{2}{3} = \frac{}{12}$

5. $\frac{3}{4} = \frac{}{16}$

6. $\frac{4}{5} = \frac{}{30}$

7. $\frac{1}{2} = \frac{2}{4} = \frac{3}{6} = \frac{}{8} = \frac{}{10} = \frac{}{12} = \frac{}{14} = \frac{}{16} = \frac{}{18}$

Practice

Write the missing numerators.

1. $\dfrac{1}{4} = \dfrac{}{12}$

2. $\dfrac{5}{6} = \dfrac{}{18}$

3. $\dfrac{3}{5} = \dfrac{}{15}$

4. $\dfrac{4}{7} = \dfrac{}{21}$

5. $\dfrac{2}{3} = \dfrac{}{12}$

6. $\dfrac{5}{6} = \dfrac{}{24}$

7. $\dfrac{5}{8} = \dfrac{}{24}$

8. $\dfrac{3}{10} = \dfrac{}{20}$

9. $\dfrac{5}{9} = \dfrac{}{18}$

10. $\dfrac{7}{8} = \dfrac{}{64}$

11. $\dfrac{3}{9} = \dfrac{}{27}$

12. $\dfrac{3}{4} = \dfrac{}{16}$

13. $\dfrac{4}{5} = \dfrac{}{20}$

14. $\dfrac{3}{7} = \dfrac{}{28}$

15. $\dfrac{5}{8} = \dfrac{}{16}$

16. $\dfrac{1}{9} = \dfrac{}{45}$

17. $\dfrac{4}{7} = \dfrac{}{21}$

18. $\dfrac{5}{9} = \dfrac{}{54}$

19. $\dfrac{3}{4} = \dfrac{}{32}$

20. $\dfrac{4}{5} = \dfrac{}{30}$

21. $\dfrac{6}{11} = \dfrac{}{33}$

22. $\dfrac{5}{12} = \dfrac{}{72}$

23. $\dfrac{3}{16} = \dfrac{}{96}$

24. $\dfrac{5}{24} = \dfrac{}{72}$

25. $\dfrac{1}{3} = \dfrac{2}{6} = \dfrac{3}{9} = \dfrac{}{12} = \dfrac{}{15} = \dfrac{}{18} = \dfrac{}{21} = \dfrac{}{24} = \dfrac{}{27}$

26. $\dfrac{2}{3} = \dfrac{4}{6} = \dfrac{6}{9} = \dfrac{}{12} = \dfrac{}{15} = \dfrac{}{18} = \dfrac{}{21} = \dfrac{}{24} = \dfrac{}{27}$

27. $\dfrac{1}{4} = \dfrac{2}{8} = \dfrac{3}{12} = \dfrac{}{16} = \dfrac{}{20} = \dfrac{}{24} = \dfrac{}{28} = \dfrac{}{32} = \dfrac{}{36}$

28. $\dfrac{3}{4} = \dfrac{6}{8} = \dfrac{9}{12} = \dfrac{}{16} = \dfrac{}{20} = \dfrac{}{24} = \dfrac{}{28} = \dfrac{}{32} = \dfrac{}{36}$

29. $\dfrac{1}{5} = \dfrac{2}{10} = \dfrac{3}{15} = \dfrac{}{20} = \dfrac{}{25} = \dfrac{}{30} = \dfrac{}{35} = \dfrac{}{40} = \dfrac{}{45}$

30. $\dfrac{1}{6} = \dfrac{2}{12} = \dfrac{3}{18} = \dfrac{}{24} = \dfrac{}{30} = \dfrac{}{36} = \dfrac{}{42} = \dfrac{}{48} = \dfrac{}{54}$

Comparing Fractions

Elaina and Kurt are trying to find out which fraction is greater, $\frac{3}{4}$ or $\frac{2}{3}$. Help them compare the fractions.

We want to know if $\frac{3}{4}$ is greater or less than $\frac{2}{3}$.

We can draw two number lines.

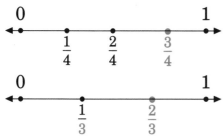

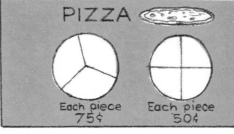

$\frac{3}{4}$ is closer to 1. Therefore $\frac{3}{4}$ is _____ than $\frac{2}{3}$.

We write: $\frac{3}{4} > \frac{2}{3}$.

We can also say $\frac{2}{3}$ **is less than** $\frac{3}{4}$. We write: $\frac{2}{3} < \frac{3}{4}$.

✔ Numbers to the right on number lines are always greater. Numbers to the left are always less.

We can also find equivalent fractions that have the same denominator. Then we can compare the numerators.

$$\frac{3 \times 3}{4 \times 3} = \frac{}{12} \qquad \frac{2 \times 4}{3 \times 4} = \frac{}{12} \qquad \frac{}{12} > \frac{}{12}$$

Getting Started

Use the number lines to compare the fractions.
Write < or > in the circle.

1. $\frac{1}{2} \bigcirc \frac{1}{4}$

2. $\frac{3}{5} \bigcirc \frac{2}{3}$

Use equivalent fractions to compare the fractions.
Write < or > in the circle.

3. $\frac{3}{4} \bigcirc \frac{3}{8}$

4. $\frac{3}{8} \bigcirc \frac{1}{2}$

5. $\frac{2}{3} \bigcirc \frac{5}{6}$

6. $\frac{5}{6} \bigcirc \frac{4}{5}$

251

Practice

Use the number lines to compare the fractions.
Write < or > in the circle.

1. $\frac{1}{3}$ ◯ $\frac{1}{5}$

2. $\frac{3}{5}$ ◯ $\frac{2}{8}$

3. $\frac{4}{6}$ ◯ $\frac{3}{4}$

4. $\frac{1}{2}$ ◯ $\frac{6}{10}$

5. $\frac{5}{8}$ ◯ $\frac{2}{3}$

6. $\frac{7}{10}$ ◯ $\frac{3}{5}$

Use equivalent fractions to compare the fractions.
Write < or > in the circle.

7. $\frac{5}{6}$ ◯ $\frac{1}{2}$

8. $\frac{5}{8}$ ◯ $\frac{3}{4}$

9. $\frac{2}{3}$ ◯ $\frac{3}{12}$

10. $\frac{1}{2}$ ◯ $\frac{4}{16}$

11. $\frac{1}{4}$ ◯ $\frac{1}{12}$

12. $\frac{1}{4}$ ◯ $\frac{3}{8}$

13. $\frac{5}{9}$ ◯ $\frac{1}{2}$

14. $\frac{3}{5}$ ◯ $\frac{5}{6}$

15. $\frac{5}{12}$ ◯ $\frac{1}{2}$

16. $\frac{7}{9}$ ◯ $\frac{2}{3}$

17. $\frac{5}{6}$ ◯ $\frac{7}{12}$

18. $\frac{3}{4}$ ◯ $\frac{4}{5}$

19. $\frac{1}{2}$ ◯ $\frac{1}{3}$

20. $\frac{3}{7}$ ◯ $\frac{3}{8}$

21. $\frac{2}{3}$ ◯ $\frac{3}{4}$

22. $\frac{3}{8}$ ◯ $\frac{5}{6}$

Apply

Solve these problems.

23. Cleve ran $\frac{2}{5}$ of a mile. Gary ran $\frac{5}{10}$ of a mile. Who ran farther?

24. Jennie read for $\frac{3}{4}$ of an hour. Myra read for $\frac{5}{6}$ of an hour. Who read longer?

Finding Simplest Terms

Mr. Granger bought 18 cans of motor oil on sale. What fraction of the case of oil did he buy?

We want to know what part of a case Mr. Granger bought.

Mr. Granger bought ____ cans of oil.

There are ____ cans in a case.

✔ Remember that the denominator names the total number of parts, and the numerator names the number of parts you are counting.

$$\underline{} = \frac{\text{the number of cans bought}}{\text{the number of cans in a case}}$$

This fraction can be **simplified.** The numerator and the denominator of a fraction are called the **terms** of a fraction. To simplify a fraction, we name it in its lowest terms. To simplify a fraction, we divide the numerator and the denominator by the same number.

$$\frac{18 \div 6}{24 \div 6} = \frac{3}{4}$$

✔ A fraction is in its lowest terms when the terms cannot be divided by any common factor other than 1.

Mr. Granger bought ____ of a case of oil.

Getting Started

Simplify each fraction.

1. $\frac{6}{8} =$ **2.** $\frac{5}{15} =$ **3.** $\frac{3}{9} =$ **4.** $\frac{10}{20} =$ **5.** $\frac{16}{24} =$

Practice

Simplify each fraction.

1. $\frac{10}{15} =$ 2. $\frac{6}{9} =$ 3. $\frac{4}{12} =$ 4. $\frac{5}{10} =$ 5. $\frac{6}{18} =$

6. $\frac{4}{20} =$ 7. $\frac{4}{24} =$ 8. $\frac{4}{16} =$ 9. $\frac{8}{12} =$ 10. $\frac{9}{18} =$

11. $\frac{6}{12} =$ 12. $\frac{14}{16} =$ 13. $\frac{15}{25} =$ 14. $\frac{6}{10} =$ 15. $\frac{3}{12} =$

16. $\frac{16}{20} =$ 17. $\frac{9}{12} =$ 18. $\frac{24}{48} =$ 19. $\frac{8}{16} =$ 20. $\frac{8}{32} =$

21. $\frac{10}{12} =$ 22. $\frac{16}{24} =$ 23. $\frac{4}{8} =$ 24. $\frac{27}{36} =$ 25. $\frac{12}{16} =$

EXCURSION

Find the missing digits.

1.
```
    7 , 0 4 2
  -  □ , □ 6 □
  ─────────────
    3 , 4 □ 7
```

2.
```
   2 □ , 0 6 8
   4 9 , 4 7 □
 + □ 5 , □ 3 4
 ─────────────
   8 9 , 2 □ 5
```

3.
```
   3 6 , 4 □ 3
   1 7 , □ 8 7
 + 1 □ , 9 6 □
 ─────────────
   □ 3 , 7 2 4
```

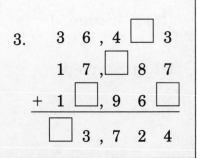

254

Understanding Mixed Numbers

Miguel is on the track team. His coach told him to run 9 laps during practice. How many miles did Miguel run?

We want to know how far Miguel ran.

Miguel ran ____ laps.

Each lap is ____ mile long.
We can use a number line to help us understand this distance.

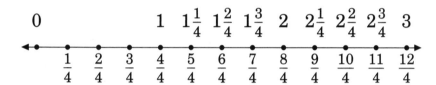

Miguel ran a total of $\frac{}{4}$ miles.

✔ A fraction whose numerator is larger than its denominator can be renamed as a **mixed number** by using division. We divide the numerator by the denominator.

We divide ____ by ____.

$$\frac{9}{4} = 4\overline{)9} \quad \begin{array}{l} 2 \leftarrow \text{whole number} \\ \underline{8} \\ 1 \leftarrow \text{number of fourths left} \end{array}$$

$$\frac{9}{4} = 2\frac{1}{4}$$

whole number   fraction

$2\frac{1}{4}$ is called a **mixed number.**

Miguel ran ____ miles.

✔ Remember to simplify fractions.

$$\frac{16}{6} = 2\frac{4}{6} = 2\frac{2}{3} \qquad \frac{15}{3} = 5$$

Getting Started

Rename each fraction as a whole or mixed number, and simplify.

1. $\frac{7}{3} =$
2. $\frac{5}{2} =$
3. $\frac{10}{8} =$
4. $\frac{8}{4} =$
5. $\frac{16}{10} =$

255

Practice

Rename each fraction as a whole or mixed number, and simplify.

1. $\frac{5}{4} =$　　2. $\frac{8}{3} =$　　3. $\frac{6}{4} =$　　4. $\frac{7}{2} =$　　5. $\frac{9}{3} =$

6. $\frac{8}{5} =$　　7. $\frac{12}{8} =$　　8. $\frac{14}{6} =$　　9. $\frac{16}{3} =$　　10. $\frac{18}{4} =$

11. $\frac{25}{10} =$　12. $\frac{30}{12} =$　13. $\frac{30}{9} =$　14. $\frac{24}{16} =$　15. $\frac{21}{7} =$

16. $\frac{44}{8} =$　17. $\frac{16}{10} =$　18. $\frac{63}{12} =$　19. $\frac{40}{6} =$　20. $\frac{86}{20} =$

21. $\frac{16}{5} =$　22. $\frac{14}{10} =$　23. $\frac{18}{8} =$　24. $\frac{36}{6} =$　25. $\frac{42}{9} =$

26. $\frac{16}{7} =$　27. $\frac{72}{9} =$　28. $\frac{9}{5} =$　29. $\frac{29}{10} =$　30. $\frac{49}{7} =$

EXCURSION

Fill in the blanks and circles with numbers and signs that correctly complete the pattern.

$9 \times 9 =$ ___　　　　$8 \ + \ 1 \ =$ ___

$9 \times 8 =$ ___　　　　___ $+$ ___ $=$ ___

$9 \times 7 =$ ___　　　　___ $\bigcirc$ ___ $=$ ___

$9 \times 6 =$ ___　　　　___ $\bigcirc$ ___ $=$ ___

$9 \times 5 =$ ___　　　　___ $\bigcirc$ ___ $=$ ___

Write a sentence that describes the pattern.

_____

_____

Understanding Fractions in Measurement

Find the length of the scissors
to the nearest $\frac{1}{4}$ inch.

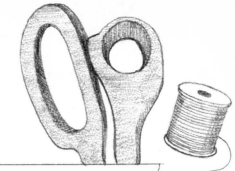

We use a ruler marked in **quarter** inches.

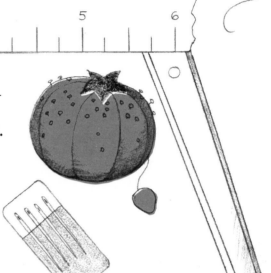

The length of the scissors is between ____

and ____ inches. It is closer to ____ inches.

To the nearest $\frac{1}{4}$ inch, the length of the

scissors is ____ inches.

Getting Started

Measure each figure to the nearest quarter inch.

1.

_____

2.

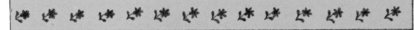

_____

3.

_____

4.

_____

257

Practice

Measure each figure to the nearest quarter inch.

1.
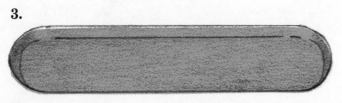

_____

2.

_____

3.

_____

4.
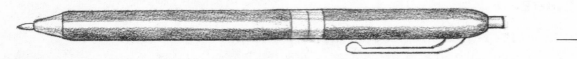

_____

5.

_____

6.

_____

EXCURSION

This **modulo-4** system contains just four numbers. Complete the addition table using the clock face as your number line.

+	0	1	2	3
0		1		
1				0
2	2	3		
3			1	2

Understanding Ratios

A **ratio** is a comparison of two quantities. The ratio of black pins to all pins on the bulletin board is 3 to 9. This can also be written as the fraction $\frac{3}{9}$. The ratio of black pins to white pins is 3 to 4, or $\frac{3}{4}$. What is the ratio of red pins to black pins?

We want to compare the number of red pins to the number of black pins.

There are _____ red pins.

There are _____ black pins.

The ratio of red pins to black pins is _____

to _____, or the fraction _____.

Getting Started

Write each comparison as a fraction.

1. white pins to black pins

2. white pins to all pins

3. red pins to black pins

4. black pins to red pins

Write each comparison as a ratio.

5. red pins to all pins

6. red pins to white pins

_____

_____

Practice

Write each comparison as a fraction.

1. white marbles to all marbles

2. white marbles to red marbles

3. black marbles to red marbles

4. red marbles to white marbles

5. black marbles to all marbles

6. red marbles to black marbles

7. white marbles to black marbles

8. red marbles to all marbles

Write each comparison as a ratio.

9. truck to cars

_____

10. cars to engines

_____

11. engines to all vehicles

_____

12. engines to trucks

_____

13. trucks to all vehicles

_____

14. trucks to engines

_____

15. trucks and cars to all vehicles

_____

16. cars to trucks and engines

_____

PROBLEM SOLVING

Selecting Notation

Jack's mother is making pudding which calls for
4 cups of milk. Show how she gets this amount
using her 7-cup and 5-cup measures.

★ SEE
We want to show how Jack's mother measures 4
cups of milk.

★ PLAN
We use ordered pairs to represent the amount of
milk in the measuring cups. The first number
represents the amount in the 7-cup measure.
The second number represents the amount in
the 5-cup measure.

★ DO

(7, 0)   She fills the _____-cup measure.

(2, 5)   She pours _____ cups from the 7-cup into the _____-cup.

(2, 0)   She empties the _____-cup into the carton.

(0, 2)   She pours _____ cups from the _____-cup to the _____-cup.

(7, 2)   She refills the _____-cup.

(4, 5)   She pours _____ cups from the _____-cup into the _____-cup.

Jack's mother now has exactly _____ cups of milk
in the first measuring cup.

★ CHECK
We can check our work by reviewing each step
in the solution and by asking ourselves these questions:

1. Did we use more than 7 cups
   for the first measuring cup
   in any step? _____

2. Did we use more than 5 cups
   for the second measuring cup
   in any step? _____

261

Apply

Select notation to help you solve these problems.

1. Fran and Beth gathered blackberries and filled an 8-quart pail. They want to divide the berries equally. Besides the 8-quart pail, they have a 5-quart pail and a 3-quart pail. Describe how they can divide the berries equally.

2. Arthur Ant wants to crawl from A to G on this cube. How many different 3-sided trips can he make? He must stay on an edge of the cube at all times.

3. Terry has a 3-ounce and a 7-ounce container. Her recipe calls for exactly 5 ounces of water. Using only these two containers, show how Terry can measure exactly 5 ounces of water.

4. The Chess Club is having a tournament. Each of the 7 members will play every other member one time. The champion will be the member with the most wins. How many games will be played?

5. Jodi's favorite clothes include four sweatshirts, three pairs of jeans and two pairs of tennis shoes. How many days in a row can she wear a different outfit using her favorite clothes?

6. At Washington School, for every 7 students who walked to school, 25 rode a school bus. At Lincoln School, the ratio was 9 to 30. At which school is the ratio of walkers to riders greater? Prove your answer.

7. In a math contest, the first 10 students to give an answer to the following challenge were given a puzzle book for a prize. "Show 3 fractions in order from least to greatest where the numerators are arranged from greatest to least." What answer would you give?

8. Tom and Juan were playing a game making up special numbers. To make up the first number, Tom said 3 and Juan said 5. To make up another number, Tom said 6 and Juan said 10. Then Tom said 9 and Juan said 15. What kind of numbers are they making up?

Write the fraction.

1. What part of the square is red?

2. What part of the coins are *not* pennies?

Find the part.

3. $\frac{1}{5}$ of 25 =

4. $\frac{3}{4}$ of 24 =

5. $\frac{7}{8}$ of a price of \$48

_____

Write the missing numerators.

6. $\frac{3}{5} = \frac{}{10}$

7. $\frac{3}{8} = \frac{}{16}$

8. $\frac{2}{3} = \frac{}{9}$

9. $\frac{5}{6} = \frac{}{24}$

Write < or > in the circle.

10. $\frac{2}{3} \bigcirc \frac{5}{9}$

11. $\frac{1}{2} \bigcirc \frac{3}{8}$

12. $\frac{7}{12} \bigcirc \frac{3}{4}$

13. $\frac{2}{3} \bigcirc \frac{1}{4}$

Simplify each fraction.

14. $\frac{6}{10} =$

15. $\frac{4}{8} =$

16. $\frac{9}{12} =$

17. $\frac{14}{16} =$

Write each fraction as a mixed number.

18. $\frac{7}{2} =$

19. $\frac{8}{3} =$

20. $\frac{16}{5} =$

21. $\frac{15}{12} =$

Measure the figures to the nearest quarter inch.

22.

23.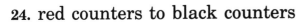

_____

Write the comparisons as fractions.

24. red counters to black counters

25. black counters to all counters

CUMULATIVE REVIEW

Circle the letter of the correct answer.

1 Round 925 to the nearest hundred.

a 800
b 900
c NG

2 What is the value of the 6 in 473,160?

a tens
b hundreds
c thousands
d NG

3
$$3,416$$
$$+ 7,396$$

a 10,702
b 10,712
c 10,812
d NG

4
$$23,089$$
$$+ 29,716$$

a 42,805
b 52,705
c 52,795
d NG

5
$$1,836$$
$$- \ \ 929$$

a 907
b 913
c 917
d NG

6
$$28,016$$
$$- 19,951$$

a 11,945
b 17,065
c 8,065
d NG

7 Choose the better estimate of weight.

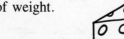

a 1 gram
b 1 kilogram

8 $4.26 × 8

a $31.08
b $32.68
c $34.08
d NG

9
$$424$$
$$\times \ \ 28$$

a 5,040
b 5,172
c 11,772
d NG

10 144 ÷ 9

a 1 R5
b 1 R6
c 1 R7
d NG

11 890 ÷ 26

a 3 R11
b 34
c 34 R6
d NG

12 Find the perimeter.

6 cm

9 cm

a 12 cm
b 18 cm
c 30 cm
d NG

13 Find the area.

a 14 units
b 20 sq units
c 24 sq units
d NG

score

ADDING AND SUBTRACTING FRACTIONS

Adding Fractions with Common Denominators

Ellen spent the afternoon at the zoo. She walked from the elephant's cage to the monkey house, and on to the lion's den. How far did Ellen walk?

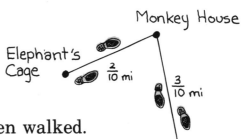

We want to find how many miles Ellen walked.

She walked ____ of a mile from the elephant's cage

to the monkey house, and ____ of a mile more to the lion's den.
To find the total distance Ellen walked, we add ____ and ____.
We can use the number line.

```
0                                                    1

◄──┼──┼──┼──┼──┼──┼──┼──┼──┼──┼──┼──►
   1    2    3    4    5    6    7    8    9
   10   10   10   10   10   10   10   10   10
```

$$\frac{5}{10} = \frac{1}{2}$$

✔ To add fractions with common denominators, we can also add the numerators and put the sum over the denominator. We simplify the answer if necessary.

$$\frac{2}{10} + \frac{3}{10} = \frac{2+3}{10} = \frac{}{10} = $$

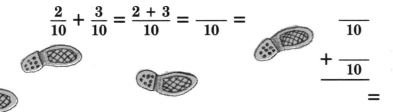

$$\begin{array}{r} \dfrac{}{10} \\ + \dfrac{}{10} \\ \hline = \end{array}$$

Ellen walked a total of ____ of a mile to reach the lion's den.

Getting Started

Add. Simplify if necessary.

1. $\dfrac{5}{12} + \dfrac{6}{12} =$

2. $\dfrac{3}{8} + \dfrac{3}{8} =$

3. $\begin{array}{r} \dfrac{3}{5} \\ + \dfrac{1}{5} \\ \hline \end{array}$

4. $\begin{array}{r} \dfrac{5}{16} \\ + \dfrac{7}{16} \\ \hline \end{array}$

Practice

Add. Simplify if necessary.

1. $\frac{3}{8} + \frac{2}{8} =$

2. $\frac{5}{7} + \frac{1}{7} =$

3. $\frac{3}{9} + \frac{3}{9} =$

4. $\frac{7}{12} + \frac{4}{12} =$

5. $\frac{3}{10} + \frac{5}{10} =$

6. $\frac{2}{6} + \frac{1}{6} =$

7. $\frac{5}{12} + \frac{3}{12} =$

8. $\frac{3}{16} + \frac{1}{16} =$

9. $\begin{array}{r} \frac{1}{6} \\ + \frac{3}{6} \\ \hline \end{array}$

10. $\begin{array}{r} \frac{5}{9} \\ + \frac{2}{9} \\ \hline \end{array}$

11. $\begin{array}{r} \frac{2}{5} \\ + \frac{2}{5} \\ \hline \end{array}$

12. $\begin{array}{r} \frac{5}{11} \\ + \frac{3}{11} \\ \hline \end{array}$

13. $\begin{array}{r} \frac{1}{4} \\ + \frac{2}{4} \\ \hline \end{array}$

14. $\begin{array}{r} \frac{5}{8} \\ + \frac{1}{8} \\ \hline \end{array}$

15. $\begin{array}{r} \frac{5}{10} \\ + \frac{1}{10} \\ \hline \end{array}$

16. $\begin{array}{r} \frac{4}{12} \\ + \frac{5}{12} \\ \hline \end{array}$

17. $\begin{array}{r} \frac{1}{6} \\ + \frac{3}{6} \\ \hline \end{array}$

18. $\begin{array}{r} \frac{3}{16} \\ + \frac{5}{16} \\ \hline \end{array}$

19. $\begin{array}{r} \frac{7}{12} \\ + \frac{3}{12} \\ \hline \end{array}$

20. $\begin{array}{r} \frac{4}{8} \\ + \frac{1}{8} \\ \hline \end{array}$

21. $\begin{array}{r} \frac{7}{9} \\ + \frac{1}{9} \\ \hline \end{array}$

22. $\begin{array}{r} \frac{5}{12} \\ + \frac{3}{12} \\ \hline \end{array}$

23. $\begin{array}{r} \frac{1}{3} \\ + \frac{1}{3} \\ \hline \end{array}$

24. $\begin{array}{r} \frac{3}{7} \\ + \frac{2}{7} \\ \hline \end{array}$

25. $\begin{array}{r} \frac{4}{10} \\ + \frac{4}{10} \\ \hline \end{array}$

26. $\begin{array}{r} \frac{5}{8} \\ + \frac{1}{8} \\ \hline \end{array}$

27. $\begin{array}{r} \frac{3}{16} \\ + \frac{9}{16} \\ \hline \end{array}$

28. $\begin{array}{r} \frac{1}{5} \\ + \frac{3}{5} \\ \hline \end{array}$

Apply

Solve these problems.

29. Wally lives $\frac{2}{5}$ of a mile from school. It is another $\frac{1}{5}$ of a mile from school to the store. How far is it from Wally's house to the store?

30. Rochelle painted $\frac{3}{8}$ of a mural. Martha painted $\frac{1}{8}$ of it. How much of the mural did the girls paint?

Subtracting Fractions with Common Denominators

Barry, Cal and Craig challenged each other to an 8-minute run around the school track. How much farther did Barry run than Cal?

We want to know how much farther Barry ran than Cal.

Barry ran ____ of a mile, while Cal ran ____ of a mile in the same period of time. To find the difference in the distance Barry and Cal ran, we subtract ____ from ____. We can use a number line.

Barry	$\frac{7}{8}$ mile
Cal	$\frac{5}{8}$ mile
Craig	$\frac{6}{8}$ mile

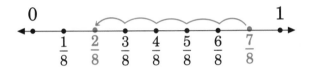

$$\frac{2}{8} = \frac{1}{4}$$

✔ To subtract fractions with common denominators, we can also subtract the numerators and write the difference over the denominator. We simplify the answer if necessary.

$$\frac{7}{8} - \frac{5}{8} = \frac{7-5}{8} = \frac{\quad}{8} =$$

$$\begin{array}{r} \overline{8} \\ - \overline{8} \\ \hline = \end{array}$$

Barry ran ____ of a mile farther than Cal.

Getting Started

Subtract. Simplify if necessary.

1. $\frac{4}{5} - \frac{1}{5} =$

2. $\frac{9}{10} - \frac{3}{10} =$

3. $\begin{array}{r} \frac{7}{8} \\ - \frac{7}{8} \\ \hline \end{array}$

4. $\begin{array}{r} \frac{8}{12} \\ - \frac{5}{12} \\ \hline \end{array}$

Practice

Subtract. Simplify if necessary.

1. $\dfrac{4}{5} - \dfrac{1}{5} =$
2. $\dfrac{5}{6} - \dfrac{2}{6} =$
3. $\dfrac{3}{11} - \dfrac{2}{11} =$
4. $\dfrac{12}{16} - \dfrac{8}{16} =$

5. $\dfrac{5}{8} - \dfrac{2}{8} =$
6. $\dfrac{7}{12} - \dfrac{4}{12} =$
7. $\dfrac{6}{7} - \dfrac{3}{7} =$
8. $\dfrac{5}{6} - \dfrac{1}{6} =$

9. $\dfrac{7}{9}$ $-\dfrac{4}{9}$
10. $\dfrac{4}{5}$ $-\dfrac{3}{5}$
11. $\dfrac{6}{8}$ $-\dfrac{1}{8}$
12. $\dfrac{11}{12}$ $-\dfrac{5}{12}$
13. $\dfrac{13}{16}$ $-\dfrac{5}{16}$

14. $\dfrac{9}{10}$ $-\dfrac{1}{10}$
15. $\dfrac{5}{7}$ $-\dfrac{2}{7}$
16. $\dfrac{7}{9}$ $-\dfrac{3}{9}$
17. $\dfrac{5}{8}$ $-\dfrac{1}{8}$
18. $\dfrac{7}{11}$ $-\dfrac{3}{11}$

19. $\dfrac{11}{16}$ $-\dfrac{9}{16}$
20. $\dfrac{7}{8}$ $-\dfrac{3}{8}$
21. $\dfrac{7}{10}$ $-\dfrac{2}{10}$
22. $\dfrac{12}{15}$ $-\dfrac{9}{15}$
23. $\dfrac{11}{12}$ $-\dfrac{2}{12}$

24. $\dfrac{2}{3}$ $-\dfrac{1}{3}$
25. $\dfrac{7}{16}$ $-\dfrac{3}{16}$
26. $\dfrac{8}{15}$ $-\dfrac{3}{15}$
27. $\dfrac{5}{10}$ $-\dfrac{2}{10}$
28. $\dfrac{9}{16}$ $-\dfrac{7}{16}$

Apply

Solve these problems.

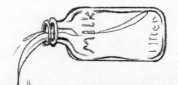

29. Cindy had $\dfrac{5}{8}$ of a liter of milk left in the bottle. She drinks $\dfrac{3}{8}$ of a liter with her lunch. How much milk does Cindy have left?

30. Clay did $\dfrac{9}{10}$ of his homework correctly. David did $\dfrac{7}{10}$ of his correctly. How much more homework did Clay do correctly?

Adding and Subtracting Fractions, Simplifying

Leah is going skiing on Tuesday, if
fresh snow falls in the mountains.
She checks with the Weather Bureau
on Monday before she packs
her gear. How much new snow
fell over the weekend?

We want to know how many inches of new snow
fell on Saturday and Sunday.

It snowed ___ of an inch on Saturday, and

___ of an inch on Sunday.
To find the total amount of snowfall for both

days, we add ___ and ___.

$$
\begin{array}{r}
\frac{9}{10} \\
+ \frac{5}{10} \\
\hline
\end{array}
\quad = \quad =
$$

✔ Remember to simplify fractions. This
includes changing fractions to whole or
mixed numbers, if necessary.

It snowed ___ inches over the weekend.

Getting Started

Add or subtract. Simplify if necessary.

1. $\frac{3}{5} + \frac{4}{5} =$ 2. $\frac{7}{8} - \frac{1}{8} =$ 3. $\frac{3}{4} + \frac{3}{4} =$ 4. $\frac{19}{12} - \frac{13}{12} =$

5. $\begin{array}{r} \frac{5}{6} \\ + \frac{4}{6} \\ \hline \end{array}$ 6. $\begin{array}{r} \frac{9}{16} \\ - \frac{1}{16} \\ \hline \end{array}$ 7. $\begin{array}{r} \frac{1}{2} \\ - \frac{1}{2} \\ \hline \end{array}$ 8. $\begin{array}{r} \frac{17}{10} \\ - \frac{3}{10} \\ \hline \end{array}$ 9. $\begin{array}{r} \frac{3}{10} \\ + \frac{7}{10} \\ \hline \end{array}$

Practice

Add or subtract. Simplify if necessary.

1. $\frac{5}{8} + \frac{6}{8} =$ 2. $\frac{11}{9} - \frac{1}{9} =$ 3. $\frac{11}{12} - \frac{3}{12} =$ 4. $\frac{7}{5} + \frac{3}{5} =$

5. $\frac{19}{8} - \frac{9}{8} =$ 6. $\frac{3}{4} + \frac{6}{4} =$ 7. $\frac{5}{6} + \frac{5}{6} =$ 8. $\frac{11}{15} - \frac{6}{15} =$

9. $\begin{array}{r} \frac{9}{10} \\ + \frac{6}{10} \\ \hline \end{array}$ 10. $\begin{array}{r} \frac{4}{7} \\ + \frac{6}{7} \\ \hline \end{array}$ 11. $\begin{array}{r} \frac{18}{9} \\ - \frac{12}{9} \\ \hline \end{array}$ 12. $\begin{array}{r} \frac{2}{3} \\ + \frac{2}{3} \\ \hline \end{array}$ 13. $\begin{array}{r} \frac{18}{10} \\ - \frac{2}{10} \\ \hline \end{array}$

14. $\begin{array}{r} \frac{14}{15} \\ + \frac{4}{15} \\ \hline \end{array}$ 15. $\begin{array}{r} \frac{10}{12} \\ + \frac{8}{12} \\ \hline \end{array}$ 16. $\begin{array}{r} \frac{7}{10} \\ + \frac{9}{10} \\ \hline \end{array}$ 17. $\begin{array}{r} \frac{9}{16} \\ - \frac{5}{16} \\ \hline \end{array}$ 18. $\begin{array}{r} \frac{9}{5} \\ + \frac{3}{5} \\ \hline \end{array}$

19. $\begin{array}{r} \frac{7}{12} \\ + \frac{8}{12} \\ \hline \end{array}$ 20. $\begin{array}{r} \frac{17}{12} \\ - \frac{3}{12} \\ \hline \end{array}$ 21. $\begin{array}{r} \frac{7}{8} \\ - \frac{1}{8} \\ \hline \end{array}$ 22. $\begin{array}{r} \frac{9}{12} \\ + \frac{7}{12} \\ \hline \end{array}$ 23. $\begin{array}{r} \frac{10}{6} \\ + \frac{4}{6} \\ \hline \end{array}$

24. $\begin{array}{r} \frac{19}{10} \\ + \frac{11}{10} \\ \hline \end{array}$ 25. $\begin{array}{r} \frac{17}{12} \\ - \frac{13}{12} \\ \hline \end{array}$ 26. $\begin{array}{r} \frac{13}{4} \\ + \frac{13}{4} \\ \hline \end{array}$ 27. $\begin{array}{r} \frac{15}{16} \\ + \frac{11}{16} \\ \hline \end{array}$ 28. $\begin{array}{r} \frac{13}{6} \\ - \frac{3}{6} \\ \hline \end{array}$

Apply

Solve these problems.

29. Bonnie drank $\frac{5}{8}$ of a quart of water before the basketball game and $\frac{7}{8}$ of a quart after. How much water did Bonnie drink?

30. A jacket button is $\frac{9}{8}$ inches wide. The button hole is $\frac{13}{8}$ inches wide. How much wider is the button hole?

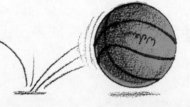

Adding Fractions, Uncommon Denominators

Following the veterinarian's advice, Tony is keeping track of his new kitten's weight gain. How many pounds has his kitten gained after 2 weeks?

We want to find the kitten's weight gain for the first two weeks.

It gained ____ of a pound the first week

and ____ of a pound the second week. To find how many pounds the kitten

gained in 2 weeks, we add ____ and ____.

The fractions do not have common denominators.	Find equivalent fractions with common denominators.	Add the fractions. Simplify.

$$\frac{1}{2}$$
$$+\frac{3}{4}$$

$$\frac{1 \times 2}{2 \times 2} = \frac{2}{4}$$
$$+\frac{3}{4} \quad = \frac{3}{4}$$

$$\frac{2}{4}$$
$$+\frac{3}{4}$$
$$=$$

Tony's kitten has gained ____ pounds in the first 2 weeks.

Getting Started

Add. Simplify if necessary.

1. $\frac{3}{5}$
    $+\frac{3}{10}$

2. $\frac{2}{3}$
    $+\frac{5}{6}$

3. $\frac{3}{8}$
    $+\frac{1}{4}$

4. $\frac{7}{12}$
    $+\frac{2}{3}$

Copy and add.

5. $\frac{1}{2} + \frac{3}{4}$

6. $\frac{2}{5} + \frac{3}{20}$

7. $\frac{1}{6} + \frac{3}{12}$

Practice

Add. Simplify if necessary.

1. $\dfrac{1}{3}$
   $+\dfrac{1}{6}$

2. $\dfrac{4}{2}$
   $+\dfrac{3}{8}$

3. $\dfrac{7}{12}$
   $+\dfrac{3}{4}$

4. $\dfrac{2}{3}$
   $+\dfrac{5}{9}$

5. $\dfrac{7}{8}$
   $+\dfrac{3}{4}$

6. $\dfrac{5}{12}$
   $+\dfrac{5}{6}$

7. $\dfrac{3}{5}$
   $+\dfrac{7}{10}$

8. $\dfrac{3}{14}$
   $+\dfrac{2}{7}$

9. $\dfrac{7}{15}$
   $+\dfrac{3}{5}$

10. $\dfrac{9}{10}$
    $+\dfrac{1}{2}$

11. $\dfrac{12}{5}$
    $+\dfrac{7}{20}$

12. $\dfrac{9}{16}$
    $+\dfrac{8}{4}$

Copy and Do

13. $\dfrac{3}{4} + \dfrac{7}{2}$

14. $\dfrac{2}{3} + \dfrac{7}{9}$

15. $\dfrac{5}{8} + \dfrac{1}{4}$

16. $\dfrac{7}{10} + \dfrac{3}{5}$

17. $\dfrac{11}{12} + \dfrac{3}{4}$

18. $\dfrac{4}{3} + \dfrac{5}{12}$

19. $\dfrac{2}{3} + \dfrac{9}{6}$

20. $\dfrac{7}{15} + \dfrac{4}{5}$

21. $\dfrac{7}{9} + \dfrac{7}{18}$

22. $\dfrac{9}{16} + \dfrac{7}{8}$

23. $\dfrac{9}{20} + \dfrac{9}{10}$

24. $\dfrac{4}{9} + \dfrac{2}{3}$

25. $\dfrac{9}{2} + \dfrac{3}{16}$

26. $\dfrac{8}{10} + \dfrac{4}{5}$

27. $\dfrac{13}{12} + \dfrac{1}{6}$

28. $\dfrac{5}{7} + \dfrac{11}{21}$

Apply

Solve these problems.

29. Jackie lost $\dfrac{2}{3}$ of a pound in one week. The next week, she lost $\dfrac{5}{6}$ of a pound. How much weight did Jackie lose all together?

30. Lanny used $\dfrac{1}{2}$ of a roll of red paper and $\dfrac{5}{8}$ of a roll of green paper to wrap gifts. How much paper did Lanny use?

Subtracting Fractions, Uncommon Denominators

Dina is making cookies to give to the new neighbors. The recipe calls for $\frac{7}{8}$ of a cup of peanut butter. How much more peanut butter does Dina need?

We want to find how much more peanut butter Dina needs to measure.

She needs ___ of a cup and has

already measured ___ of a cup. To find how much more peanut butter

is needed, we subtract ___ from ___.

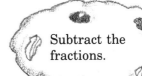

The fractions do not have common denominators.	Find equivalent fractions with common denominators.	Subtract the fractions.

$$\frac{7}{8}$$
$$-\frac{1}{2}$$

$$\frac{7}{8} = \frac{7}{8}$$
$$-\frac{1}{2} \times \frac{4}{4} = \frac{4}{8}$$

$$\frac{7}{8}$$
$$-\frac{4}{8}$$

Dina needs ___ of a cup more peanut butter.

Getting Started

Subtract.

1. $\frac{5}{6}$
   $-\frac{1}{3}$

2. $\frac{7}{12}$
   $-\frac{1}{2}$

3. $\frac{15}{16}$
   $-\frac{3}{4}$

4. $\frac{7}{9}$
   $-\frac{2}{3}$

Copy and subtract.

5. $\frac{5}{8} - \frac{1}{2}$

6. $\frac{11}{12} - \frac{2}{3}$

7. $\frac{17}{15} - \frac{4}{5}$

8. $\frac{6}{3} - \frac{7}{12}$

273

Practice

Subtract.

1. $\dfrac{3}{4}$
   $-\dfrac{1}{2}$

2. $\dfrac{5}{8}$
   $-\dfrac{1}{4}$

3. $\dfrac{7}{2}$
   $-\dfrac{9}{10}$

4. $\dfrac{7}{9}$
   $-\dfrac{2}{3}$

5. $\dfrac{9}{6}$
   $-\dfrac{7}{12}$

6. $\dfrac{8}{5}$
   $-\dfrac{5}{10}$

7. $\dfrac{9}{12}$
   $-\dfrac{2}{3}$

8. $\dfrac{11}{4}$
   $-\dfrac{7}{8}$

9. $\dfrac{15}{6}$
   $-\dfrac{7}{12}$

10. $\dfrac{17}{10}$
    $-\dfrac{4}{5}$

11. $\dfrac{13}{5}$
    $-\dfrac{9}{15}$

12. $\dfrac{7}{6}$
    $-\dfrac{2}{3}$

Copy and Do

13. $\dfrac{7}{9} - \dfrac{1}{3}$

14. $\dfrac{8}{3} - \dfrac{5}{6}$

15. $\dfrac{7}{5} - \dfrac{8}{10}$

16. $\dfrac{15}{16} - \dfrac{7}{8}$

17. $\dfrac{11}{12} - \dfrac{1}{4}$

18. $\dfrac{9}{4} - \dfrac{3}{8}$

19. $\dfrac{7}{3} - \dfrac{5}{9}$

20. $\dfrac{9}{2} - \dfrac{7}{4}$

21. $\dfrac{8}{5} - \dfrac{13}{10}$

22. $\dfrac{13}{16} - \dfrac{1}{4}$

23. $\dfrac{16}{12} - \dfrac{5}{4}$

24. $\dfrac{11}{6} - \dfrac{4}{3}$

25. $\dfrac{24}{15} - \dfrac{7}{5}$

26. $\dfrac{16}{3} - \dfrac{26}{9}$

27. $\dfrac{7}{4} - \dfrac{7}{8}$

28. $\dfrac{25}{12} - \dfrac{5}{4}$

Apply

Solve these problems.

29. A recipe for custard calls for $\dfrac{3}{4}$ of a cup of milk. Joel has only $\dfrac{1}{2}$ of a cup of milk. How much milk does Joel need to borrow?

30. Naomi lives $\dfrac{3}{5}$ of a mile from Deven. She has walked $\dfrac{5}{10}$ of a mile so far. How much further must she walk to get to Deven's?

Adding and Subtracting Fractions, Finding Common Multiples

Marty's Allowance

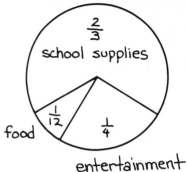

Marty spends her allowance on school supplies, food and entertainment. What part of her allowance does she spend on school supplies and entertainment?

We want to know what fractional part of her money Marty spends on school supplies and entertainment.

Marty spends ____ of her allowance on school

supplies and ____ of her allowance on entertainment.
To find the total portion spent on these two

things, we add ____ and ____.
We need to find the smallest number that is a multiple of both 3 and 4. This is called the **least common multiple.**

Multiples of 3:   3   6   9   12   15
Multiples of 4:   4   8   12   16

The least common multiple of 3 and 4 is ____.
Use the least common multiple as the common denominator.
Find the equivalent fractions and add.

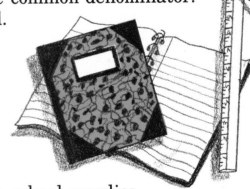

$$\frac{2}{3} \times \frac{\underline{}}{\underline{}} = \frac{}{12}$$

$$+\frac{1}{4} \times \frac{\underline{}}{\underline{}} = \frac{}{12}$$

Marty spends ____ of her allowance on school supplies and entertainment.

Getting Started

Add or subtract.

1. $\frac{3}{5}$
    $+\frac{1}{3}$

2. $\frac{5}{6}$
    $-\frac{1}{4}$

3. $\frac{2}{3}$
    $+\frac{1}{2}$

Copy and add or subtract.

4. $\frac{21}{3} - \frac{11}{9}$

5. $\frac{1}{7} + \frac{1}{3}$

6. $\frac{3}{4} + \frac{5}{6}$

7. $\frac{8}{6} - \frac{2}{5}$

275

Practice

Add or subtract.

1. $\frac{1}{5}$
$+\frac{1}{3}$

2. $\frac{1}{4}$
$+\frac{5}{6}$

3. $\frac{2}{3}$
$-\frac{1}{2}$

4. $\frac{3}{8}$
$-\frac{1}{6}$

5. $\frac{3}{4}$
$+\frac{4}{5}$

6. $\frac{7}{3}$
$-\frac{3}{4}$

7. $\frac{3}{4}$
$+\frac{5}{8}$

8. $\frac{11}{12}$
$-\frac{2}{3}$

9. $\frac{7}{8}$
$-\frac{3}{16}$

10. $\frac{3}{2}$
$+\frac{2}{3}$

11. $\frac{7}{10}$
$+\frac{4}{5}$

12. $\frac{18}{5}$
$-\frac{9}{4}$

Copy and Do

13. $\frac{1}{2} + \frac{1}{9}$

14. $\frac{7}{4} - \frac{5}{3}$

15. $\frac{5}{6} - \frac{4}{9}$

16. $\frac{7}{8} + \frac{5}{3}$

17. $\frac{2}{3} - \frac{1}{5}$

18. $\frac{11}{12} - \frac{5}{6}$

19. $\frac{13}{9} - \frac{25}{36}$

20. $\frac{5}{9} + \frac{7}{6}$

21. $\frac{1}{2} - \frac{2}{5}$

22. $\frac{3}{5} + \frac{1}{4}$

23. $\frac{11}{6} - \frac{8}{9}$

24. $\frac{9}{8} + \frac{4}{3}$

25. $\frac{7}{8} + \frac{5}{6}$

26. $\frac{7}{10} + \frac{4}{5}$

27. $\frac{5}{8} + \frac{1}{12}$

28. $\frac{9}{4} - \frac{6}{7}$

Apply

Use the chart to help solve these problems.

29. How much rain fell on
Monday and Wednesday? _____

30. How much more rain fell on
Monday than on Tuesday? _____

Rainfall in Inches	
Monday	$\frac{3}{4}$ inch
Tuesday	$\frac{2}{3}$ inch
Wednesday	$\frac{3}{5}$ inch

Adding Mixed Numbers

Betsy answers the telephone afternoons, at the library. How many hours does Betsy's time card show she has worked this week?

Betsy Kline	
Day	**Hours**
Monday	$3\frac{3}{4}$
Tuesday	$2\frac{1}{2}$
Wednesday	
Thursday	

We want to know Betsy's part-time hours.

Betsy worked _____ hours on Monday and

_____ hours on Tuesday.

To find her total hours, we add ___ and ___.

Add the fractions. Add the whole numbers.

$$3\frac{3}{4} = 3\frac{3}{4}$$
$$+\ 2\frac{1}{2} = 2\frac{2}{4}$$
$$\overline{\qquad 5\frac{5}{4}}$$

Simplify by trading.

$$5\frac{5}{4} = 5 + \frac{4}{4} + \frac{1}{4}$$
$$5 + 1 + \frac{1}{4} = 6\frac{1}{4}$$

✔ Remember that a fraction with the same numerator and denominator, is equal to one.

Betsy has worked ___ hours this week.

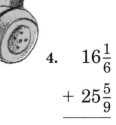

Getting Started

Add. Simplify your answers if necessary.

1. $3\frac{1}{2}$
    $+\ 7\frac{7}{8}$

2. $5\frac{2}{3}$
    $+\ 2\frac{1}{6}$

3. $9\frac{1}{2}$
    $+\ 5\frac{2}{3}$

4. $16\frac{1}{6}$
    $+\ 25\frac{5}{9}$

Copy and add.

5. $10\frac{2}{3} + 4\frac{1}{6}$

6. $5\frac{1}{9} + 5\frac{3}{18}$

7. $8\frac{2}{5} + 9\frac{8}{10}$

8. $11\frac{1}{4} + 2\frac{1}{3}$

Practice

Add. Simplify your answers if necessary.

1.
$$5\frac{1}{6}$$
$$+\ 6\frac{1}{2}$$

2.
$$4\frac{2}{3}$$
$$+\ 7\frac{5}{8}$$

3.
$$6\frac{3}{4}$$
$$+\ 5\frac{1}{3}$$

4.
$$9\frac{1}{2}$$
$$+\ 7\frac{1}{8}$$

5.
$$16\frac{3}{5}$$
$$+\ \ 9\frac{3}{4}$$

6.
$$6\frac{7}{8}$$
$$+\ 15\frac{5}{6}$$

7.
$$1\frac{2}{3}$$
$$+\ 6\frac{5}{8}$$

8.
$$6\frac{3}{5}$$
$$+\ 7\frac{3}{4}$$

Copy and Do

9. $5\frac{3}{8} + 2\frac{1}{2}$

10. $9\frac{7}{16} + 3\frac{7}{8}$

11. $4\frac{2}{3} + 16\frac{3}{4}$

12. $7\frac{3}{5} + 15\frac{1}{4}$

13. $6\frac{7}{10} + 16\frac{3}{4}$

14. $14\frac{7}{10} + 8\frac{5}{6}$

15. $9\frac{7}{8} + 7\frac{11}{12}$

16. $7\frac{2}{3} + 9\frac{5}{9}$

17. $6\frac{5}{6} + 18\frac{3}{7}$

18. $2\frac{4}{5} + 6\frac{3}{8}$

19. $5\frac{7}{8} + 7\frac{5}{7}$

20. $3\frac{2}{3} + 6\frac{3}{5}$

EXCURSION

Use the diagram to answer **true** or **false** for each statement.

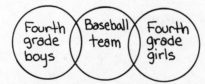

1. All of the fourth grade boys play on the baseball team. _____

2. Only fourth graders play on the baseball team. _____

3. There are boys and girls on the team. _____

4. Some fourth graders do not play on the team. _____

Adding Three Mixed Numbers

Marianne built a model trading fort as part of her project on fur traders in Colonial America. Find the perimeter of her triangular fort.

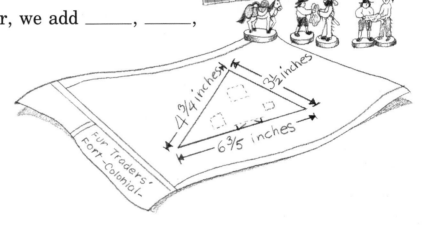

We want to know the perimeter of Marianne's fort.

The sides of the triangle measure _____ inches, _____ inches and _____ inches.

To find the perimeter, we add _____, _____, and _____.

$$4\frac{3}{4} = 4\frac{15}{20}$$
$$3\frac{1}{2} = 3\frac{10}{20}$$
$$+\ 6\frac{3}{5} = 6\frac{12}{20}$$
$$\overline{\phantom{+\ 6\frac{3}{5} =\ }13\frac{37}{20} = 14\frac{17}{20}}$$

The perimeter of Marianne's fort is _____ inches.

Getting Started

Add.

1. $2\frac{1}{2}$
   $3\frac{5}{8}$
   $+\ 2\frac{1}{4}$

2. $3\frac{1}{3}$
   $6\frac{5}{9}$
   $+\ 4\frac{5}{6}$

3. $9\frac{1}{2}$
   $3\frac{4}{5}$
   $+\ 7\frac{5}{6}$

4. $7\frac{5}{12}$
   $9\frac{3}{8}$
   $+\ 4\frac{5}{6}$

Copy and add.

5. $10\frac{3}{4} + 2\frac{1}{2} + 7\frac{1}{4}$

6. $5\frac{1}{3} + 11\frac{5}{6} + \frac{1}{12}$

7. $11\frac{1}{4} + 3\frac{2}{3} + 2\frac{1}{2}$

279

Practice

Add.

1. $5\frac{1}{5}$
$7\frac{3}{10}$
$+4\frac{9}{20}$

2. $6\frac{2}{3}$
$5\frac{1}{6}$
$+7\frac{5}{9}$

3. $3\frac{2}{5}$
$4\frac{1}{2}$
$+9\frac{5}{10}$

4. $2\frac{5}{8}$
$3\frac{5}{12}$
$+4\frac{1}{4}$

5. $7\frac{5}{9}$
$6\frac{1}{3}$
$+4\frac{5}{6}$

6. $7\frac{3}{4}$
$2\frac{1}{3}$
$+11\frac{5}{6}$

7. $8\frac{5}{8}$
$7\frac{1}{2}$
$+9\frac{2}{3}$

8. $16\frac{3}{4}$
$2\frac{1}{2}$
$+5\frac{2}{3}$

Copy and Do

9. $5\frac{1}{8} + 6\frac{2}{3} + 9\frac{1}{2}$

10. $7\frac{3}{4} + 5\frac{3}{8} + 7\frac{1}{2}$

11. $9\frac{2}{3} + 4\frac{3}{5} + 6\frac{7}{10}$

12. $4\frac{1}{3} + 8\frac{5}{6} + 12\frac{5}{9}$

13. $16\frac{1}{2} + 5\frac{2}{3} + 8\frac{1}{4}$

14. $7\frac{5}{6} + 9\frac{1}{2} + 8\frac{2}{3}$

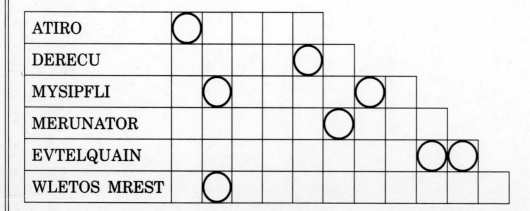

EXCURSION

Unscramble each word, writing one letter in a box. To find the mystery word, unscramble the circled letters.

ATIRO		◯							
DERECU				◯					
MYSIPFLI		◯			◯				
MERUNATOR				◯					
EVTELQUAIN						◯◯			
WLETOS MREST	◯								

Mystery Word: ⬜⬜⬜⬜⬜⬜⬜⬜⬜

Writing an Open Sentence

A mouse walks around the outside of a rectangular-shaped piece of cheese whose length is twice its width. If the mouse walks a total of 12 inches, what are the dimensions of the piece of cheese?

★ **SEE**

We want to find the length and the width of the piece of cheese.
The perimeter of the cheese is _____ inches.
The length of cheese is double that of its width.
If the width were 1 inch, the length would be _____ inches.

★ **PLAN**

We make a sketch of the rectangle of cheese with notation. If we label the width with the letter W, then the length is $2 \times W$. This is written: **2W.**

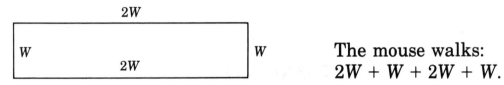

The mouse walks:
$2W + W + 2W + W$.

★ **DO**

The **open sentence** that represents the distance the mouse walks is:

$2W + W + 2W + W = 12$

$\qquad\qquad 6W = 12$ (We add all the W's. $2 + 1 + 2 + 1 = 6$)

$\qquad\qquad\ \ W = 2$ (We reason if 6 times $W = 12$, the value of W must be 2 because $6 \times 2 = 12$.)

If $W = 2$, then $2W =$ _____.

The width of the cheese is _____ inches and the length is _____ inches.

★ **CHECK**

We can check by adding the lengths and widths together.

$4 + 2 + 4 + 2 =$ _____

Apply

Write an open sentence to solve each problem.

1. What is the perimeter of a square checkerboard 12 inches on a side?

2. Find the distance around a square pasture 45 meters on each side.

3. There are 12 months in a year. Write an open sentence to find how many months are in 10 years. How many months are in 100 years?

4. A basketball game is played where a team scored 55 points. Twenty baskets were made and each is worth two points. A free throw is worth one point. Write an open sentence to help find how many free throws were made.

5. The sum of two numbers is 90. The first number is twice the second number. What are the two numbers?

6. Jason has saved 3 nickels, 8 dimes and an unknown number of quarters. The total amount he saved is $2.20. Write an open sentence that will help determine the number of quarters Jason has.

7. Read Exercise 4 again and the open sentence that you wrote. What if the team scored 60 points? How would you change your open sentence to fit this new situation?

8. Read Exercise 5 again. Rewrite the exercise so that the second number is twice the first number. Then explain how this changes the answer.

9. Write an addition sentence to show two like fractions that have a sum with a different denominator.

10. Explain how you could write many different number sentences where 1 is the sum of two like fractions.

Calculators and Fractions

Mr. Smalley is writing a
newspaper advertisement for
computers and stereos in
his store. What are the
sale prices of the computers
and the stereos?

We want to know the sale prices of the
computers and the stereos.

The original price of a computer was _____.

The original price of a stereo was _____.

Mr. Smalley is offering ___ off each
original price.
To find sale prices, we first must find the
money that the customer saves. This is called
the **discount.** To find the discount, we find $\frac{3}{5}$

of the original price. We multiply _____ by

_____ and divide by _____.

599 ⊠ 3 ÷ 5 ⊜ ⬭

The discount on the computer is _____.
To find the sale price, we subtract the discount

from the original price. We subtract _____

from _____.

The sale price of the computer is _____.
Complete the codes to find the sale price of
the stereo.

____ ⊠ ____ ÷ ____ ⊜ ⬭

The discount on the stereo is _____.

____ ⊟ ____ ⊜ ⬭

The sale price of the stereo is _____.

283

Practice

Use your calculator to find these discounts.

1. $\frac{2}{3}$ of $186

2. $\frac{5}{8}$ of $924

3. $\frac{4}{5}$ of $625

Complete the table.

4.

Original Price	$1,260	$2,124	$1,125	$5,275
Fraction Off	$\frac{3}{4}$	$\frac{5}{6}$	$\frac{2}{9}$	$\frac{1}{2}$
Discount				
Sale Price				

Apply

Solve these problems.

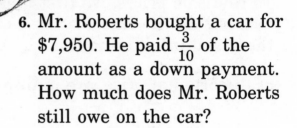

5. Miss Ortiz received a bonus equal to $\frac{2}{5}$ of her yearly salary. Her yearly salary is $37,500. How much is her bonus?

6. Mr. Roberts bought a car for $7,950. He paid $\frac{3}{10}$ of the amount as a down payment. How much does Mr. Roberts still owe on the car?

EXCURSION

Steve figured out a shortcut to help Mr. Smalley find the sale prices faster. He figured that if the customer was going to **save** $\frac{3}{5}$ of the original price, he would **pay** $\frac{2}{5}$ of it. Steve used this calculator code to find the sales price of the stereo.

$$750 \ \boxed{\times} \ 2 \ \boxed{\div} \ 5 \ \boxed{=} \ \boxed{}$$

Complete this table to show that Steve's shortcut works everytime.

Original Price	Fraction Off	Sale Price
$870	$\frac{2}{3}$	
$850	$\frac{1}{4}$	
$648	$\frac{5}{9}$	
$1,026	$\frac{5}{6}$	
$460	$\frac{3}{10}$	

Add or subtract. Simplify your answers.

1. $\dfrac{3}{5}$
$+\dfrac{1}{5}$

2. $\dfrac{7}{8}$
$-\dfrac{4}{8}$

3. $\dfrac{2}{7}$
$+\dfrac{4}{7}$

4. $\dfrac{5}{9}$
$-\dfrac{4}{9}$

5. $\dfrac{11}{12}$
$-\dfrac{5}{12}$

6. $\dfrac{5}{10}$
$+\dfrac{3}{10}$

7. $\dfrac{1}{8}$
$+\dfrac{5}{8}$

8. $\dfrac{5}{6}$
$+\dfrac{1}{6}$

9. $\dfrac{2}{3}$
$+\dfrac{3}{4}$

10. $\dfrac{7}{8}$
$-\dfrac{1}{4}$

11. $\dfrac{3}{5}$
$+\dfrac{1}{3}$

12. $\dfrac{7}{4}$
$+\dfrac{5}{6}$

13. $\dfrac{9}{8}$
$-\dfrac{5}{6}$

14. $\dfrac{11}{10}$
$-\dfrac{4}{5}$

15. $\dfrac{9}{6}$
$+\dfrac{7}{9}$

16. $\dfrac{15}{12}$
$-\dfrac{9}{8}$

17. $3\dfrac{5}{8}$
$+2\dfrac{3}{4}$

18. $7\dfrac{2}{3}$
$+8\dfrac{1}{4}$

19. $6\dfrac{3}{4}$
$+6\dfrac{1}{6}$

20. $3\dfrac{2}{3}$
$+9\dfrac{1}{8}$

21. $\dfrac{1}{2} + \dfrac{3}{7}$

22. $\dfrac{2}{3} - \dfrac{2}{7}$

23. $4\dfrac{3}{5} + 2\dfrac{1}{2}$

24. $7\dfrac{3}{10} - 1\dfrac{1}{4}$

Circle the letter of the correct answer.

1 Round 6,296 to the nearest thousand.

a 6,000
b 7,000
c NG

2 What is the place value of the 7 in 736,092?

a hundreds
b thousands
c hundred thousands
d NG

3　　5,629
　　+ 24,751

a 29,380
b 30,370
c 30,380
d NG

4　　8,096
　　− 1,998

a 7,008
b 7,098
c 7,902
d NG

5 Choose the better estimate of weight.

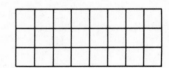

a 1 gram
b 1 kilogram

6　$3.26
　×　　6

a $18.26
b $18.56
c $19.56
d NG

7 67 × 53

a 536
b 3,451
c 3,551
d NG

8 8)265

a 3 R1
b 30 R1
c 33 R1
d NG

9 760 ÷ 42

a 1 R4
b 18 R4
c 180 R4
d NG

10 Find the perimeter.

12 in.　　12 in.

15 in.

a 24 in.
b 27 in.
c 39 in.
d NG

11 Find the area.

a 24 sq units
b 48 sq units
c 48 units
d NG

12 $\frac{2}{3}$ of 48 = n
　　　n = ?

a 8
b 16
c 32
d NG

☐ score

14

DECIMALS

Understanding Tenths

Rita is painting scenery panels for the class play. What decimal represents the number of panels Rita has painted so far?

We want to know how many panels are painted.

Each panel has _____ equal parts.

Rita has painted _____ complete panels, and _____ parts of another panel.
We can write this as the mixed number $2\frac{6}{10}$.

$2\frac{6}{10}$ is also written as **2.6.**

Decimal point

→2.6←

Whole number **Decimal number**

ones	tenths
2	6

We say:
two and six tenths.

Rita has painted _____ panels so far.

✔ Decimal numbers can name parts less than 1. Rita still has 0.4 of a panel to paint.

→0.4←
0 ones   **4 tenths**

We say: **four tenths.**

✔ Whole numbers can be written as decimal numbers. When she completes her job, Rita will have painted 3.0 panels.

→3.0←
3 ones   **0 tenths**

We say: **three.**

Getting Started

Write the decimal numbers to show how many panels are painted.

1. _____

2.  _____

Practice

Write the decimal number to show how many panels are painted.

1. 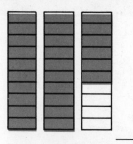 _____

2.  _____

3. 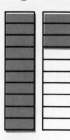 _____

4. 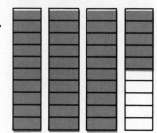 _____

5. 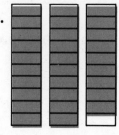 _____

6.  _____

Write the decimal numbers.

7. six and four tenths _____

8. three and seven tenths _____

9. eight tenths _____

10. $\frac{7}{10}$ _____

11. eight _____

12. four and one tenth _____

13. $5\frac{9}{10}$ _____

14. one and nine tenths _____

15. seven and two tenths _____

Write the decimal numbers in words.

16. 4.3

_____

17. 5.9

_____

18. 6.0

_____

19. 2.7

_____

20. 7.0

_____

21. 6.9

_____

22. 9.9

_____

23. 5.3

_____

24. 1.5

_____

Understanding Hundredths

Dick is making a mosaic tile picture to enter in the art contest. What decimal represents the part of the picture that Dick has tiled so far?

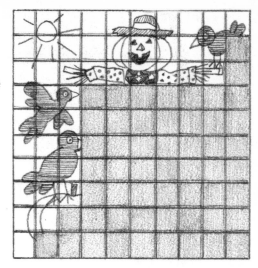

We want to know what part of the picture is finished.

The mosaic will be made up of _____ tiles.

Dick has used _____ of the tiles so far. We can write this as the fraction $\frac{46}{100}$.

$\frac{46}{100}$ is also written as **0.46.**

0.46

Whole number   Decimal number

ones	tenths	hundredths
0	4	6

We say:

forty-six hundredths.

Dick has finished _____ of the mosaic tile picture so far.

Getting Started

Write the decimal number for the part that has been tiled.

1.

2.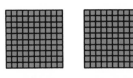

3.

_____   _____   _____

Write the decimal numbers.

Write the decimal numbers in words.

4. six and twelve   5. $3\frac{36}{100}$ 6. 0.08

hundredths _____   _____   _____

Practice

Write the decimal number for the part that has been tiled.

1.  _____

2. 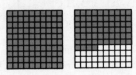 _____

3. _____

4. _____

5.  _____

6. _____

Write the decimal numbers.

7. four and twenty-five hundredths _____

8. six and nine hundredths _____

9. $14\frac{12}{100}$ _____

10. five hundredths _____

11. seven and thirty-seven hundredths _____

12. seventy-eight hundredths _____

Write the decimal numbers in words.

13. 3.29

_____

_____

14. 6.01

_____

_____

15. 3.09

_____

_____

16. 7.50

_____

_____

17. 0.16

_____

_____

18. 0.03

_____

_____

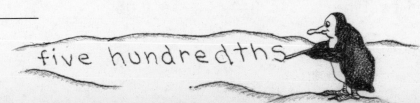

five hundredths

Understanding Thousandths

Mr. Half Moon buys supplies
for the school cafeteria.
He is purchasing a quantity
of meat. How much meat
is he buying?

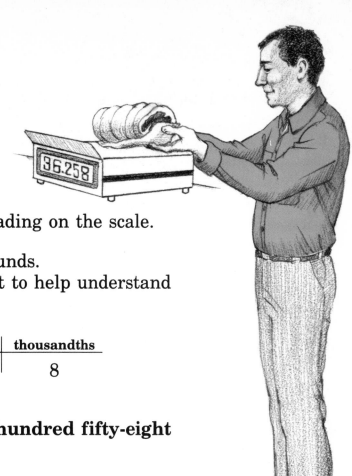

We want to understand the reading on the scale.

The scale reads _____ pounds.
We can use a place value chart to help understand
the weight of the meat.

tens	ones	tenths	hundredths	thousandths
3	6	2	5	8

We say: **thirty-six and two hundred fifty-eight
thousandths.**

Mr. Half Moon bought _____ pounds of meat.

Getting Started

Name the place value of the red digit.

1. 76.259 _____

2. 116.326 _____

3. 4.405 _____

Name the place value of 4 in each number.

4. 390.421 _____

5. 26.045 _____

6. 5.324 _____

Write the decimal numbers.

7. two and sixteenth thousandths

8. seven thousandths

_____

_____

Write the decimal numbers in words.

9. 29.752 _____

10. 5.308 _____

Practice

Name the place value of the red digit.

1. 13.26 _____

2. 67.154 _____

3. 7.041 _____

4. 216.107 _____

5. 2.478 _____

6. 23.840 _____

Name the value of the 6 in each number.

7. 21.684 _____

8. 16.273 _____

9. 143.86 _____

10. 4.156 _____

11. 29.465 _____

12. 3.006 _____

Write the decimal numbers.

13. five and fifty-seven thousandths _____

14. twelve and one hundred thirty-nine thousandths _____

15. two hundred and four hundred eight thousandths _____

16. eighty-one and seven thousandths _____

17. fifty-three and seventy-five thousandths _____

Write the decimal numbers in words.

18. 16.25 _____

19. 3.246 _____

20. 7.915 _____

21. 12.021 _____

22. 14.6 _____

23. 29.003 _____

24. 114.218 _____

25. 16.255 _____

26. 39.608 _____

Comparing Decimals

Three friends competed in the
Special Olympics. One of their
best events was the 100-meter
dash. In what order did they
finish the race?

100 meter dash		
Bert	42	13.6
Dennis	12	13.65
Daryle	8	13.57

We want to know in what order the boys
finished the race.

We can arrange _____, _____ and _____ in order
on a number line.

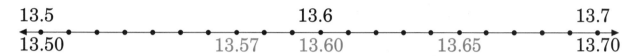

13.5   13.6   13.7
13.50   13.57   13.60   13.65   13.70

✔ Notice that 13.5 and 13.50 are the same value.
Zeros to the far right of a decimal number do not
change its value.
We can also compare them one place value at a time.

13.60	13.60	13.60	13.65
13.65	13.65	13.65	
13.57	13.57		
Same number of ones	13.57 has fewer tenths, 13.57 is the least.	13.60 has fewer hundredths. 13.60 is less than 13.65.	13.65 is the greatest.

_____ finished the race first. _____ was second

and _____ finished third.

Getting Started

Write <, = or > in the circle.

1. 9.35 ◯ 9.27

2. 3.09 ◯ 3.90

3. 7.5 ◯ 7.50

4. 0.3 ◯ 0.2

5. 4.24 ◯ 4.28

6. 8.6 ◯ 8.66

Write the numbers in order from least to greatest.

7. 2.3, 1.67, 1.95

8. 7.1, 6.9, 7

9. 3.5, 3.49, 3.2

_____   _____   _____

Practice

Write <, = or > in the circle.

1. 5.64 ◯ 5.78
2. 3.21 ◯ 3.30
3. 5.71 ◯ 5.17

4. 9.03 ◯ 9.30
5. 7.50 ◯ 7.5
6. 2.39 ◯ 2.35

7. 8.6 ◯ 8.68
8. 9.23 ◯ 9.32
9. 0.6 ◯ 0.60

10. 4.75 ◯ 4.6
11. 8.25 ◯ 8.3
12. 0.16 ◯ 0.17

Write the numbers in order from least to greatest.

13. 4.6, 3.5, 3.9

_____

14. 6.26, 6.38, 6.16

_____

15. 8.15, 8.1, 8

_____

16. 7.1, 7.15, 7.09

_____

17. 4.36, 4.16, 5.03

_____

18. 9.2, 9.14, 9.27

_____

19. 18.21, 18.12, 18.22

_____

20. 37.08, 38.7, 37.8

_____

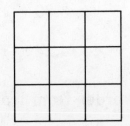

294

Adding Decimals

Iron is an important mineral in each person's diet. It is recommended that young people, 11 to 14 years old, have at least 18 milligrams of iron daily. How much iron is found in a meal of sirloin steak and spinach?

PORK & BEANS
½ cup 2.95mg

SPINACH
⅔ cup 2.67mg

STEAK
4½ ounces 3.75mg

We want to find the amount of iron in a meal of steak and spinach.

The steak has _____ milligrams of iron.

The spinach has _____ milligrams of iron.
To find the total milligrams of iron, we add

_____ and _____.

Add the hundredths. Trade if needed.	Add the tenths. Trade if needed. Place the decimal point.	Add the ones.
1 3.7**5** + 2.6**7** **2**	1 1 3.75 + 2.67 .4**2**	1 3.75 + 2.67 6.4**2**

The steak and the spinach contain _____ milligrams of iron.

✔ When adding decimals, alignment of the decimal point and place values is important.

7.4 + 8.62 should be set up:

$$
\begin{array}{r}
7.4 \\
+\ 8.62 \\
\hline
16.02
\end{array}
$$

Getting Started

Add.

1. $\begin{array}{r} 4.9 \\ + 2.6 \\ \hline \end{array}$

2. $\begin{array}{r} 5.83 \\ + 2.16 \\ \hline \end{array}$

3. $\begin{array}{r} 17.59 \\ + \ \ 8.6 \\ \hline \end{array}$

4. $\begin{array}{r} 37.25 \\ + 18.77 \\ \hline \end{array}$

Copy and add.

5. 39.2 + 18.5

6. 47.3 + 21.19

7. 13.6 + 92.5 + 53.8

Practice

Add.

1.
$$\begin{array}{r} 5.3 \\ + 2.4 \\ \hline \end{array}$$

2.
$$\begin{array}{r} 9.2 \\ + 3.5 \\ \hline \end{array}$$

3.
$$\begin{array}{r} 7.72 \\ + 6.13 \\ \hline \end{array}$$

4.
$$\begin{array}{r} 3.64 \\ + 8.3 \\ \hline \end{array}$$

5.
$$\begin{array}{r} 7.8 \\ + 3.9 \\ \hline \end{array}$$

6.
$$\begin{array}{r} 4.86 \\ + 2.71 \\ \hline \end{array}$$

7.
$$\begin{array}{r} 39.5 \\ + 8.64 \\ \hline \end{array}$$

8.
$$\begin{array}{r} 17.763 \\ + 26.389 \\ \hline \end{array}$$

9.
$$\begin{array}{r} 7.8 \\ 13.2 \\ + 15.7 \\ \hline \end{array}$$

10.
$$\begin{array}{r} 26.4 \\ 19.7 \\ + 38.6 \\ \hline \end{array}$$

11.
$$\begin{array}{r} 9.87 \\ 11.586 \\ + 27.197 \\ \hline \end{array}$$

12.
$$\begin{array}{r} 52.174 \\ 48.8 \\ + 19.78 \\ \hline \end{array}$$

Copy and Do

13. 39.7 + 18.58

14. 72.69 + 28.36

15. 78.15 + 87.85

16. 38.09 + 27.284

17. 46.9 + 52.48

18. 37.75 + 39.28

19. 58.164 + 9.283

20. 15.96 + 83.48

21. 10.36 + 15.4 + 12.75

22. 39.75 + 48.16 + 58.03

23. 87.51 + 93.78 + 48.62

Apply

Solve these problems.

24. Lee swam the first lap of the butterfly-stroke race in 25.48 seconds. She swam the second lap in 27.59 seconds. What was Lee's total time?

25. A container holds 3.25 liters of liquid. Another container holds 4.65 liters. How much liquid can both containers hold when they are filled?

Subtracting Decimals

A barometer is used to help forecast the weather. As the barometer rises, the weather becomes clear and dry. How much did the barometer change from noon to 9:00 PM?

Noon	76.28 cm
3:00	75.38 cm
6:00	74.75 cm
9:00	74.57 cm

We want to know the change in the barometer between noon and 9 PM.

At noon the barometer read _____ centimeters.

At 9:00 PM the barometer read _____ centimeters.

To find the total change, we subtract _____

from _____.

Subtract the hundredths. Trade if needed.	Subtract the tenths. Trade if needed. Place the decimal point.	Subtract the ones.

$$\begin{array}{r} 76.2\,8 \\ -\,74.5\,7 \\ \hline 1 \end{array}$$

$$\begin{array}{r} {}^{5\ \ 12}\\ 7\,6.2\,8 \\ -\,74.5\,7 \\ \hline .7\,1 \end{array}$$

$$\begin{array}{r} {}^{5}\\ 7\,6.2\,8 \\ -\,74.5\,7 \\ \hline 1.7\,1 \end{array}$$

The barometer dropped _____ centimeters.

✔ Remember to align the decimal points and place values before you subtract.

Getting Started

Add.

1. $\begin{array}{r} 8.9 \\ -\,3.6 \end{array}$

2. $\begin{array}{r} 14.25 \\ -\,11.21 \end{array}$

3. $\begin{array}{r} 89.145 \\ -\,17.964 \end{array}$

4. $\begin{array}{r} 57.04 \\ -\,29.17 \end{array}$

Copy and subtract.

5. 82.7 − 39.9

6. 485.18 − 210.16

7. 280.36 − 198.75

297

Practice

Subtract.

1.   4.7
    − 3.2

2.   8.9
    − 2.5

3.   7.84
    − 6.31

4.   9.79
    − 5.16

5.   41.56
    − 14.81

6.   59.27
    − 28.93

7.   38.28
    − 26.57

8.   67.35
    − 48.72

9.   74.117
    − 29.585

10.   87.68
    − 52.99

11.   38.046
    − 19.787

12.   51.168
    − 38.274

Copy and Do

13. 8.36 − 4.51   14. 12.97 − 7.83   15. 19.21 − 11.75   16. 27.36 − 18.58

17. 73.09 − 5.78   18. 35.59 − 14.96   19. 68.25 − 19.68   20. 40.65 − 29.76

21. 92.17 − 37.82   22. 80.034 − 27.389   23. 73.17 − 29.98   24. 53.706 − 19.851

Apply

Solve these problems.

25. Jim's long jump measured 4.26 meters. Dave's was 5.03 meters long. How much longer was Dave's jump?

26. A paint can held 5.36 liters of paint. The handyman poured out 4.75 liters. How much paint was left in the can?

27. A pair of slacks costs $29.79. A shirt costs $7.95. How much will one pair of slacks and two shirts cost?

28. How much change will be left if a suit costing $89.50, is paid for with a one hundred dollar bill?

298

Adding and Subtracting Decimals

Two animals known for their speed are the quarterhorse and the greyhound. Both were timed over a distance of a quarter mile. How much faster is the quarterhorse?

We want to know how much faster the quarterhorse ran the quarter mile.

	Miles Per Hour
Quarterhorse	47.5
Greyhound	39.35

The quarterhorse ran _____ miles per hour.

The greyhound ran _____ miles per hour.

To compare the two speeds, we subtract _____

from _____.

✔ Remember that writing a zero to the far right of a decimal number does not change its value.

$$
\begin{array}{r}
47.5 \\
-39.35
\end{array}
\longrightarrow
\begin{array}{r}
47.50 \\
-39.35
\end{array}
$$

The quarterhorse ran _____ miles per hour faster than the greyhound.

Getting Started

Add or subtract.

1. $\begin{array}{r} 9.7 \\ +11.39 \end{array}$

2. $\begin{array}{r} 27.56 \\ -13.9 \end{array}$

3. $\begin{array}{r} 54.275 \\ +13.3 \end{array}$

4. $\begin{array}{r} 96 \\ -12.85 \end{array}$

Copy and add or subtract.

5. $14.68 - 7.32$

6. $9.63 + 2.7 + 3$

7. $(12 - 7.5) + 6.2$

Practice

Add or subtract.

1.	5.6 + 7.15	2.	6.23 + 5.9	3.	9.27 − 3.1	4.	8.5 − 6.15

5.	7.24 + 11.6	6.	5.28 − 1.965	7.	8 + 3.5	8.	9.27 − 6.9

9.	17.21 − 9	10.	25.3 + 48.68	11.	76.467 + 80.984	12.	14 − 9.52

Copy and Do

13. 39 + 6.58

14. 27.39 − 19.8

15. 4.26 + 8.2 + 9.5

16. 17.9 − 11.764

17. 15.2 + 36.48 + 9

18. (28.39 + 14.6) − 9.8

19. (48 − 16.3) + 8.25

20. (47.8 − 15.27) − 7.3

21. (43 + 18.12) − 6.9

Apply

Solve these problems.

22. How much more does the sugar packet weigh than the salt?

23. Find the total snowfall.

Monday	3.6 cm
Tuesday	2.48 cm
Wednesday	2 cm

24. How much longer is the knife than the fork?

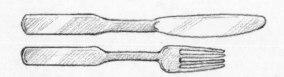

25. Find the perimeter.

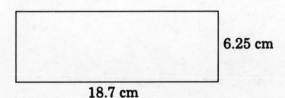

6.25 cm

18.7 cm

Multiplying a Whole Number and a Decimal

Joe and Melissa are using a square table to display their fresh vegetables at the town centennial. They want to hang bunting along 3 sides of the table. How many meters of bunting do they need?

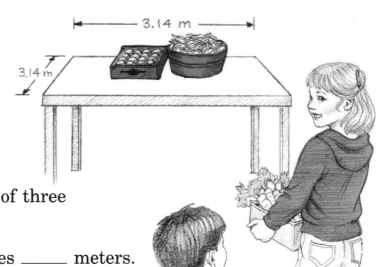

3.14 m

3.14 m

We want to know the length of three sides of a square table.

One side of the table measures _____ meters. To find the length of three sides, we multiply the length of one side by three.

We multiply _____ by _____.

Multiply as whole numbers.

$$3.14 \leftarrow \text{2 decimal places}$$
$$\times \quad 3 \leftarrow \text{0 decimal places}$$
$$9.42 \leftarrow \text{2 decimal places}$$

✔ Remember the product has the same number of decimal places as the factors.

Joe and Melissa need _____ meters of bunting.

Getting Started

Place the decimal points in these products.

1.	8.12	2.	12.9	3.	79	4.	7.08
	× 5		× 3		× 2.5		× 56
	40 60		38 7		197 5		396 48

Copy and multiply.

5. 9.43×7 6. 14.3×12 7. 17×0.39 8. 2.06×37

Practice

Place the decimal points in these products.

1. 7.29
    ×   8
    ——
    58 32

2. 14.6
    ×   6
    ——
    87 6

3.   85
    × 4.1
    ——
    348 5

4. 7.48
    ×   21
    ——
    157 08

5. 15.2
    ×   7
    ——
    106 4

6. 3.25
    ×   9
    ——
    29 25

7. 9.6
    × 9
    ——
    86 4

8. 7.05
    ×   8
    ——
    56 40

Multiply.

9.   8.8
    ×   6

10.   15
    × 2.9

11. 281
    × 5.3

12. 8.65
    ×   9

13. 3.75
    × 17

14. 6.85
    × 60

15. 325
    × 0.28

16. 5.9
    × 36

Copy and Do

17. 96 × 3.5

18. 8.7 × 27

19. 3.25 × 9

20. 12 × 7.36

21. 18 × 0.29

22. 4.8 × 37

23. 0.73 × 9

24. 85 × 7.83

25. 5.9 × 372

26. 28.9 × 6

27. 1.75 × 8

28. 85 × 0.16

Apply

Solve these problems.

29. A dictionary weighs 2.15 pounds. How much does a stack of four dictionaries weigh?

30. Find the area of a rectangle that has a length of 6.75 inches and a width of 9 inches.

Multiplying Decimals

A barrel of maple syrup holds 1.5 times as much syrup as a pail. How much syrup does a barrel hold?

PAIL 4.5 L

BARREL ? L

We want to know how much maple syrup a barrel holds.

A pail holds ____ liters of syrup.

A barrel holds ____ times as much syrup. To find how much a barrel can hold, we

multiply ____ by ____.

Multiply as whole numbers.

```
   4.5
 × 1.5
 ─────
   225
   45
 ─────
   675
```

The product has the same number of decimal places as both factors together.

```
   4.5  ←── 1 place
 × 1.5  ←── 1 place
 ─────
   225
   45
 ─────
  6.75  ←── 2 places
```

A barrel holds _____ liters of syrup.

Getting Started

Multiply.

1. 3.7
   × 2.4

2. 8.9
   × 5

3. 3.8
   × 0.7

4. 0.9
   × 0.6

Copy and multiply.

5. 18 × 3.5

6. 0.24 × 3

7. 12.6 × 1.9

8. 8.5 × 6.8

Practice

Multiply.

1.   4.6
   × 2.7
	2. 3.26
	    × 8
		3. 12.7
		     × 6
			4. 14.3
			   × 2.5

5.   7.09
    × 5
	6. 16
	   × 8.5
		7. 4.9
		  × 5.7
			8. 0.92
			    × 7

9.   0.8
  × 0.6
	10. 36.2
	    × 1.4
		11. 49
		  × 7.3
			12. 46.8
			   × 4.3

Copy and Do

13. 6.3×4.8 14. 16×0.15 15. 1.6×9 16. 37×8.4

17. 0.7×0.7 18. 8.3×7.6 19. 27×4.9 20. 12×0.9

21. 64×6.8 22. 0.67×23 23. 1.59×3 24. 62.5×7.6

Apply

25. A can of nails weighs 4.8 pounds. How much do 2.5 cans weigh?

26. Find the area of a rectangle that is 5.2 centimeters long and 7.6 centimeters wide.

5.2 cm

7.6 cm

EXCURSION

If a year's supply of pencils for the world, laid end to end, circled the earth 5 times, how many times would an $8\frac{3}{4}$ year's supply circle the earth? Write your answer as a decimal. _____

Using a Formula

Mr. Glove must drive his son to college. The trip takes $5\frac{1}{2}$ hours while traveling at an average rate of 50 miles per hour. How many miles away is the college?

★ **SEE**

We are looking for the distance Mr. Glove must travel to his son's college.

He will drive at the rate of _____ miles per hour.

It will take him _____ hours to make the trip.

★ **PLAN**

We can use the formula **D = R × T,** where **D** represents the distance traveled, R represents the average rate of speed of the car and **T** represents the time it takes the car to travel **D** miles. For our situation, **R** = 50 miles per hour and **T** = 5.5 hours. $\left(5\frac{1}{2} = 5.5\right)$

★ **DO**

D = R × T

D = 50 × 5.5

$$\begin{array}{r} 5.5 \\ \times\ 50 \\ \hline \end{array}$$

D = _____ miles

Mr. Glove will travel _____ miles to take his son to college.

★ **CHECK**

We can reason that if Mr. Glove travels

50 miles in 1 hour,

he will travel 100 miles in 2 hours,

150 miles in 3 hours,

_____ miles in 4 hours,

_____ miles in 5 hours,

and _____ miles in $5\frac{1}{2}$ hours.

Apply

Use the given formulas to solve these problems.

1. The area of a square is side times side. $A = S \times S$. Find the area of a square if its side measures 15 centimeters.

2. The perimeter of a square is 4 times a side. $P = 4 \times S$ or $P = 4S$. Find the perimeter of a square that is 12 units long on one side.

3. The perimeter of a rectangle is two lengths plus two widths. $P = 2L + 2W$. Find the perimeter of a rectangle having a width of 7 feet and a length of 12 feet.

4. The area of a rectangle is length times width. $A = L \times W$ or $A = LW$. Find the area of a rectangle which is 4 centimeters long and 2 centimeters wide.

5. Use the formula in Exercise 3. Suppose the perimeter of a rectangle is 24 feet and the width is 4 feet. Explain how to find the length.

6. What if the width of a rectangle were given in feet and the length were given in inches? How would you find the perimeter?

7. What if you doubled the length of a rectangle like the one in Exercise 4? How would this affect the area?

8. What if you doubled both the length and the width of a rectangle? How would this affect the area?

9. Write a formula for the number of days in **W** weeks.

10. Write a formula for the number of months in **Y** years.

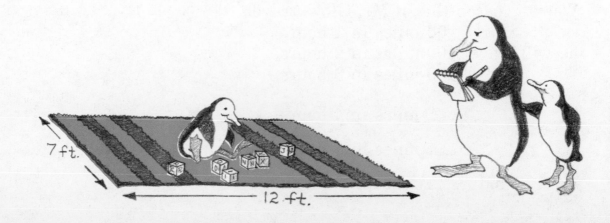

7 ft.

12 ft.

Calculators and Percents

Valerie grew roses this year for the first time. She is buying a crystal vase to display them in her living room. What is the total amount of the bill for the vase?

We need to find the total amount of the bill.

The price of the vase is _____.

The rate of sales tax is _____%.
We must find the amount of sales tax and add it to the cost of the vase.

To find the sales tax, we find 5% of _____.
Complete this code:

25 ⨉ 5 % (⎯⎯)

✔ When a percent of a number is found on a calculator, the = key is not used. The number on the display is in dollars and cents.

The sales tax is _____.

To find the total amount, we add _____ and _____.

25 + 1.25 = (⎯⎯)

The total cost of the vase is _____.
Complete the code to find the total cost of a crystal bell that costs $9.

9 ⨉ 5 % + 9 = (⎯⎯)

✔ Note that on a calculator, you can find the total cost in one code.

The cost of the bell is _____.

Practice

Find the percent of each number.

1. 8% of $150 = _____

2. 10% of $256 = _____

3. 25% of $364 = _____

4. 50% of $750 = _____

Complete the table.

5.

Amount spent	$855	$760	$2,578	$3,745
Percent of sales tax	6%	5%	7%	4%
Amount of sales tax				
Total cost				

Apply

Solve these problems.

6. Angelo bought a used car for $2,650. He had to pay 8% of the cost of the car as a down payment. How much did Angelo have to pay down?

7. Donna earned a salary of $26,000 a year as a city planner. This year Donna also received a bonus of 5% of her salary. How much did Donna earn this year?

EXCURSION

Valerie has a short-cut way to find the total amount of a bill, when the tax rate is given. Valerie uses this code to find the total cost.

25 $\boxed{\times}$ 105 $\boxed{\%}$ $\boxed{\qquad}$

Use her method to complete the chart.

Cost	Rate of Sales Tax	Total Cost
$650	6%	
$495	8%	
$810	9%	
$735	12%	

What is the value of the 4 in each number?

1. 84.21

2. 156.43

3. 20.148

4. 47.296

_____   _____   _____   _____

What is the value of the 7 in each number?

5. 639.74

6. 387.28

7. 200.07

8. 583.957

_____   _____   _____   _____

Write <, = or > in the circle.

9. 3.46 ◯ 3.64   10. 8.4 ◯ 8.40   11. 7.3 ◯ 7.39   12. 0.231 ◯ 0.22

13. 7.05 ◯ 7.5   14. 0.13 ◯ 0.031   15. 65.1 ◯ 65.09   16. 8.7 ◯ 8.70

Add.

17.   5.9
    + 3.6

18.   27.25
    + 48.397

19.   96.5
    + 48.76

20.   53.47
    + 16.7

Subtract.

21.   8.9
    − 2.5

22.   37.038
    − 15.969

23.   38.7
    − 19.58

24.   89.25
    − 27.5

Multiply.

25.   3.2
    ×   8

26.   12.6
    × 0.4

27.   13.7
    × 0.6

28.   8.9
    × 4.7

29.   24.8
    × 7.2

30.   1.6
    ×   7

31.   5.1
    × 0.06

32.   0.09
    ×   7

CUMULATIVE REVIEW

Circle the letter of the correct answer.

1 Round 4,500 to the nearest thousand.

a 4,000
b 5,000
c NG

2 13,296
+ 8,758

a 21,954
b 22,054
c 22,064
d NG

3 9,241
− 8,658

a 583
b 1,417
c 1,583
d NG

4 Choose the better estimate of length.

a 2 cm
b 2 meters

5 409 × 6

a 2,454
b 2,456
c 24,054
d NG

6 16)328

a 2 R8
b 20 R8
c 28
d NG

7 Find the perimeter.

16 feet

a 16 sq ft
b 64 sq ft
c 48 feet
d NG

8 Find the area.

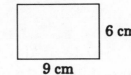

6 cm

9 cm

a 15 cm
b 15 sq cm
c 30 sq cm
d NG

9 $\frac{3}{4}$ of 16 = ?

a 4
b 8
c 12
d NG

10 Simplify $\frac{16}{24}$.

a $\frac{1}{2}$
b $\frac{2}{3}$
c $\frac{3}{4}$
d NG

11 $\frac{2}{3}$
+ $\frac{3}{5}$

a $\frac{5}{8}$
b $1\frac{4}{5}$
c $1\frac{4}{15}$
d NG

12 $\frac{5}{8} - \frac{1}{8}$

a $\frac{1}{2}$
b $\frac{3}{4}$
c 4
d NG

score

GRAPHING AND PROBABILITY

Tallies and Bar Graphs

Mr. Ryan is keeping a **tally** of the different types of books checked out of the library. Complete the **bar graph** to show which type is the most popular.

Library Book Checkout

Mystery	ЖЖ Ж III
Biography	ЖЖ III
Sports	ЖЖ ЖЖ I
Romance	ЖЖ ЖЖ ЖЖ I

We want to show the most popular type of book on a bar graph.

There were ____ mysteries, ____ biographies,

____ sports books and ____ romance books checked out.

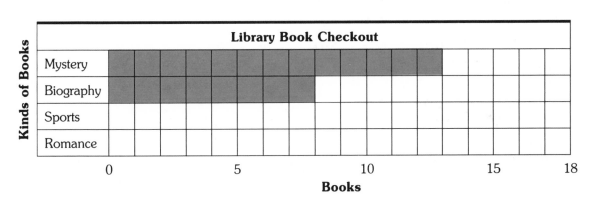

The most popular type of book checked out is the _____ book.

Getting Started

Use the graph above to answer these questions.

1. How many sports books were checked out?

   ____

2. How many more mystery books than biographies were checked out?

   ____

3. How many books were checked out altogether?

   ____

4. How many checked-out books were not romances?

   ____

Practice

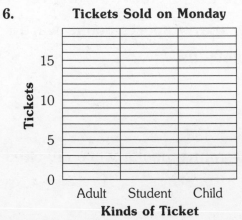

Use the tally chart to complete the bar graph and answer the questions.

Class Votes for President	
Eduardo	||||| ||
Nick	||||| ||||
Janet	||||| |||||	
Kim	||||| |||||

Class Votes for President

Candidates	1	2	3	4	5	6	7	8	9	10	11	12
Eduardo												
Nick												
Janet												
Kim												

Votes

1. Who won the election?

   _____

2. How many more votes did Nick get than Eduardo?

   ____

3. How many votes were cast altogether?

   ____

4. How many votes did the boys get together?

   ____

Complete the bar graphs using the information on the tally charts.

Games Won	
Baily	||||| ||||| |||
Smith	||||| |||||
Lincoln	||||| ||||| |||||

FRISBEE - TOSS TOURNAMENT

5.

Games Won

Wins

15
10
5
0

Baily   Smith   Lincoln

Teams

Tickets Sold on Monday	
Adult	||||| ||||| ||||| |||
Student	||||| ||||| |||||
Child	||||| |||||

6.

Tickets Sold on Monday

Tickets

15
10
5
0

Adult   Student   Child

Kinds of Ticket

Picture Graphs

A **picture graph** uses pictures to represent data on a graph. Here we can see how the construction industry changes with the seasons. How many new houses were started in June?

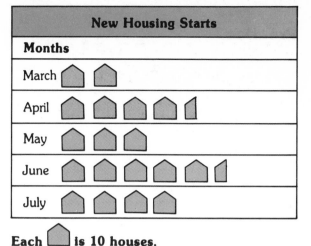

New Housing Starts	
Months	
March	🏠 🏠
April	🏠 🏠 🏠 🏠 ◗
May	🏠 🏠 🏠
June	🏠 🏠 🏠 🏠 🏠 ◗
July	🏠 🏠 🏠 🏠

Each 🏠 is 10 houses.

We want to know how many houses were started in June.

Each full house on the graph means

____ houses started.

A half of a house means ____ houses started.

There are ____ full houses and ____ half house pictured for June.

(____ × 10) + ____ = ____

There were ____ houses started in June.

Getting Started

Use the picture graph to answer these questions.

1. Which month had the fewest new houses started?

   _____

2. How many houses were started in April?

   _____

3. How many more houses were started in July than March?

   _____

4. In which month were only 30 houses started?

   _____

5. What was the monthly average of housing starts?

   _____

6. Which months were above average in number of housing starts?

   _____

313

Practice

Use the picture graph to answer these questions.

1. How many games did Bush win? _____

2. How many games did Jones win? _____

3. Which team won exactly 10 games? _____

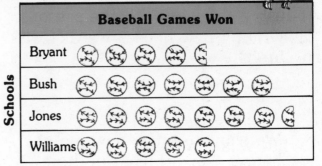

Baseball Games Won							
Bryant	⚾	⚾	⚾	⚾	◖		
Bush	⚾	⚾	⚾	⚾	⚾	⚾	⚾
Jones	⚾	⚾	⚾	⚾	⚾	⚾	⚾ ◖
Williams	⚾	⚾	⚾	⚾	⚾		

Each ⚾ is 2 games.

Use the tally chart to make a picture graph.
Then answer the questions.

Birds Sighted	
Bluebird	IIII IIII IIII I
Robin	IIII IIII II
Cardinal	IIII IIII IIII
Blackbird	IIII IIII

4.

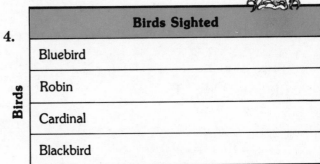

Birds Sighted
Bluebird
Robin
Cardinal
Blackbird

Each _____ means 4 birds.

5. How many birds were sighted? _____

6. What was the average number of each kind of bird sighted? _____

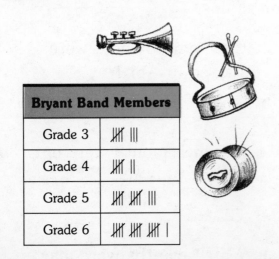

Bryant Band Members	
Grade 3	IIII III
Grade 4	IIII II
Grade 5	IIII IIII III
Grade 6	IIII IIII IIII I

7.

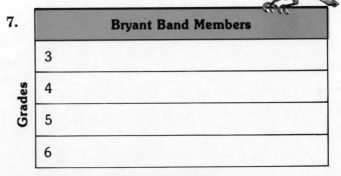

Bryant Band Members
3
4
5
6

Each _____ means 2 children.

8. How many more Grade 6 band members are there than Grade 4? _____

9. Which grades have more than the average number of members? _____

314

Line Graphs

A **line graph** is a
good way to show
changes in information.
This line graph
shows the high
temperatures for each
day for the first
two weeks in May.
What was the high
temperature on
May 6?

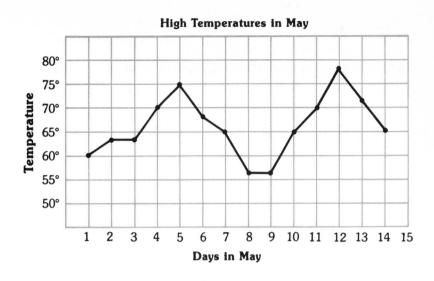

High Temperatures in May

We want to find the high temperature
for May 6 on the line graph.

The _____ is shown up the side
of the graph.

The _____ are shown along the bottom.
To find the high temperature for May 6, we
follow along the bottom of the graph until
we reach the sixth day. Then we go up the
vertical line until we reach the dot. The
temperature is the reading in degrees
directly opposite that dot. On May 6, the

high temperature was ____.

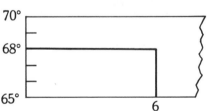

Getting Started

Use the line graph above to answer the questions.

1. What was the high temperature

   on May 10? _____

2. On what day was the high
   temperature exactly 72°?

   _____

3. On how many days was the
   high temperature exactly 70°?

   _____

4. What was the average high
   temperature for May 12, May
   13 and May 14? _____

315

Practice

Use the line graph to answer the questions.

New Car Sales

1. How many cars were sold in

   October? _____

2. How many cars were sold in

   February? _____

3. Did sales go up or down from
   June through September?

   _____

4. In what month did the sales
   of cars increase the most over

   the month before? _____

5. In which month were the most

   cars sold? _____

6. In which month were the least

   cars sold? _____

7. How many more cars were
   sold in April than September?

   _____

8. What was the average
   monthly car sales during the

   last four months? _____

Number Pairs

Number pairs can be used to give locations on a number grid. The pair (4, 3) shows the location of point *A*. What number pair locates point *D*?

We want to know what number pair identifies point *D*.

We know that point *A* is ___ units

over and ___ units up.

✔ To find a number pair, we start at the origin on the grid. The **first** number tells how far **over** to move. The **second** number tells how far **up** to move.

Point *D* is ___ over and ___ up.

The number pair (___, ___) locates point *D*.

We write: **D (2, 5).** We say: **Point *D* is the number pair two, five.**

Getting Started

Write the letter identified by each number pair.

1. ___(6, 1)   **2.** ___(9, 2)   **3.** ___(3, 6)   **4.** ___(6, 6)

Write the number pair that identifies each letter.

5. *I*(___, ___)   **6.** *E*(___, ___)   **7.** *C*(___, ___)   **8.** *F*(___, ___)

317

Practice

Write the letter identified by each number pair.

1. ____(5, 2)

2. ____(6, 4)

3. ____(2, 5)

4. ____(1, 6)

5. ____(4, 6)

6. ____(2, 8)

7. ____(7, 2)

8. ____(1, 1)

9. ____(7, 4)

10. ____(3, 4)

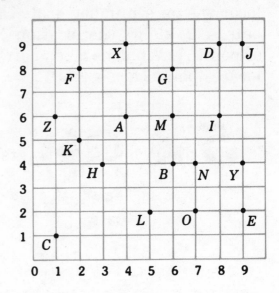

Write the number pair that identifies each letter.

11. M(____, ____)

12. X(____, ____)

13. I(____, ____)

14. O(____, ____)

15. E(____, ____)

16. G(____, ____)

17. J(____, ____)

18. Y(____, ____)

EXCURSION

Take the numbers from the first square, and rearrange them in the second square so that each column, row and diagonal has the same sum.

15	1	11
5	9	13
7	17	3

Graphing Number Pairs

Graph the points $C(3, 6)$ and $D(7, 6)$.
Use a ruler to draw $\overline{AB}$, $\overline{BD}$, $\overline{DC}$
and $\overline{CA}$. What kind of figure did
you draw?

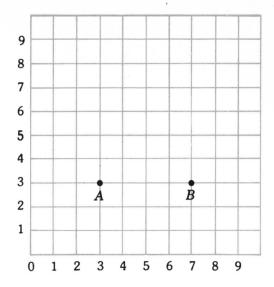

We graph and label points C and D.

Point C is ___ units over

and ___ units up.

Point D is ___ units over

and ___ units up.

We draw line segments ___, ___,

___ and ___.

✔ Remember that $\overline{AB}$ is a line
segment from point A to point B.

The figure $ABCD$ is a _____.

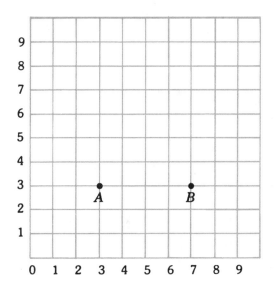

Getting Started

Graph these points. Draw line
segments AB, BC and CA.
$A(2, 9)$ $B(6, 9)$
$C(4, 5)$

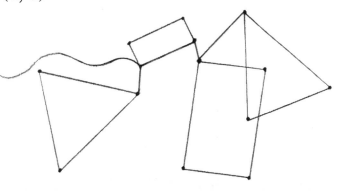

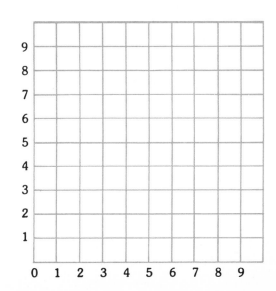

319

Practice

1. Graph and label these points.

$A(3, 6)$ $B(4, 8)$ $C(5, 6)$

$D(4, 6)$ $F(3, 4)$

$E(4, 5)$ $G(5, 4)$

Use a ruler to draw $\overline{AB}$, $\overline{BC}$, $\overline{AC}$, $\overline{DE}$, $\overline{FE}$ and $\overline{EG}$.

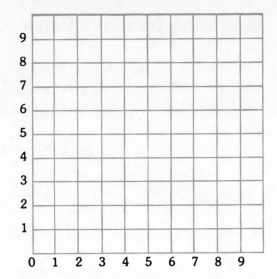

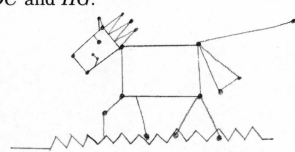

2. Graph and label these points.

$A(2, 2)$ $B(2, 6)$

$C(4, 2)$ $D(4, 6)$

$E(2, 4)$ $F(4, 4)$

$G(7, 2)$ $H(7, 6)$

Use a ruler to draw $\overline{AB}$, $\overline{EF}$, $\overline{DC}$ and $\overline{HG}$.

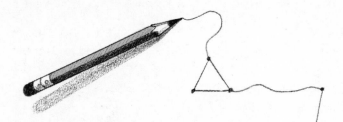

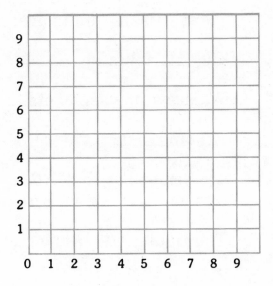

3. Graph and label these points.

$A(1, 1)$ $J(4, 8)$ $K(5, 8)$ $D(5, 1)$

$E(3, 4)$ $B(2, 4)$ $C(5, 4)$ $H(4, 4)$

$G(4, 6)$ $F(3, 6)$ $L(5, 7)$ $M(4, 7)$

Use a ruler to draw $\overline{AB}$, $\overline{BC}$, $\overline{CD}$, $\overline{EF}$, $\overline{FG}$, $\overline{HJ}$, $\overline{JK}$, $\overline{KL}$ and $\overline{LM}$.

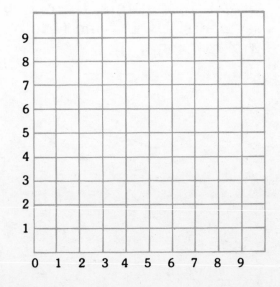

320

Understanding Probability

Jean is working a **probability** experiment for her class by drawing numbers from a hat. Each number is equally likely to be drawn. What is the probability that she will pick a 3?

We want to know how likely it is that Jean will pick a 3 from the hat.

There are ___ papers in the hat.

The papers are numbered ___, ___, ___,

___ and ___.

Each number that is drawn is called an **outcome**. Since there are five possible outcomes in this experiment, we say the probability of Jean picking a 3, the first time, is **1 out of 5.**

The ___ in this probability tells how many 3's there are in the hat.

The ___ tells how many numbers there are altogether in the hat.

The probability of Jean picking a 3 is _____.

Getting Started

Answer these questions based on the papers in the hat.

1. What is the probability of drawing a 2?

   _____

2. What is the probability of drawing a 5?

   _____

3. What is the probability of drawing an odd number?

   _____

4. What is the probability of drawing a number greater than 2?

   _____

5. What is the probability of drawing a number divisible by 2?

   _____

6. What is the probability of drawing a number greater than 6?

   _____

Practice

A cube has the letters *A, B, C, D, E* and *F* printed on its faces. The outcome is the letter printed on the top of the cube after a toss.

1. What are the possible outcomes?

   _____

2. How many different outcomes are possible?

   _____

3. What is the probability of tossing an A?

   _____

4. What is the probability of tossing a C?

   _____

5. What is the probability of tossing a D?

   _____

6. What is the probability of tossing an X?

   _____

A spinner is divided into three equal parts numbered 1, 2 and 3. If the spinner lands on a line it doesn't count.

7. What are the possible outcomes?

   _____

8. How many different outcomes are possible?

   _____

9. What is the probability of spinning a 1?

   _____

10. What is the probability of spinning a 2 or 3?

    _____

11. What is the probability of spinning a 5?

    _____

12. What is the probability of spinning an odd number?

    _____

Listing Outcomes

Tim is playing a game in which he spins the wheel twice each turn. His move on the board is determined by the two numbers the arrow points to. List all the possible outcomes Tim could spin in one turn.

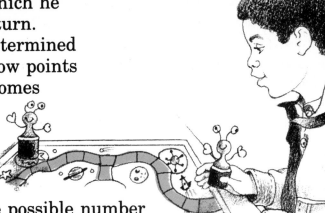

We want a list of all the possible number combinations Tim could spin.

We know the numbers on the wheel are ___,

 ___, ___, ___, ___, ___, ___ and ___.

Tim could spin:

1, 1	2, 1	3, 1	4, 1	5, 1	___	___	___
1, 2	2, 2	3, 2	4, 2	5, 2	___	___	___
1, 3	2, 3	3, 3	4, 3	5, 3	___	___	___
1, 4	2, 4	3, 4	4, 4	5, 4	___	___	___
1, 5	2, 5	3, 5	4, 5	5, 5	___	___	___
1, 6	2, 6	3, 6	4, 6	5, 6	___	___	___
1, 7	2, 7	3, 7	4, 7	5, 7	___	___	___
1, 8	2, 8	3, 8	4, 8	5, 8	___	___	___

There are ___ different possible outcomes.

Getting Started

Tracy tosses a nickel and a dime in the air to see if she will get heads or tails. List all the possible outcomes she could get.

_____   _____

323

Practice

1. Each of the letters in the word COURAGE are written on a piece of paper and put into a box. List all the possible outcomes, if two papers are pulled out at a time. (All papers are returned to the box after each turn.)

_____

_____

_____

_____

2. List all the possible partner combinations for a chess game if Team A plays Team B.

_____

_____

_____

Team A	Team B
Alexi	Danielle
Bruce	Erica
Carl	Flo
	Gerry

3. Complete these diagrams to show all possible combinations of candidates for president and vice-president of the safety squad. The people running for the jobs are Greg, Lee, Kristine, Lin and Heather.

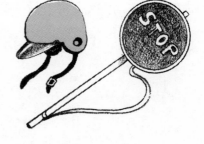

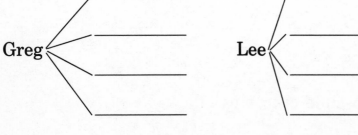

Greg

Lee

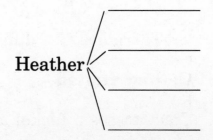

Heather

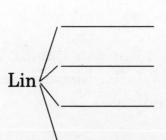

Kristine

Lin

Review

The four-step plan can help us to be better problem solvers. A review of this plan can remind us of ways to use it.

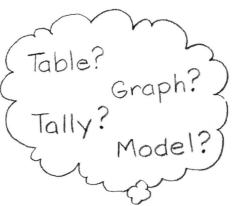

★ **SEE**

We decide what we are looking for.
We state all the facts we know that
will help us to solve the problem.

★ **PLAN**

We think about the important facts and choose
a plan to solve the problem.
Some of the things we have learned to do to
help us solve problems are:

> Guessing and checking
> Making an organized list
> Acting it out
> Looking for a pattern
> Making a table
> Drawing a picture or diagram
> Making a model
> Making a tally
> Making a graph
> Restating the problem
> Selecting notations
> Writing an open sentence
> Using a formula

★ **DO**

We carry out the plan and reach a solution to
the problem.

★ **CHECK**

We check the problem for careless errors.
We see if the solution makes sense.
We look for another way to work the problem.

Apply

Use one or more of the things you have learned
to do to help solve each problem.

1. Angela, Barbara, Cheryl, Dorothy and Eve are in a foot race. At the finish line, Angela is 20 meters behind Barbara. Barbara is 50 meters ahead of Cheryl. Cheryl is 10 meters behind Eve. Dorothy is 30 meters ahead of Angela. In what order did they finish?

2. Ling spent half of the money in his pocket for his school lunch. On the way home, he spent half of his remaining money at the music store. Ling then had $1.15 in his pocket. How much money did Ling have in his pocket before lunch?

3. Forgetful Fred was cleaning out his desk and discovered a library book that was 12 days overdue. Write an open sentence that will help find Fred's library debt, if the fine is 8 cents for each of the 12 days.

4. A school bus starts its morning route and picks up one passenger at the first stop, two passengers at the second stop, three at the third and so on. After the twelfth stop, how many passengers are on the bus?

5. Suppose you know that it is more likely to rain tomorrow than it is to snow. What do you know is true about the probability of rain and the probability of snow?

6. A spinner with different colors is used in a game. Suppose the probability of spinning the color red is 3 out of 5. If you spin 20 times, how many times can you expect to spin red?

7. Fred and Freida are drawing a map of their town on a grid. Fred says, "The school is at (5,3)." Freida says, "No, the school is at (3,5)." What is alike about these number pairs and what is different?

8. Barney and Betty buy old bicycles and fix them up to sell. They bought a bicycle for $40, used $20 worth of parts to repair it, and then sold it for $80. Rewrite this problem so that they make a profit of $40.

Calculator Review

You have used a calculator to work with the basic operations involving whole numbers, money, fractions and percents. Now let's use your calculator to have some fun.

Activity 1: A Magic Square

Fill in the squares with 7, 14, 21, 28, 42, 49, 56 and 63 so each row, column, and diagonal has a sum of 105.

	35	

Activity 2: Palindromes

A number that is read the same forward or backward is called a **palindrome.** Reverse the digits and add. Continue to reverse and add each new sum until it becomes a palindrome.

Pick a number.	215
Reverse the digit.	512
Add.	727 A palindrome

Find the palindrome for each number.

1. 623   2. 807   3. 285   4. 518   5. 374

Activity 3: Patterns

Find the product of the first three problems. Use the pattern to guess the fourth product. Check your guess with your calculator.

1. $99 \times 2 = $ _____

   $99 \times 3 = $ _____

   $99 \times 4 = $ _____

   $99 \times 7 = $ _____

2. $999 \times 2 = $ _____

   $999 \times 3 = $ _____

   $999 \times 4 = $ _____

   $999 \times 7 = $ _____

3. $9,999 \times 2 = $ _____

   $9,999 \times 3 = $ _____

   $9,999 \times 4 = $ _____

   $9,999 \times 7 = $ _____

Activity 4: Cross-Number Puzzle

Across
1. 56 × 28
3. 12 × 12
5. 494 + 379
6. 1,680 ÷ 112
7. 16,808 − 9,783
8. 25 × 225
10. 64 × 16 × 56
13. 26 × 26 − 294
14. 4,739 + 4,769

Down
1. 39 + 16 + 48
2. 4,225 ÷ 65
3. 12,360 ÷ 12
4. 7,653 − 2,968
6. 219 × 75
8. 9,546 − 3,877
9. 2,938 + 2,640
11. 33,495 ÷ 35 ÷ 29
12. 16,575 ÷ 39

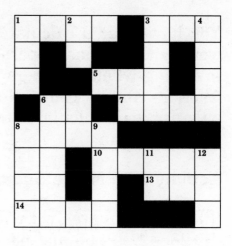

Activity 5: A Game of Markout for 2 People

Use the numbers 12, 15, 21, 36, 48, 64 and 52. Pick two numbers each turn and find their product, using the calculator. Then find your answer on the chart, and mark out the number with your initial. The first to mark out a horizontal or vertical path across the chart wins.

540	441	1,092	180	1,488
1,344	432	576	780	624
3,072	2,704	2,304	252	1,008
768	756	315	1,872	225
1,296	2,496	960	144	720

Activity 6: Mystery Numbers

Find each pair of mystery numbers.

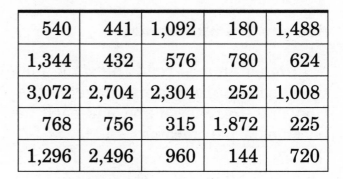

1. Their sum is 70 and their difference is 16.

_____

2. Their sum is 30 and their product is 216.

_____

3. Their difference is 50 and their quotient is 3.

_____

4. Their product is 45 and their quotient is 5.

_____

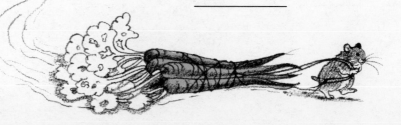

Find the average of each set of numbers.

1. 18, 26 _____   2. 16, 47, 51 _____   3. 23, 35, 45, 15, 32 _____

Use the graphs to answer questions 8 and 9.

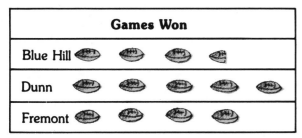

Games Won				
Blue Hill				
Dunn				
Fremont				

Each 🏈 means 2 games.

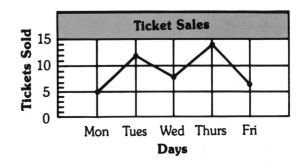

4. How many games did

   Fremont win? _____

5. How many tickets were sold

   on Thursday? _____

Use the graph to do exercise 6 through 9.

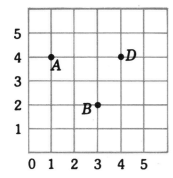

6. Give the letter for (3, 2). _____

7. Give the number pair for point *A*. _____

8. Graph and label point *C*(2, 4).

9. Graph and label point *E*(4, 2).

Ten lettered pieces of paper are placed in a box.
One letter is drawn.

10. What is the probability the letter will be a B?

    _____

11. What is the probability the letter will be a C?

    _____

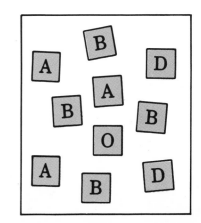

329

Circle the letter of the correct answer.

16,245
+ 45,682

a 51,827
b 61,927
c 62,927
d NG

2   7,046
  − 4,895

a 2,151
b 3,851
c 11,941
d NG

3 36 × 28

a 360
b 908
c 1,308
d NG

4 8)109

a 1 R35
b 13 R5
c 135
d NG

5 Find the perimeter.

38 35 38
30 46 30

a 215 units
b 217 units
c 225 units
d NG

6 Find the area.

8 in.

6 in.

a 48 in.
b 28 sq in.
c 48 sq in.
d NG

7 $\frac{2}{3}$ of 24 = n
    n = ?

a 8
b 12
c 16
d NG

8   $2\frac{2}{3}$
  $+ 3\frac{1}{2}$

a $5\frac{1}{6}$
b $5\frac{3}{5}$
c $6\frac{1}{6}$
d NG

9   $\frac{15}{8}$
  $- \frac{3}{4}$

a $\frac{14}{4}$
b $\frac{1}{8}$
c $1\frac{1}{8}$
d NG

10 7.9 + 9.8

a 1.77
b 17.7
c 177
d NG

11   15.9
  − 8.73

a 7.17
b 7.23
c 7.27
d NG

12   5.9
  × 0.3

a 1.77
b 17.7
c 177
d NG

13 Find the average.
    16, 24, 23

a 6
b 20
c 23
d NG

☐ score

Compare these numbers.

1. $9 \bigcirc 25$　　　2. $36 \bigcirc 63$　　　3. $47 \bigcirc 49$　　　4. $88 \bigcirc 82$

Add.

5. $6 + 4 =$ _____　　6. $8 + 8 =$ _____　　7. $7 + 6 =$ _____　　8. $6 + 9 =$ _____

9. $\begin{array}{r} 2 \\ + 8 \\ \hline \end{array}$　　　10. $\begin{array}{r} 7 \\ + 5 \\ \hline \end{array}$　　　11. $\begin{array}{r} 9 \\ + 8 \\ \hline \end{array}$　　　12. $\begin{array}{r} 4 \\ 5 \\ + 8 \\ \hline \end{array}$

13. $\begin{array}{r} 3 \\ 7 \\ + 6 \\ \hline \end{array}$　　　14. $\begin{array}{r} 6 \\ 2 \\ 8 \\ + 7 \\ \hline \end{array}$　　　15. $\begin{array}{r} 7 \\ 1 \\ 6 \\ + 1 \\ \hline \end{array}$　　　16. $\begin{array}{r} 2 \\ 6 \\ 3 \\ 4 \\ + 1 \\ \hline \end{array}$

17. $(6 + 3) + 2 =$ _____　　18. $3 + (7 + 1) =$ _____　　19. $(8 + 1) + 4 =$ _____

20. $4 + (0 + 7) =$ _____　　21. $(2 + 5) + 8 =$ _____　　22. $9 + (4 + 7) =$ _____

Subtract.

23. $8 - 5 =$ _____　24. $16 - 7 =$ _____　25. $12 - 7 =$ _____　26. $13 - 5 =$ _____

27. $\begin{array}{r} 11 \\ - 6 \\ \hline \end{array}$　　　28. $\begin{array}{r} 14 \\ - 7 \\ \hline \end{array}$　　　29. $\begin{array}{r} 9 \\ - 5 \\ \hline \end{array}$　　　30. $\begin{array}{r} 6 \\ - 6 \\ \hline \end{array}$

Write the missing addends.

31. $4 + n = 7$

$n =$ ____

32. $n + 6 = 14$

$n =$ ____

33. $\begin{array}{r} 9 \\ + n \\ \hline 12 \end{array}$

$n =$ ____

34. $\begin{array}{r} 6 \\ + n \\ \hline 12 \end{array}$

$n =$ ____

Write the place value of the red digits.

1. 4,621

2. 11,624

3. 7,243

4. 127,640

_____ _____ _____ _____

5. 64,327

6. 4,681,000

7. 161,121

8. 34,691,200

_____ _____ _____ _____

Write the numbers.

9. two hundred ninety-five   10. seven thousand, four hundred twenty-nine

_____   _____

11. six million, four hundred thousand, fifty-one

_____

Write the missing words.

12. 27,653 twenty-seven _____, six _____ fifty-three

13. 34,006,126 thirty four _____, six _____, one _____,
twenty-six

Compare these numbers.

14. 7,826 ◯ 3,271

15. 4,362 ◯ 4,623

16. 6,327 ◯ 6,273

Round to the nearest ten.

17. 4,565 _____

18. 6,212 _____

19. 9,287 _____

Round to the nearest hundred or dollar.

20. 657 _____

21. 387 _____

22. $5.27 _____

23. 4,582 _____

24. $6.72 _____

25. 349 _____

Add.

1. 47
    + 32

2. 61
    + 17

3. 93
    + 28

4. 27
    + 84

5. 246
    + 221

6. 302
    + 459

7. 364
    + 252

8. 974
    + 668

9. 1,324
    + 3,361

10. 5,536
    + 3,528

11. 8,317
    + 3,835

12. 4,635
    + 7,977

13. 6,452
    + 8,693

14. 7,958
    + 4,655

15. 2,976
    + 5,493

16. 9,498
    + 3,784

Estimate the sum after rounding to the nearest hundred or dollar.

17. 683
    + 326

18. 179
    + 420

19. 6,877
    + 2,416

20. $23.50
    + 19.64

Estimate the sum after rounding to the nearest thousand.

21. 6,426
    + 2,397

22. 4,956
    + 2,631

23. 2,751
    + 3,284

24. 6,421
    + 3,791

Add.

25. 736
    254
    + 323

26. 6,436
    1,527
    + 3,375

27. 13,276
    3,184
    + 27,722

28. $45.67
    8.23
    + 36.51

Subtract and check.

1. 75
-62

2. 47
-32

3. 94
-37

4. 67
-48

5. 659
-324

6. 763
-256

7. 927
-565

8. 715
-287

9. 702
-431

10. 503
-218

11. $\$6.04$
$-\ 3.48$

12. $\$7.00$
$-\ 4.95$

13. $8,483$
$-3,674$

14. $\$96.43$
$-\ 48.27$

15. $27,466$
$-19,598$

16. $\$654.18$
$-\ 247.73$

17. $8,005$
$-4,679$

18. $\$60.00$
$-\ 15.49$

19. $50,003$
$-36,357$

20. $\$700.36$
257.38

Estimate each difference.

Round to the nearest thousand.

21. $6,421$
$-2,716$

22. $7,056$
$-2,194$

23. $4,809$
$-3,674$

24. $9,362$
$-3,212$

Round to the nearest hundred.

25. 697
-356

26. 387
-126

27. 428
-287

28. 949
-655

Multiply.

1. $\begin{array}{r} 8 \\ \times\,6 \\ \hline \end{array}$	**2.** $\begin{array}{r} 9 \\ \times\,0 \\ \hline \end{array}$	**3.** $\begin{array}{r} 8 \\ \times\,3 \\ \hline \end{array}$	**4.** $\begin{array}{r} 7 \\ \times\,7 \\ \hline \end{array}$	**5.** $\begin{array}{r} 0 \\ \times\,8 \\ \hline \end{array}$	**6.** $\begin{array}{r} 8 \\ \times\,9 \\ \hline \end{array}$	**7.** $\begin{array}{r} 9 \\ \times\,3 \\ \hline \end{array}$
8. $\begin{array}{r} 7 \\ \times\,8 \\ \hline \end{array}$	**9.** $\begin{array}{r} 6 \\ \times\,2 \\ \hline \end{array}$	**10.** $\begin{array}{r} 6 \\ \times\,6 \\ \hline \end{array}$	**11.** $\begin{array}{r} 2 \\ \times\,6 \\ \hline \end{array}$	**12.** $\begin{array}{r} 7 \\ \times\,9 \\ \hline \end{array}$	**13.** $\begin{array}{r} 6 \\ \times\,7 \\ \hline \end{array}$	**14.** $\begin{array}{r} 2 \\ \times\,7 \\ \hline \end{array}$
15. $\begin{array}{r} 1 \\ \times\,6 \\ \hline \end{array}$	**16.** $\begin{array}{r} 6 \\ \times\,5 \\ \hline \end{array}$	**17.** $\begin{array}{r} 5 \\ \times\,7 \\ \hline \end{array}$	**18.** $\begin{array}{r} 7 \\ \times\,6 \\ \hline \end{array}$	**19.** $\begin{array}{r} 6 \\ \times\,9 \\ \hline \end{array}$	**20.** $\begin{array}{r} 5 \\ \times\,9 \\ \hline \end{array}$	**21.** $\begin{array}{r} 2 \\ \times\,8 \\ \hline \end{array}$
22. $\begin{array}{r} 6 \\ \times\,3 \\ \hline \end{array}$	**23.** $\begin{array}{r} 5 \\ \times\,5 \\ \hline \end{array}$	**24.** $\begin{array}{r} 9 \\ \times\,6 \\ \hline \end{array}$	**25.** $\begin{array}{r} 4 \\ \times\,7 \\ \hline \end{array}$	**26.** $\begin{array}{r} 8 \\ \times\,4 \\ \hline \end{array}$	**27.** $\begin{array}{r} 4 \\ \times\,5 \\ \hline \end{array}$	**28.** $\begin{array}{r} 0 \\ \times\,0 \\ \hline \end{array}$
29. $\begin{array}{r} 3 \\ \times\,5 \\ \hline \end{array}$	**30.** $\begin{array}{r} 4 \\ \times\,9 \\ \hline \end{array}$	**31.** $\begin{array}{r} 7 \\ \times\,4 \\ \hline \end{array}$	**32.** $\begin{array}{r} 9 \\ \times\,5 \\ \hline \end{array}$	**33.** $\begin{array}{r} 3 \\ \times\,6 \\ \hline \end{array}$	**34.** $\begin{array}{r} 8 \\ \times\,8 \\ \hline \end{array}$	**35.** $\begin{array}{r} 4 \\ \times\,8 \\ \hline \end{array}$

Solve for n.

36. $(6 \times 4) + 3 = n$

$n =$ ____

37. $(8 - 5) \times 3 = n$

$n =$ ____

38. $5 \times (3 + 4) = n$

$n =$ ____

39. $30 + (6 \times 5) = n$

$n =$ ____

40. $45 - (9 \times 5) = n$

$n =$ ____

41. $(6 \times 6) - 26 = n$

$n =$ ____

42. $6 \times n = 42$

$n =$ ____

43. $n \times 9 = 45$

$n =$ ____

44. $n \times 4 = 36$

$n =$ ____

45. $n \times 7 = 49$

$n =$ ____

46. $n \times 3 = 24$

$n =$ ____

47. $8 \times n = 0$

$n =$ ____

Write the first nine multiples of each of these numbers.

1. 2 ———, ———, ———, ———, ———, ———, ———, ———, ———

2. 6 ———, ———, ———, ———, ———, ———, ———, ———, ———

3. 8 ———, ———, ———, ———, ———, ———, ———, ———, ———

Skip-count by 9.

4. 27, ———, ———, ———, ———, ———, ———, ———, 99

Skip-count by 7.

5. 21, ———, ———, ———, ———, ———, ———, ———, 77

Solve for n.

6. $9 \times (0 \times 2) = n$ 7. $8 \times 6 = n$ 8. $(6 \times 3) + (9 \times 2) = n$

$n = $ ___ $n = $ ___ $n = $ ___

9. $5 \times (7 \times 2) = n$ 10. $(7 \times 0) + (7 \times 0) = n$ 11. $11 \times 7 = n$

$n = $ ___ $n = $ ___ $n = $ ___

Multiply.

12.
$$\begin{array}{r} 43 \\ \times\ 2 \\ \hline \end{array}$$

13.
$$\begin{array}{r} 13 \\ \times\ 3 \\ \hline \end{array}$$

14.
$$\begin{array}{r} 22 \\ \times\ 4 \\ \hline \end{array}$$

15.
$$\begin{array}{r} 11 \\ \times\ 6 \\ \hline \end{array}$$

16.
$$\begin{array}{r} 27 \\ \times\ 3 \\ \hline \end{array}$$

17.
$$\begin{array}{r} 24 \\ \times\ 4 \\ \hline \end{array}$$

18.
$$\begin{array}{r} 13 \\ \times\ 5 \\ \hline \end{array}$$

19.
$$\begin{array}{r} 37 \\ \times\ 2 \\ \hline \end{array}$$

20.
$$\begin{array}{r} \$0.46 \\ \times\ \ \ \ \ 5 \\ \hline \end{array}$$

21.
$$\begin{array}{r} \$0.63 \\ \times\ \ \ \ \ 7 \\ \hline \end{array}$$

22.
$$\begin{array}{r} \$0.84 \\ \times\ \ \ \ \ 8 \\ \hline \end{array}$$

23.
$$\begin{array}{r} \$0.49 \\ \times\ \ \ \ \ 6 \\ \hline \end{array}$$

Divide.

1. $6\overline{)48}$ 2. $7\overline{)28}$ 3. $6\overline{)30}$ 4. $3\overline{)12}$ 5. $2\overline{)18}$

6. $5\overline{)20}$ 7. $2\overline{)18}$ 8. $9\overline{)45}$ 9. $6\overline{)0}$ 10. $7\overline{)49}$

11. $72 \div 9 =$ ___   12. $35 \div 5 =$ ___   13. $8 \div 8 =$ ___   14. $40 \div 8 =$ ___

15. $6 \div 6 =$ ___   16. $63 \div 7 =$ ___   17. $72 \div 8 =$ ___   18. $64 \div 8 =$ ___

Divide. Show your work.

19. $6\overline{)50}$ 20. $9\overline{)46}$ 21. $8\overline{)34}$ 22. $7\overline{)37}$

23. $6\overline{)66}$ 24. $3\overline{)96}$ 25. $4\overline{)96}$ 26. $2\overline{)36}$

27. $5\overline{)77}$ 28. $4\overline{)98}$ 29. $3\overline{)97}$ 30. $2\overline{)73}$

31. $6\overline{)62}$ 32. $7\overline{)86}$ 33. $4\overline{)67}$ 34. $8\overline{)86}$

Write the times. Include AM or PM.

1. 25 minutes before nine in the morning

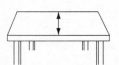

2. 2 hours and 25 minutes after 7:25 PM

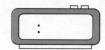

Circle the best estimate for each measurement.

3.

   6 in. 6 ft 6 mi

4.

   7 in. 7 ft 7 yd

5.

   1 pt 1 qt 1 gal

6.

   10 in. 10 yd 10 mi

7.

   36 in. 36 ft 36 yd

8.

   2 mL 2 L 2 kL

9.

   100 g 100 kg

10.

   1 cm 1 m 1 km

11.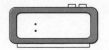

   50 g 50 kg

12.

   2 kg 2 T

Multiply. Use estimation to check your answers.

1. 214
    × 3

2. $5.16
    × 5

3. 747
    × 6

4. 637
    × 5

5. 6,307
    × 4

6. 3,652
    × 8

7. $27.32
    × 3

8. 8,456
    × 5

9. 12
    × 24

10. 62
    × 13

11. 42
    × 22

12. 64
    × 43

13. 83
    × 45

14. 67
    × 76

15. 93
    × 68

16. 37
    × 75

17. 527
    × 48

18. $6.27
    × 56

19. 548
    × 36

20. 458
    × 77

21. 752
    × 63

22. $6.84
    × 39

23. 498
    × 75

24. 596
    × 87

25. 397
    × 54

26. 429
    × 36

27. $9.89
    × 47

28. 434
    × 38

Divide. Show your work.

1. $4\overline{)488}$ 2. $3\overline{)666}$ 3. $5\overline{)557}$ 4. $7\overline{)918}$

5. $3\overline{)703}$ 6. $2\overline{)800}$ 7. $3\overline{)622}$ 8. $4\overline{)835}$

9. $5\overline{)365}$ 10. $8\overline{)344}$ 11. $7\overline{)505}$ 12. $7\overline{)651}$

13. $3\overline{)\$6.18}$ 14. $9\overline{)\$7.38}$ 15. $3\overline{)\$8.22}$ 16. $6\overline{)\$3.66}$

17. $22\overline{)176}$ 18. $42\overline{)260}$ 19. $32\overline{)236}$ 20. $64\overline{)259}$

21. $24\overline{)288}$ 22. $35\overline{)\$7.35}$ 23. $47\overline{)953}$ 24. $37\overline{)555}$

Find the average of each set of numbers.

25. 6, 4, 8, 3, 4   26. 39, 42, 65, 26

_____   _____

27. 74, 68, 116, 92, 45   28. 262, 434, 204

_____   _____

ALTERNATE CHAPTER TEST

Write the name for each figure.

1.  X ——— Y

2. X ——— Z

3.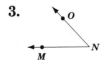

_____   _____   _____

Name each kind of polygon.

4. ▢

5. △

6. ⬡

_____   _____   _____

Find the perimeter.

7. ▢ 11 cm

8. ▭ 9 m 20 m

_____   _____

Find the area.

9. ▯ 12 cm 10 cm

10. ▢ 9 m

_____   _____

Find the volume.

11.

12.

_____   _____

Write the fraction.

1. What part of the figure is red?

2. What part of the coins are pennies?

Find the part.

3. $\frac{1}{3}$ of 45 =

4. $\frac{2}{5}$ of 30 =

5. $\frac{3}{4}$ of the price of $56

_____

Write the missing numerators.

6. $\frac{2}{3} = \frac{}{9}$

7. $\frac{2}{3} = \frac{}{12}$

8. $\frac{3}{4} = \frac{}{8}$

9. $\frac{4}{8} = \frac{}{24}$

Write < or > in the circle.

10. $\frac{3}{4} \bigcirc \frac{3}{8}$

11. $\frac{5}{8} \bigcirc \frac{1}{2}$

12. $\frac{4}{12} \bigcirc \frac{1}{2}$

13. $\frac{4}{5} \bigcirc \frac{3}{4}$

Simplify each fraction.

14. $\frac{20}{24} = \frac{}{6}$

15. $\frac{14}{18} = \frac{}{9}$

16. $\frac{9}{15} = \frac{}{5}$

17. $\frac{12}{18} = \frac{}{3}$

Write each fraction as a mixed number.

18. $\frac{8}{6} =$

19. $\frac{9}{2} =$

20. $\frac{17}{6} =$

21. $\frac{18}{12} =$

Measure the figures to the nearest quarter inch.

22.  _____

23. _____

Write the comparisons as fractions.

24. red counters to black counters

25. black counters to all counters

ALTERNATE CHAPTER TEST

Add or subtract. Simplify your answers.

1. $\dfrac{3}{7}$
    $+\dfrac{2}{7}$

2. $\dfrac{6}{8}$
    $-\dfrac{3}{8}$

3. $\dfrac{7}{9}$
    $-\dfrac{3}{9}$

4. $\dfrac{7}{10}$
    $-\dfrac{3}{10}$

5. $\dfrac{10}{11}$
    $-\dfrac{7}{11}$

6. $\dfrac{3}{8}$
    $+\dfrac{3}{8}$

7. $\dfrac{5}{6}$
    $-\dfrac{2}{6}$

8. $\dfrac{3}{6}$
    $-\dfrac{1}{6}$

9. $\dfrac{1}{6}$
    $+\dfrac{1}{4}$

10. $\dfrac{5}{12}$
    $-\dfrac{1}{4}$

11. $\dfrac{10}{14}$
    $+\dfrac{2}{7}$

12. $\dfrac{6}{8}$
    $+\dfrac{8}{12}$

13. $\dfrac{9}{12}$
    $-\dfrac{3}{8}$

14. $\dfrac{6}{8}$
    $-\dfrac{3}{16}$

15. $\dfrac{3}{4}$
    $+\dfrac{5}{6}$

16. $\dfrac{11}{9}$
    $-\dfrac{2}{6}$

17. $4\dfrac{4}{9}$
    $+1\dfrac{6}{18}$

18. $6\dfrac{4}{6}$
    $+3\dfrac{1}{4}$

19. $24\dfrac{2}{8}$
    $+16\dfrac{3}{4}$

20. $3\dfrac{3}{5}$
    $+8\dfrac{1}{3}$

21. $\dfrac{2}{3} + \dfrac{1}{5} =$ _____

22. $\dfrac{3}{4} - \dfrac{1}{7} =$ _____

23. $2\dfrac{1}{6} + 3\dfrac{3}{4} =$ _____

24. $8\dfrac{1}{2} - 3\dfrac{1}{6} =$ _____

What is the value of the 4 in each number?

1. 27.43

2. 621.84

3. 164.32

4. 297.364

_____ _____ _____ _____

What is the value of the 7 in each number?

5. 937.63

6. 432.71

7. 562.437

8. 263.07

_____ _____ _____ _____

Write <, = or > in the circle.

9. 2.97 ◯ 2.79 10. 6.19 ◯ 6.1 11. 0.246 ◯ 2.46 12. 9.04 ◯ 9.40

13. 6.7 ◯ 6.07 14. 0.15 ◯ 0.051 15. 8.20 ◯ 8.2 16. 72.08 ◯ 72.1

Add.

17.
$$\begin{array}{r} 5.4 \\ + 2.7 \\ \hline \end{array}$$

18.
$$\begin{array}{r} 17.36 \\ + 36.255 \\ \hline \end{array}$$

19.
$$\begin{array}{r} 47.3 \\ + 84.91 \\ \hline \end{array}$$

20.
$$\begin{array}{r} 86.24 \\ + 19.8 \\ \hline \end{array}$$

Subtract.

21.
$$\begin{array}{r} 6.4 \\ - 3.1 \\ \hline \end{array}$$

22.
$$\begin{array}{r} 26.147 \\ - 15.369 \\ \hline \end{array}$$

23.
$$\begin{array}{r} 47.6 \\ - 28.29 \\ \hline \end{array}$$

24.
$$\begin{array}{r} 67.13 \\ - 15.4 \\ \hline \end{array}$$

Multiply.

25.
$$\begin{array}{r} 4.5 \\ \times \quad 4 \\ \hline \end{array}$$

26.
$$\begin{array}{r} 23.4 \\ \times \quad 0.3 \\ \hline \end{array}$$

27.
$$\begin{array}{r} 15.3 \\ \times \quad 0.7 \\ \hline \end{array}$$

28.
$$\begin{array}{r} 7.6 \\ \times 3.4 \\ \hline \end{array}$$

29.
$$\begin{array}{r} 32.6 \\ \times \quad 4.3 \\ \hline \end{array}$$

30.
$$\begin{array}{r} 8.9 \\ \times \quad 4 \\ \hline \end{array}$$

31.
$$\begin{array}{r} 6.1 \\ \times 0.05 \\ \hline \end{array}$$

32.
$$\begin{array}{r} 0.07 \\ \times \quad 8 \\ \hline \end{array}$$

Find the average of each set of numbers.

1. 32, 46 ____

2. 24, 27, 72 ____

3. 15, 21, 42, 62 ____

Use the graphs to answer questions 4 and 5.

Games Won					
Jets	⚾	⚾	⚾	⚾	⚾
Bulls	⚾	⚾	⚾		
Rockets	⚾	⚾	⚾	⚾	⚾

Each ⚾ means 2 games.

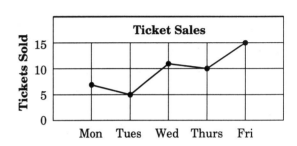

4. How many games did the Rockets win? ____

5. How many tickets were sold on Tuesday? ____

Use the graph to do exercise 6 through 9.

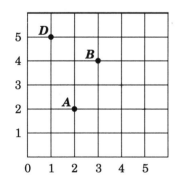

6. Give the letter for (2,2). ____

7. Give the number for point B. _____

8. Graph and label point *C* (5,2).

9. Graph and label point *E* (4,3).

Ten lettered pieces of paper are placed in a box. One letter is drawn.

10. What is the probability the letter will be an A?

_____

11. What is the probability the letter will be an O?

_____

Glossary

Addend   A number that is added to another number.

Angle   The figure made by two straight lines that meet at one endpoint, or vertex.

Area   The measure of a surface surrounded by a boundary.
The shaded part of the square is its area.

Average   The number obtained by adding two or more quantities and dividing by the number of quantities added.
The average of 2, 5 and 11 is 6;
2 + 5 + 11 = 18; 18 ÷ 3 = 6

Bar graph   A representation of numerical facts using lengths of bars to show information.

Calculator code   A set of numbers and symbols representing the order for pressing keys on a calculator keyboard.

Centimeter (cm)   A metric unit of length.
100 centimeters = 1 meter

Common denominator   Denominator that is a multiple of two or more denominators.

Congruent figures   Figures of exactly the same size and shape.

 and   are congruent triangles.

Congruent sides   Line segments of equal length.

Cup (c)   A customary unit of liquid measure.
1 cup = 8 ounces

Customary units   Standard measures of length, weight, volume and capacity.
Inches, miles, pounds, cubic feet and ounces are examples of customary units.

Decimal   A fractional part that uses place value and a decimal point to show tenths, hundredths and so on.
0.6 is the decimal equivalent of the fraction $\frac{3}{5}$.

Decimeter (dm)   A metric unit of length.
10 decimeters = 1 meter

Denominator   The number below the line in a fraction.
In $\frac{3}{5}$, 5 is the denominator.

Diagram   A drawing, chart or figure used to illustrate an idea.

Difference   The answer in a subtraction problem.

Digit   Any one of the ten number symbols: 0, 1, 2, 3, 4, 5, 6, 7, 8 and 9.

Dividend   The number that is being divided in a division problem.
In 42 ÷ 7 = 6, 42 is the dividend.

Divisor   The number that is being divided into the dividend.
In 42 ÷ 7 = 6, 7 is the divisor.

Edge   A segment that is the side of a face on a solid figure.

Entry   A number or symbol recorded on a calculator.

Endpoint   A point at the end of a segment or ray.

Equivalent fractions   Fractions that name the same number.

Face   A plane figure making up part of a solid figure.

Fact family   The set of four related facts having the same three numbers in their equations.

Factor   A number to be multiplied.
In 2 × 3 = 6, both 2 and 3 are factors.

Foot (ft)   A customary unit of length.
1 foot = 12 inches

Formula   A general rule expressed using symbols.

Fraction   A number that names a part of a whole.
$\frac{1}{2}$ is a fraction.

Gallon (gal)   A customary unit of liquid measure.
1 gallon = 4 quarts or 8 pints.

Gram (g)   A basic metric unit of weight.
1000 grams = 1 kilogram

Graphing   Drawing a picture of relationships among numbers and quantities.

Grouping property of addition   When the grouping of 3 or more addends is changed, the sum remains the same.
(2 + 5) + 1 = 2 + (5 + 1)

347

Grouping property of multiplication When the grouping of 3 or more factors is changed, the product remains the same.

$$(5 \times 3) \times 2 = 5 \times (3 \times 2)$$

Inch (in.) A customary unit of length.
12 inches = 1 foot

Intersect To meet and cross over at a point.

Line AB intersects
line CD at point P.

Kilogram (kg) A metric unit of weight.
1 kilogram = 1,000 grams

Kilometer (km) A metric unit of length.
1 kilometer = 1,000 meters

Least common multiple (LCM) The smallest number that is a common multiple of two or more numbers.
The LCM of 4 and 6 is 12.

Line A set of points whose straight path extends indefinitely in opposite directions.

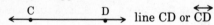 line CD or $\overleftrightarrow{CD}$

Line graph A representation of numerical facts using points and lines on a grid to show information.

Liter (L) A basic metric unit of liquid measure.
1 liter = 1,000 milliliters

Meter (m) A basic metric unit of length.
1 meter = 1,000 millimeters

Metric system A decimal system of weights and measures whose basic units are the meter, liter and gram.

Mile (mi) A customary unit of length.
1 mile = 5, 280 feet

Milliliter (mL) A metric unit of liquid measure.
1 milliliter = $\frac{1}{1000}$ liter

Minuend A number or quantity from which another is subtracted.
In 18 − 5 = 13, 18 is the minuend.

Mixed number A fractional number greater than 1 that is written as a whole number and a fraction.
$5\frac{2}{3}$ is a mixed number.

Multiple The product of a particular number and another number.
8 is a multiple of 2.

Multiplication-addition property The property that allows the first factor to be multiplied separately with each addend whose sum represents the second factor.

$$5 \times (4 + 6) = (5 \times 4) + (5 \times 6)$$
$$5 \times 10 \quad = 20 \qquad + 30$$
$$50 \quad = 50$$

Multiples of 10 The product of any factor multiplied by 10.

Number pair Two numbers that define one point on a grid; the first number names the distance across, and the second names the distance up.

Number sentence Numbers and symbols that express an equation or inequality.
3 + 4 = 7; 10 > 2

Numerator The number above the line in a fraction.
In $\frac{3}{5}$, 3 is the numerator.

One property of multiplication Any factor multiplied by one equals the original factor.

Order property of addition The order of the addends does not change the sum.
5 + 7 = 7 + 5

Order property of multiplication The order of the factors does not change the product.
3 × 4 = 4 × 3

Ounce (oz) A customary unit of weight.
16 ounces = 1 pound

Outcome The single result in a probability experiment.

Palindrome A number which reads the same backward and forward.
838 and 61,416 are palindromes.

Parallel lines Lines in the same plane that do not meet.

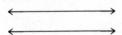

Parallelogram A quadrilateral having two pairs of opposite, congruent, parallel sides.

Percent A word meaning hundredths.
37 percent is written 37%
and means 0.37 or $\frac{37}{100}$.

Perimeter The distance around a shape that is the sum of the lengths of all of its sides.

Picture graph A representation of numerical facts using pictures.

Pint (pt) A customary unit of liquid measure.
1 pint = 16 ounces or 2 cups

Plane figure A shape that appears on a flat surface.
A circle, square, and triangle are plane figures.

Polygon A many-sided plane figure.

Pound (lb) A customary unit of weight.
1 pound = 16 ounces

Probability A number which tells how likely it is that a certain event will happen.

Product   The answer to a multiplication problem. In $4 \times 5 = 20$, 20 is the product.

Quadrilateral   A four-sided plane figure.

Quart (qt)   A customary unit of liquid measure. 1 quart = 32 ounces   4 quarts = 1 gallon

Quotient   The answer to a division problem.

In $7\overline{)63}$ with 9 above, 9 is the quotient.

Ratio   A comparison of two quantities. The ratio of 3 to 4 can be written $\frac{3}{4}$.

Ray   A part of a line having one endpoint.

E •————→ F   ray EF or $\overrightarrow{EF}$

Rectangle   A four-sided plane figure with two pairs of opposite congruent sides and four right angles.

Remainder   The number left over in a division problem.

Right angle   An angle with the same shape as the vertex of a square; 90 degrees.

In this square, □ 90° all angles are right angles.

Rounding   Estimating a number's value by raising or lowering any of its place values.

Rule of order   The order for working operations in a mathematical sentence.

Operations within parentheses should be worked before multiplication.
Work all multiplications left to right.
Work all additions and subtractions left to right.

Segment   A part of a line having two endpoints.

A ——————— B   segment AB or $\overline{AB}$

Similar figures   Plane figures that have the same shape.

Simplify   To rename a fraction as an equivalent fraction or mixed number whose numerator and denominator cannot be divided by any common factor other than 1.

simplest form   **simplest form**
$\frac{12}{26} = \frac{1}{3}$ $\frac{36}{10} = 3\frac{6}{10} = 3\frac{3}{5}$

Also, to rename an improper fraction as an equivalent whole number.

simplest form
$\frac{35}{7} = 5$

Skip-counting   Naming the multiples of a number one after another.

Solid figure   A figure that is in more than one plane.

Square   A plane figure with four congruent sides and four right angles.

Subtrahend   The number that is subtracted from the minuend. In $18 - 5 = 13$, 5 is the subtrahend.

Sum   The answer to an addition problem. In $8 + 9 = 17$, 17 is the sum.

Tally   Marks used to count by fives. ⅧⅢ ⅧⅢ Ⅲ

Terms   The numerator and the denominator of a fraction.

Ton (T)   A customary unit of weight. 1 ton = 2,000 pounds

Total   The answer to an addition problem, the same as the sum.

Triangle   A three-sided plane figure.

Unit cost   The cost of a single base unit of measurement.

Unit fraction   A fraction whose numerator is 1. $\frac{1}{5}$ is a unit fraction.

Vertex (pl. vertices)   The point at which two sides of an angle, two sides of a plane figure, or three or more sides of a solid figure meet.

Volume   The number of cubic units needed to fill a solid figure. The volume of this cube is 8 cubic units.

Whole numbers   Those numbers used in counting, including zero.

Yard (yd)   A customary unit of length. 1 yard = 3 feet or 36 inches

Zero properties of subtraction   When zero is subtracted from a minuend, the difference is the same as the minuend.
$8 - 0 = 8$
Subtracting a number from itself leaves zero.
$9 - 9 = 0$

Zero property of addition   When one addend is zero, the sum is the other addend.
$3 + 0 = 3$

Zero property of multiplication   When one factor is zero, the product is zero.
$4 \times 0 = 0$

349

Index

A

Addends, 3–8, 13–14

Addition
  calculator codes, 57–58
  column, 5–8, 53–54
  decimals, 295–296, 299–300
  estimating, 49–50
  facts, 3–4, 17
  fractions, 265–266, 269–272,
    275–280
  mixed numbers, 277–280
  money, 53–54
  multi-digit numbers, 45–52
  properties, 7–8
  two-digit numbers, 43–44

Angles, 221–222

Area, 231–232

Averages, 211–212

C

Calculators
  bank accounts, 99–100
  codes, 57–58
  comparison shopping, 215–216
  data from an ad, 77–78
  decimal key, 187–188
  division key, 139–140
  fractions, 283–284
  keys, 57–58
  money, 57–58, 77–78, 187–188
  multiplication key, 117–118
  percents, 307–308
  review, 327–328
  unit cost, 215–216

Centimeters, 153–156

Common factors, 253

Common multiples, 275–276

Comparing
  decimals, 293–294
  fractions, 251–252
  whole numbers, 1–2, 29–30

Congruent
  figures, 225–226
  sides, 227–228

Counting
  money, 25–26
  skip, 103–104
  tallies, 311–312

Cubic units, 235–236

Customary measurement
  capacity, 149–150
  length, 147–148
  liquid, 149–150
  weight, 151–152

D

Decimals
  adding, 295–296, 299–300
  comparing, 293–294
  multiplying, 301–304
  place value, 287–292
  subtracting, 297–300

Decimeters, 155–156

Diagrams, 137–138

Division
  averages, 211–212
  calculators, 139–140, 215–216
  checking, 205–206
  divisors,
    one-digit, 121–136, 139–140,
      191–200
    two-digit, 201–210
  facts, 121–130
  larger dividends, 197–198
  money, 199–200, 215–216
  multiples of ten, 201–204
  ones, 129–130
  partial dividends, 209–210
  remainders, 131–132, 135–136,
    193–198, 203–210
  three-digit quotients, 191–196
  trial quotients, 207–208
  two-digit quotients, 133–136,
    197–200, 203–204, 209–210
  zeros in, 129–130, 195–196

E

Estimating
  differences, 71–72
  products, 183–184
  quotients, 207–208
  sums, 49–50

F

Fact families, 11

Feet, 147–148

Four-step plan, 15–16

Fractions
  adding, 265–266, 269–272,
    275–280
  calculator, 283–284
  common denominator, 265–268,
  common multiples, 275–276
  comparing, 251–252
  equivalent, 247–250
  finding a fraction of a number,
    243–246
  in measurement, 257–258
  least common denominator,
    275–276
  simplest terms, 253–254

mixed numbers, 255–256,
    277–280
  naming, 241–242
  non-unit, 245–256
  ratios, 259–260
  simplifying, 253–256, 265–272,
    277–280
  subtracting, 267–270, 273–276
  uncommon denominators,
    271–280
  unit, 243–244

G

Gallons, 149–150

Geometry
  angles, 221–222
  congruent figures, 225–226
  congruent sides, 225–226
  lines, 219–220
  line segments, 219–220
  plane figures, 223–232
  similar figures, 225–226
  solid figures, 233–236

Grams, 159–160

Graphs
  bar, 311–312
  line, 315–316
  number pairs, 317–320
  picture, 313–314
Grouping, property of addition, 7
Grouping property of
    multiplication, 105

I

Inches, 147–148

K

Kilograms, 159–160

Kilometers, 155–156

L

Lines, 219–220

Liters, 157–158

M

Measuring
  area, 231–232
  capacity, 149–150, 157–158
  customary units, 147–152
  length, 147–148, 153–156
  metric units, 153–160, 229–232
  perimeter, 229–230
  time, 143–146
  volume, 235–236
  weight, 151–152, 159–160

Meters, 155–156

Metric measurement
   capacity, 157–158
   length, 153–156, 229–230
   liquid, 157–158
   weight, 159–160
   volume, 235–236

Miles, 147–148

Milliliters, 157–158

Missing addends, 13–14

Missing factors, 95–96

Money
   adding, 53–54, 57–58, 77–78
   calculators, 77–78, 187–188,
     215–216
   counting, 25–26
   dividing, 199–200, 215–216
   multiplying, 113–114, 169–170
   place value, 23–24
   subtracting, 63–74, 77–78

Multiplication
   calculators, 117–118, 187–188
   decimals, 301–304
   estimation, 183–184
   facts, 81–86, 91–94
   money, 113–114, 169–174,
     181–184, 187–188
   multiples, 103–104
   multiples of ten, 175–176
   of multi-digit numbers,
     167–168, 171–174, 181–182
   of two-digit numbers, 107–112,
     175–180
   powers of 10, 165–166
   properties, 87–88, 105–106

N

Number pairs, 317–320

Numbers
   comparing, 1–2, 29–30
   rounding, 31–34

O

One property of multiplication,
   87

Order of operations, 89–90

Order property of addition, 7

Order property of multiplication,
   87

Ounces, 151–152

P

Parallelograms, 227–228

Percents, 307–308

Perimeter, 229–230

Pints, 149–150

Place Value
   decimals, 287–292
   hundreds, tens, ones, 21–22
   millions, 37–38
   money, 23–24
   ten thousands, hundred
     thousands, 35–36
   thousands, 27–28

Plane figures, 223–232

Points, 219–222

Pounds, 151–152

Powers of ten, 165–166

Probability, 321–324

Problem Solving
   acting it out, 75–76
   drawing a picture or diagram,
     137–138
   guessing and checking, 39–40
   looking for a pattern, 97–98
   making a graph, 213–214
   making a model, 161–162
   making a systematic listing or
     table, 55–56, 115–116
   making a tally, 185–186
   properties, 7, 11
   restating the problem, 237–238
   review, 325–326
   selecting suitable notation,
     261–262
   using a formula, 305–306
   using a 4-step plan, 15–16
   writing an open sentence,
     281–282

Q

Quarts, 149–150

R

Rays, 221–222

Rounding
   money, 31–32, 71–72
   whole numbers, 31–34, 49–50
     71–72

Rule of order, 89–90

S

Segments, 219–220

Similar figures, 225–226

Skip-counting, 103–104

Solid figures, 233–236

Subtraction
   calculators, 77–78, 99–100
   checking, 11–12, 73–74
   decimals, 297–300

   estimating, 71–72
   facts, 9–12, 18
   fractions,
     common denominators,
       267–270
     uncommon denominators,
       273–276
   minuends with zeros, 65–66,
     69–70
   money, 63–74, 77–78
   multi-digit numbers, 67–70
   three-digit numbers, 63–66
   two-digit numbers, 61–62

T

Time, 143–146

Tons, 151–152

V

Volume, 235–236

Y

Yards, 147–148

Z

Zero
   calculators, 57
   in addition, 7–8
   in division, 129–130, 195–196
   in multiplication, 87–88
   in subtraction, 11–12, 65–66,
     69–70